Ready®
4
Mathematics
PRACTICE AND
PROBLEM SOLVING
Indiana
IAS Edition
Built for the Indiana
Academic Standards

Vice President of Education: Adam Berkin
Editorial Director: Cynthia Tripp
Director, Customization and Correlations: Abigail Jungreis
Executive Editors: Penny Dowdy, Kathy Kellman
Editors: Stacie Cartwright, Ruth Estabrook, Pamela Halloran,
Grace Izzi, Sarah Kraus, Djana Paper, Lauren Van Wart
Project Managers: Deborah Golumbek, Grace Izzi, Sherry Pilkerton
Cover Designer and Illustrators: Julia Bourque, Matt Pollock
Illustrator: Sam Valentino
Composition: Edward Scanlon, Mark Nodland, Scott Hoffman
Photography Credit: wk1003mike/Shutterstock (front cover background)

ISBN 978-1-4957-3513-4

North Billerica, MA 01862

15 14 13 12 11 10 9 8 7 6

800354

Table of Contents

Family Letter available with every lesson.

Unit 4: Fractions

Unit 5: Measurement and Data Analysis

Family Letter available with every lesson.

Unit 6: Geometry

Family Letter available with every lesson.

Dear Family,

This week your child is exploring place value in numbers.

Our number system is based on a pattern of tens. The value of a digit in a number is based on the place where the digit appears in the number.

A digit in one place has 10 times the value that the same digit would have in the place to its right.

Thousands Period			Ones Period		
Hundred Thousands	**Ten Thousands**	**Thousands**	**Hundreds**	**Tens**	**Ones**
4	6	7	8	8	2

This number is written in **standard form:**	467,882
This number is written in **word form:**	Four hundred sixty-seven thousand, eight hundred eighty-two
This number is written in **expanded form:**	400,000 + 60,000 + 7,000 + 800 + 80 + 2

Invite your child to share what he or she knows about place value by doing the following activity together.

Place Value Activity

Do an activity with your child to practice exploring place value in real-life numbers.

The distance from Earth to the moon is about 238,855 miles.

This number is written in standard form.

238,855

- Have your child read the number aloud. (two hundred thirty-eight thousand, eight hundred fifty-five)
- Cover the standard form of the number above so that your child cannot see it. Read the number aloud and have your child write the number in standard form.
- Now, let your child make up a 6-digit number for you to write.
- Ask your child to check your work.

Look for other real-life opportunities to practice exploring place value of numbers with your child.

Name: 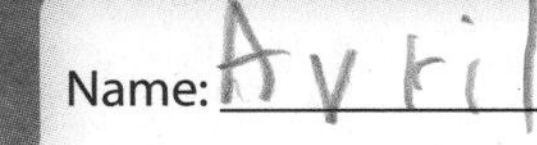

Prerequisite: How do you know the place value of each digit in a number?

Study the example that shows how a place-value chart shows the value of each digit in a number. Then solve problems 1–8.

Example

The place-value chart shows the number 435.

Hundreds	Tens	Ones
4	3	5

Word form: *four hundred thirty-five*

The 4 in the hundreds place has a value of 400.
The 3 in the tens place has a value of 30.
The 5 in the ones place has a value of 5.

So, another way to write 435 is 400 + 30 + 5.

1 Show the number 762 in the following place-value chart.

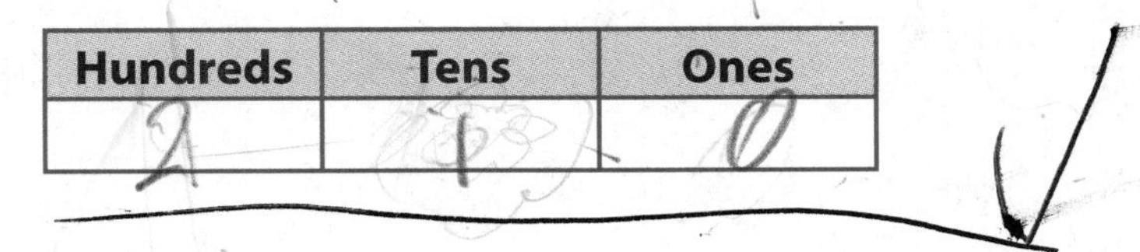

Hundreds	Tens	Ones

2 What is the value of 7 in 762? ______

3 What is the value of the digit in the tens place in 762? ______

4 Use place value to show another way to write 762.

762 = ______ + ______ + ______

Vocabulary

word form how a number is written with words or said aloud.

value the amount a digit is worth.

Solve.

5 Use the place-value chart below to help you think about the value of each digit in the number.

Hundreds	Tens	Ones
5	2	2

a. Write the number. _______

b. Write the number in word form.

Five _____________ twenty-_____________

c. Write the number another way.

_______ = _______ + _______ + _______

6 Look at the place-value chart in problem 5.

a. The digit in the ones place is _______.

The value of the digit in the ones place is _______.

b. The digit in the tens place is _______.

The value of the digit in the tens place is _______.

c. $20 =$ _______ $\times 2$

7 a. What is the value of 3 in 123? _______

b. What is the value of 3 in 231? _______

c. What is the value of 3 in 312? _______

d. $30 =$ _______ $\times 3$ $\quad 300 = 10 \times$ _______

8 Use the digits 4, 5, and 6 to write a number in which 4 has a value of 400. Explain your thinking.

____

____

____

Name: ______________________

Use Place Value

Study how the example uses a place-value chart to show the value of the digits in a number. Then solve problems 1–8.

Example

Look at the place-value chart below. What is the value of the 3?

Then, use place value to explain the value of 3 if it were in the ten thousands place.

Hundred Thousands	Ten Thousands	Thousands	Hundreds	Tens	Ones
2	0	3	5	5	4

Standard form: 203,554
Expanded form: 200,000 + 3,000 + 500 + 50 + 4
Word form: *two hundred three thousand, five hundred fifty-four*

The 3 is in the thousands place, so it has a value of 3,000.
If 3 were in the ten thousands place, its value would be 30,000.

1 Write 70,681 in the following place-value chart.

Hundred Thousands	Ten Thousands	Thousands	Hundreds	Tens	Ones

2 Write 70,681 in expanded form and word form.

____

____

3 What would be the value of 8 if it were in the thousands place? ______________

4 What is the value of the 6 in 70,681? Explain how you know.

____

____

Vocabulary

value the amount a digit is worth.

Solve.

5 What number is one thousand less than 921,438? Explain how you know.

____

____

____

6 What number is one hundred thousand more than 75,000? Explain how you know.

____

____

____

7 Show some different ways you can make 7,502.

_______ hundreds + _______ tens + _______ ones

_______ tens + _______ ones

_______ ones

8 What are three different ways to make the number 15,638 with only hundreds, tens, and ones?

____

____

____

9 Solve the following base ten riddle:

I have 30 ones, 82 thousands, 4 hundred thousands, 60 tens, and 100 hundreds. What number am I?

Solution: ______________________________

Name: ______________________

Reason and Write

Study the example. Underline two parts that you think make it a particularly good answer and a helpful example.

Example

Emma looked at the numbers 4,075 and 1,806. Her thinking is shown below.

The number 1,806 has more hundreds than 4,075 because 1,806 has 8 in the hundreds place, and 4,075 has 0 in the hundreds place. 8 hundreds is more than 0 hundreds.

Tell why Emma's thinking is incorrect. Then explain why there are more hundreds in 4,075 than in 1,806.

Show your work. Use a place-value chart, words, and numbers to explain your answer.

Hundred Thousands	Ten Thousands	Thousands	Hundreds	Tens	Ones
		4	0	7	5
		1	8	0	6

Emma looked only at the digits 0 and 8 in the hundreds place. She needed to also look at the digits in the thousands place.

4,075 has 4 thousands, or 40 hundreds, not 0 hundreds.

1,806 has 1 thousand, or 10 hundreds, plus 8 hundreds for a total of 18 hundreds, not 8 hundreds.

40 hundreds is more than 18 hundreds. There are more hundreds in 4,075 than in 1,806.

Where does the example . . .

- use a chart to show the place value of digits?
- use words and numbers to explain?
- give details?

Solve the problem. Use what you learned from the model.

Tyler looked at the numbers 10,020 and 20,010. His thinking is shown below.

> *The number 10,020 has more tens than 20,010 because 10,020 has 2 in the tens place, and 20,010 has 1 in the tens place. 2 tens is more than 1 ten.*

Tell why Tyler's thinking is incorrect. Then explain why there are more tens in 20,010 than in 10,020.

Show your work. Use a place-value chart, words, and numbers to explain your answer.

Did you . . .

- use a chart to show the place value of digits?
- use words and numbers to explain?
- give details?

Name: ______________________

Round Whole Numbers

Solve the problems.

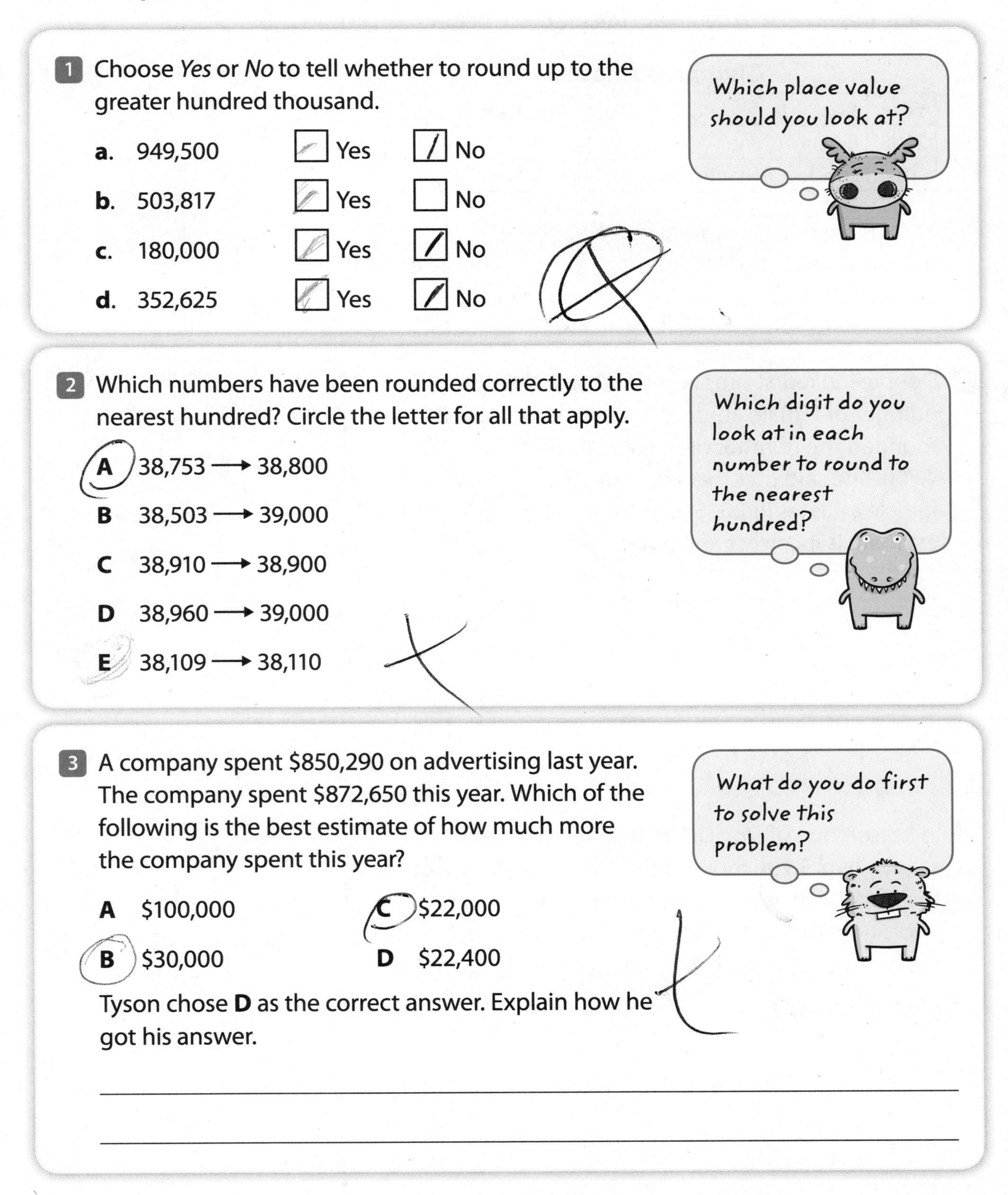

1 Choose *Yes* or *No* to tell whether to round up to the greater hundred thousand.

a. 949,500 ☐ Yes ☐ No

b. 503,817 ☐ Yes ☐ No

c. 180,000 ☐ Yes ☐ No

d. 352,625 ☐ Yes ☐ No

2 Which numbers have been rounded correctly to the nearest hundred? Circle the letter for all that apply.

A 38,753 ⟶ 38,800

B 38,503 ⟶ 39,000

C 38,910 ⟶ 38,900

D 38,960 ⟶ 39,000

E 38,109 ⟶ 38,110

3 A company spent $850,290 on advertising last year. The company spent $872,650 this year. Which of the following is the best estimate of how much more the company spent this year?

A $100,000

B $30,000

C $22,000

D $22,400

Tyson chose **D** as the correct answer. Explain how he got his answer.

____

____

Solve.

4 Look at the table below. Round all the numbers to the same place value to complete the sentence below.

Olympic Athletes

Year	City	Total	Female	Male
2008	Beijing, China	10,942	4,637	6,305
2012	London, Great Britain	10,568	4,676	5,892

Each of the two Olympic games had about __________ total athletes, including about ___________ female athletes, and about ___________ male athletes.

5 Debbie looked at problem 4 and rounded the number of female athletes in 2008 to 5,000. She rounded the number of female athletes in 2012 to 4,700. She said that there were about 300 more female athletes in 2008. Explain why Debbie's estimate is incorrect and find a correct estimate.

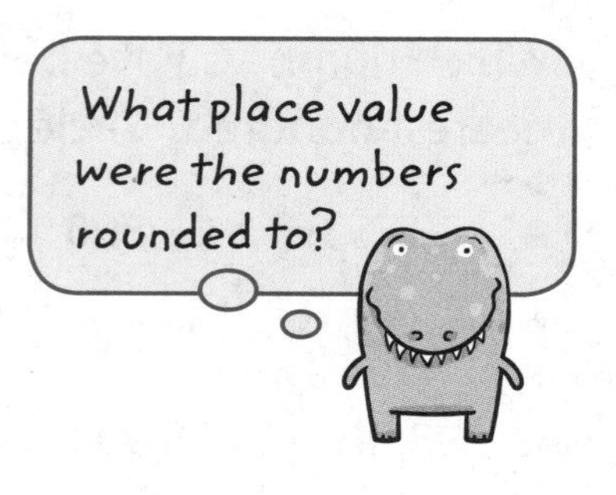

____

____

____

____

6 In season one of *Sing Off*, 16,865 people tried out. In season two, 5,296 more people tried out. In season three, 1,834 fewer people tried out than in season two. Show two different ways to round and estimate the number of people who tried out in season three.

Show your work.

Solution: ______________________________________

Unit 1 Game

Name: ______________________

Subtraction Action

What you need: Recording Sheet, 3 sets of digit cards (0–9)

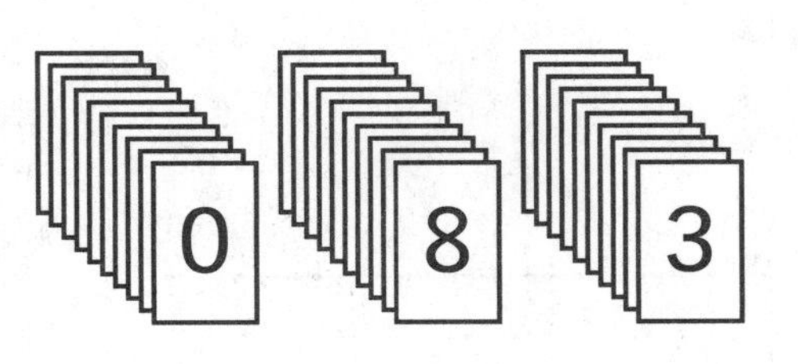

Directions

8 5 9 2 1

8 5 9 1 2

- Mix the digit cards and place them facedown in a stack. Each player takes 5 cards.
- Players each make two different 5-digit numbers using their 5 cards. The goal is to make two numbers that are as close in value to each other as possible.
- Both players subtract their lesser number from their greater number. The difference tells how close the two numbers are. Players write their subtraction problems on the Recording Sheet.

Name: ______________________

Subtraction Action Recording Sheet

Mike Player A Name		Sofia Player B Name
1. 85,921 − 85,912 9	1. 9 < 18	1. 76,053 − 76,035 18

- Players compare their differences and write the comparison on the Recording Sheet. The player with the lesser difference made two numbers that are closer together. This player wins the round.
- Put all the cards back and remix. Play 5 rounds. The player with more wins after 5 rounds wins the game.

I subtracted 85,912 from 85,921. My difference of 9 is less than your difference of 18, so I win the first round.

Name: ____________________

Subtraction Action Recording Sheet

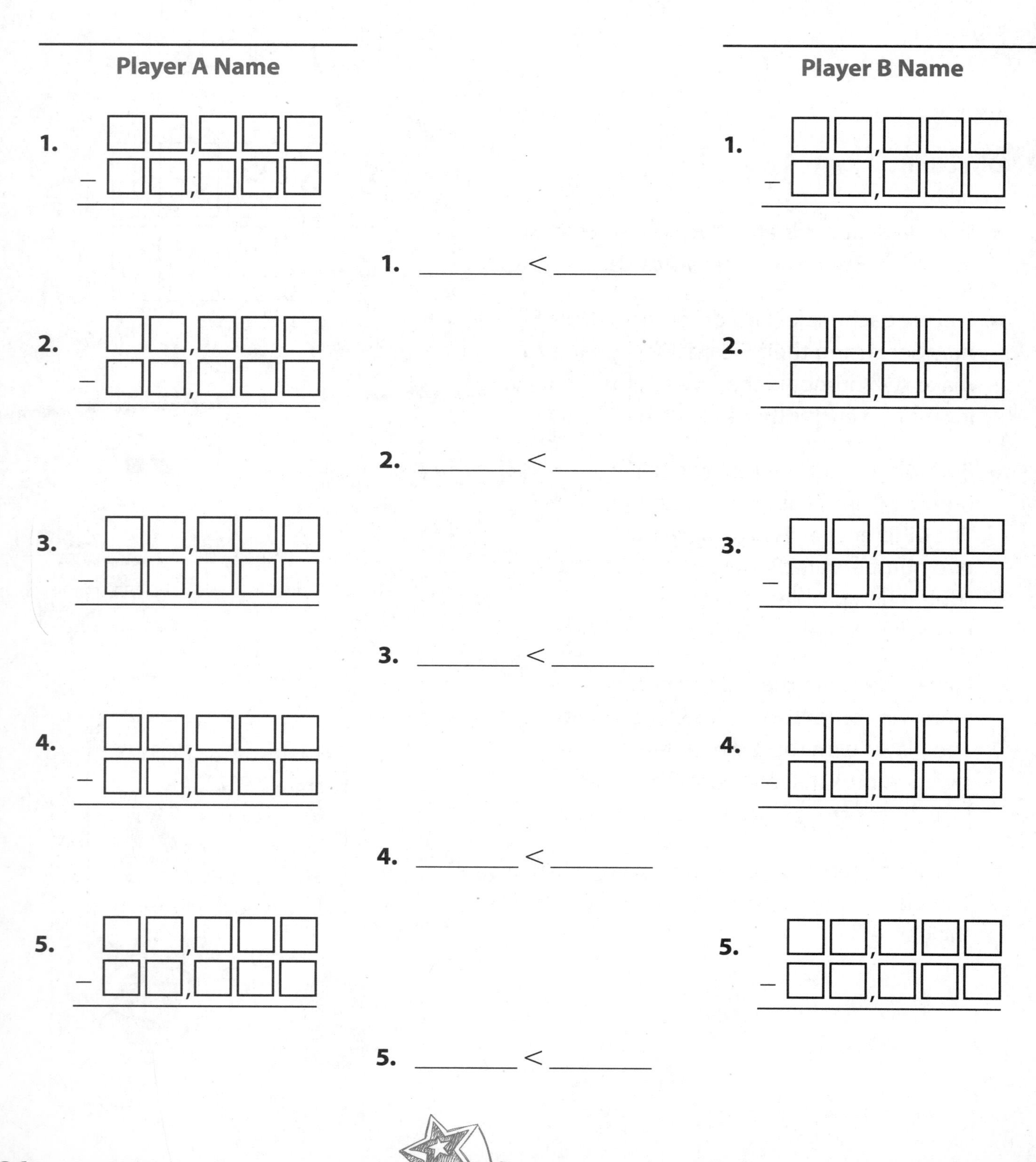

Unit 1 Practice

Name: ____________________

Whole Numbers

In this unit you learned to:	Lesson
read and write numbers using number names, for example: 495 is *four hundred ninety-five.*	1
read and write numbers using expanded form, for example: 352 = 300 + 50 + 2.	1
compare two multi-digit whole numbers, for example: 6,131 > 6,113.	2
add multi-digit whole numbers, for example: 3,966 + 7, 550 = 11,516.	3
subtract multi-digit whole numbers, for example: 25,082 − 11,919 = 13,163.	3
round multi-digit whole numbers, for example: 528 rounded to the nearest ten is 530.	4

Use these skills to solve problems 1–6.

1 Use <, >, or = to complete each number sentence.

a. 790,599 ◯ 791,043

b. 52,180 ◯ 50,000 + 2,000 + 10 + 8

c. 99,999 ◯ 100,000

d. 55 hundreds + 2 tens ◯ 5,520

e. 200,000 + 10,000 + 300 + 50 ◯ 210,305

2 A publishing company printed 920,500 copies of a book. The company sold 843,255 copies. How many books did not sell?

Show your work.

Solution: ____________________

Solve.

3 The second longest bridge in the world, the Tianjin Grand Bridge, is 373,000 feet long. Its length is 167,700 feet less than the length of the longest bridge in the world. What is the length of the longest bridge?

Show your work.

Solution: ____________________

4 Use the clues below to guess the mystery number.

- The number is less than 190,000 and greater than 180,000.
- 5,000 more than the number has 187 thousands.
- 200 less than the number has 4 hundreds.

Solution: ____________________

5 Round each number in the table to the given place value. Then, write $<$, $>$, or $=$ to compare the rounded numbers.

Round to . . .	95,498	Compare (>, <, or =)	95,607
Tens			
Hundreds			
Thousands			
Ten Thousands			

6 Juan's company spent $2,350 on an event. They spent about $1,500 on food and about $900 on entertainment. What could the actual cost of the food and entertainment be?

Show your work.

Solution: food ____________ entertainment ____________

Unit 1 Performance Task

Name: ____________________

Answer the questions and show all your work on separate paper.

The fourth-graders at Windy Hill Elementary School are collecting box tops to raise money for a robotics science program. The students need to collect 20,000 box tops in all to reach the goal.

The chart below shows how many box tops each fourth-grade class has collected in the first five months.

	Room 4A	Room 4B	Room 4C	Room 4D
Number of Box Tops	3,078	2,145	2,569	2,034

The science teacher wants to know how many box tops, to the nearest hundred, each class has collected and about how close the students are to reaching the goal of 20,000 box tops. Write an email to the science teacher describing how close the fourth-graders are to the goal and estimating how much more time the students need to reach the goal. In the email you should show your work and explain your reasoning.

Checklist

Did you . . .

- ☐ organize the information?
- ☐ use estimation in your calculations?
- ☐ write a clear explanation?

Reflect on the Process Standards

After you complete the task, choose one of the following questions to answer.

1. **Reason Mathematically** How did you use the information in the table to estimate how close the fourth-graders are to the goal?

2. **Model** What equations did you write to solve the problem?

Performance Task Tips

Word Bank Here are some words that you might use in your answer.

equal	sum	round
add	total	hundred
estimate	difference	about
halfway		

Models Here are some models that you might use to find the solution.

Thousands	Hundreds	Tens	Ones

Sentence Starters Here are some sentence starters that might help you write an explanation.

I rounded ______________________________

I estimated the total by ______________________

The sum of ______________________________

The difference between __________ is __________

To reach their goal, the classes need ____________

Unit 1 Vocabulary

Name: ______________________

My Examples

value

the amount a digit is worth

word form

how a number is written with words or said aloud

standard form

how a number is written with numerals

expanded form

how a number is written to show the place value of each digit

My Examples

period

digits in groups of three in a large number

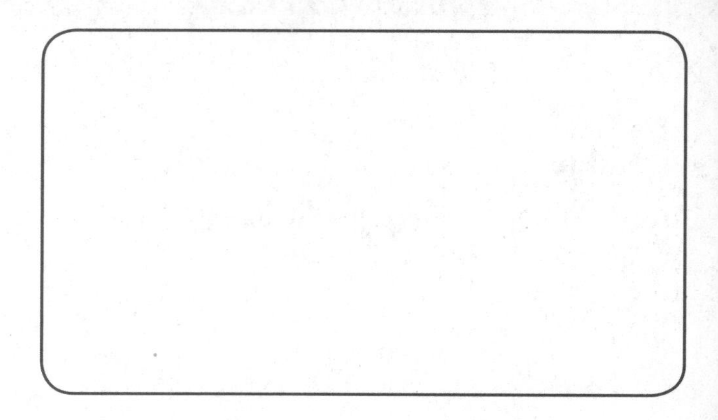

compare

to decide if one number is greater than, less than, or equal to another number

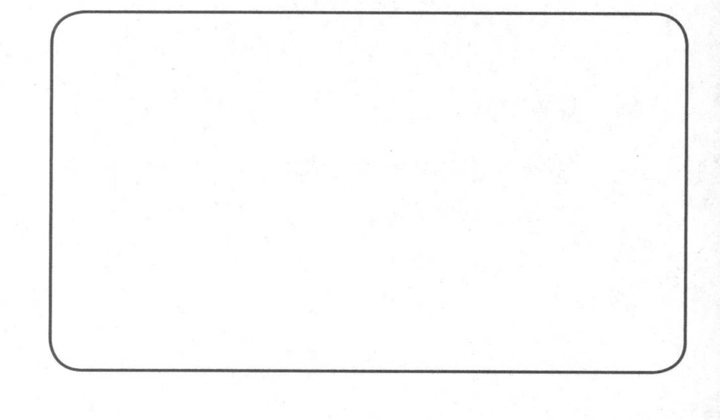

greater than (>)

a comparison that says one number has greater value than another number

less than (<)

a comparison that says one number has less value than another number

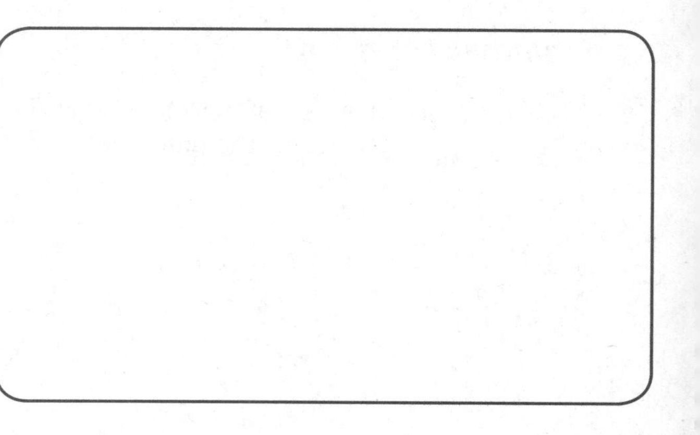

Dear Family,

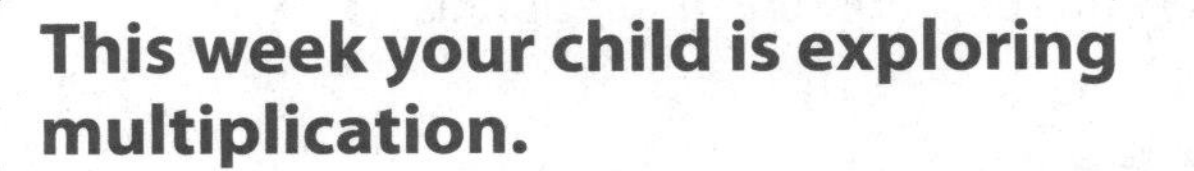

Your child is learning about multiplication as a way to compare two numbers.

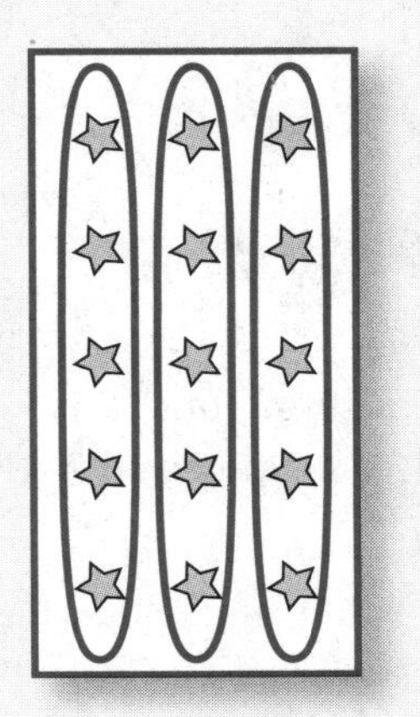

This model shows that
15 is 3 times as many as 5.
You can write the comparison as a multiplication equation:
$15 = 3 \times 5$

This model shows that
15 is 5 times as many as 3.
You can write the comparison as a multiplication equation:
$15 = 5 \times 3$

Your child is also learning how to use bar models to help understand multiplication as a comparison.

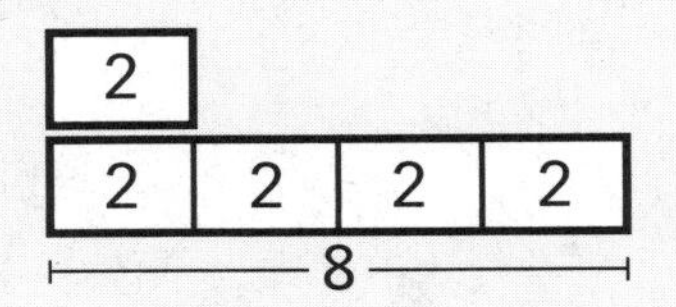

This bar model shows that 8 is 4 times as many as 2: $8 = 4 \times 2$.

Invite your child to share what he or she knows about multiplication by doing the following activity together.

Multiplication Activity

Do an activity with your child to explore multiplication as a way to compare two numbers.

Materials: 20 pennies or other small identical objects

With your child, arrange 10 pennies to show that 10 is 2 times as many as 5. The pennies should look like this:

- Now ask your child to arrange 10 pennies to show that 10 is 5 times as many as 2. (The pennies should be arranged in 5 rows with 2 pennies in each row.)
- Ask your child to arrange pennies to show other multiplication comparisons.

Examples:
14 is 7 times as many as 2.
14 is 2 times as many as 7.
12 is 4 times as many as 3.
12 is 3 times as many as 4.

Look for real-life opportunities to practice multiplication as a comparison of two numbers with your child.

Lesson 5A

Understand Multiplication

Name: ____________________

Prerequisite: How do you show and write multiplication?

Study the example showing multiplication with an array and a number sentence. Then solve problems 1–5.

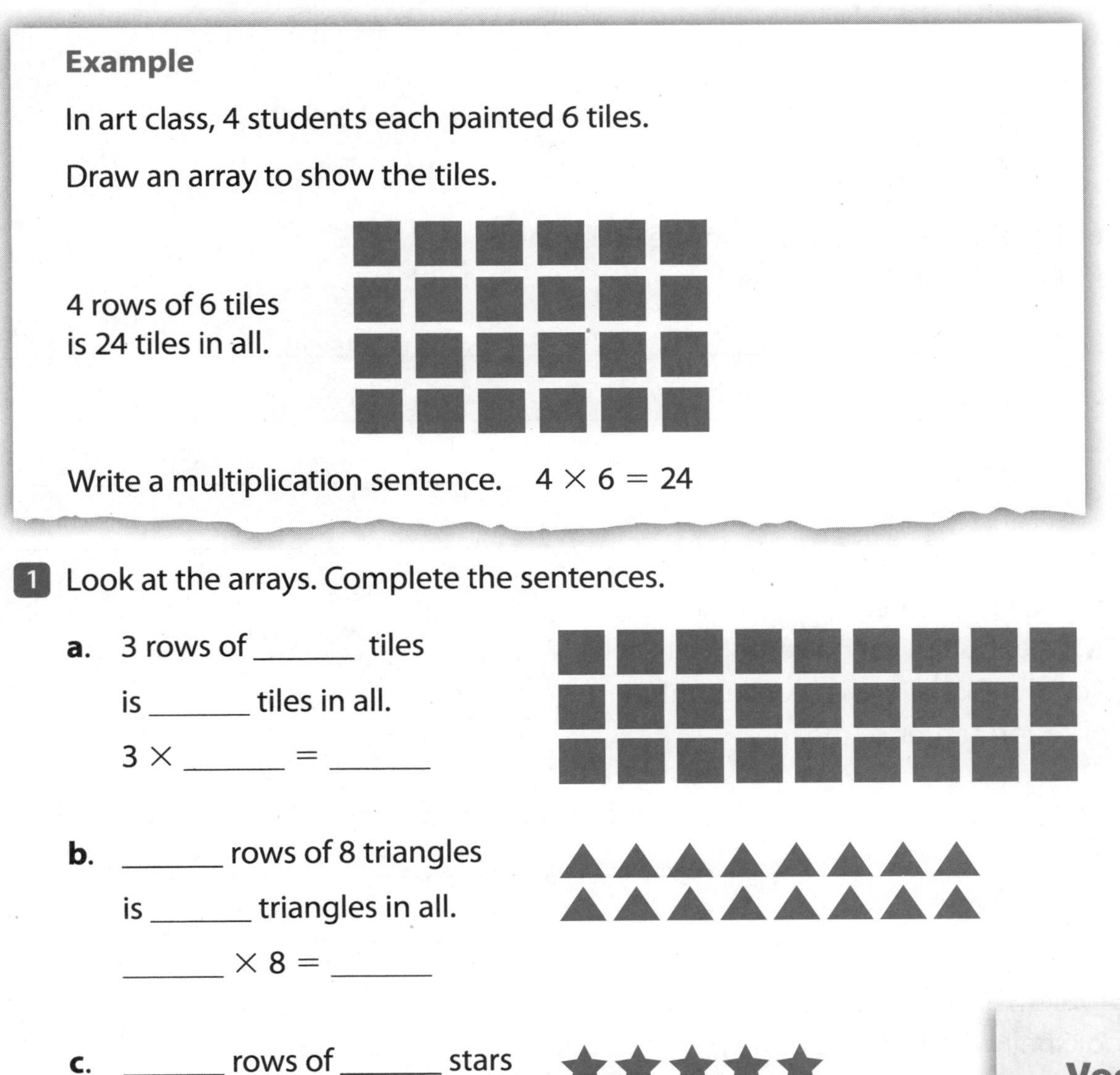

Example

In art class, 4 students each painted 6 tiles.

Draw an array to show the tiles.

4 rows of 6 tiles is 24 tiles in all.

Write a multiplication sentence. $4 \times 6 = 24$

1 Look at the arrays. Complete the sentences.

a. 3 rows of ______ tiles

is ______ tiles in all.

$3 \times$ ______ $=$ ______

b. ______ rows of 8 triangles

is ______ triangles in all.

______ $\times 8 =$ ______

c. ______ rows of ______ stars

is ______ stars in all.

______ $\times$ ______ $=$ ______

Vocabulary

multiplication an operation used to find the total number of items in equal-sized groups.

Solve.

2 Each of 3 students in a book club read 7 books. Draw an array and write a multiplication sentence to show the number of books read.

3 Write a word problem that could be modeled by the multiplication sentence $6 \times 8 = 48$.

____

____

____

____

4 Leila's bookshelf has 4 shelves. Each shelf has 9 books. Write a multiplication sentence to tell about the books. Explain what each number in the multiplication sentence means.

____

____

____

5 Look at problem 4. Suppose Leila moves her books onto a bookshelf with 6 shelves. She puts an equal number of books on each shelf. Describe what the array for this problem looks like and write a multiplication sentence.

____

____

Name: ______________________

Show Multiplication

Study the example showing how a bar model is used to show multiplication as a comparison. Then solve problems 1–7.

Example

Harris rides his bike 5 blocks to school. Daniel rides his bike 3 times as far as Harris. How far does Daniel ride his bike to school?

You can use a bar model to show multiplication as a comparison.

15 is 3 times as many as 5.
$15 = 3 \times 5$

Harris | 5 |

Daniel | 5 | 5 | 5 |

15

1 Use the bar model to the right to describe the comparison and write an equation.

| 6 |

| 6 | 6 | 6 | 6 | 6 | 6 | 6 | 6 |

48

48 is _______ times as many as _______.

_______ = _______ × _______

2 Draw and label a bar model to show a number that is 5 times as many as 7.

3 Write a word problem that the bar model in problem 2 could represent.

____

____

____

Solve.

4 Tara scored 6 times as many soccer goals as Leah during one season. Leah scored 3 goals. Draw a bar model and write an equation that represents the number of goals Tara scored.

5 What two comparisons does the equation $4 \times 2 = 8$ show?

a. _______ is _______ times as many as _______.

b. _______ is _______ times as many as _______.

6 Draw two different bar models to represent $2 \times 4 = 8$.

7 A pet caretaker walks dogs 9 times a day. He walks dogs from Monday to Friday, 5 days a week. Draw and label a bar model to show the total number of times the caretaker walks dogs in a week.

Name: ______________________

Reason and Write

Study the example. Underline two parts that you think make it a particularly good answer and a helpful example.

Example

Sylvie needs 2 cups of flour to make one loaf of bread. She wants to make 3 loaves of bread. She says she needs 5 cups of flour.

Is Sylvie correct? What did she do right? What did she do wrong?

Show your work. Use a bar model, an equation, and words to explain.

Sylvie is not correct. She used the numbers 2 and 3, but she added $2 + 3$ instead of multiplying 2×3.

Sylvie needs 2 cups of flour for one loaf of bread, so she needs 3 times as many cups of flour for 3 loaves of bread.

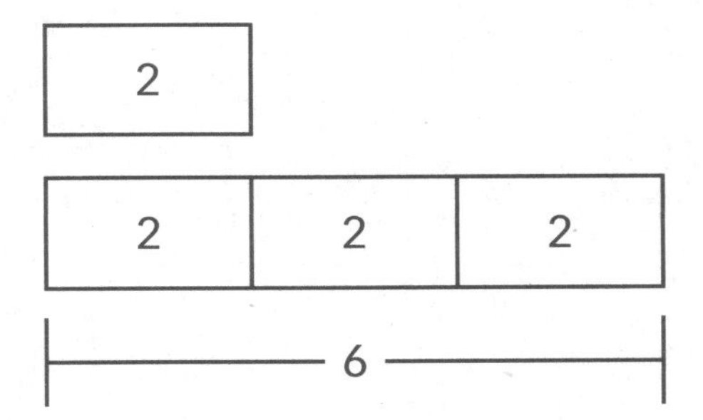

6 is 3 times as many as 2.
$6 = 3 \times 2$

Sylvie needs 6 cups of flour to make 3 loaves of bread.

Where does the example ...

- answer the questions?
- use a bar model to explain?
- use numbers in an equation to explain?
- use words to explain?

Solve the problem. Use what you learned from the model.

Victor needs 3 teaspoons of salt to make dough for one pizza. He wants to make dough for 8 pizzas. Victor says he needs 24 teaspoons of salt.

Is Victor correct? What did he do right? What did he do wrong?

Show your work. Use a bar model, an equation, and words to explain.

Did you . . .

- answer the questions?
- use a bar model to explain?
- use numbers in an equation to explain?
- use words to explain?

Dear Family,

This week your child is learning about how to use multiplication properties.

Your child is learning about using order, grouping, and renaming to solve multiplication problems.

- This model is about order. It shows that $5 \times 4 = 4 \times 5$.
- The **factors** are the numbers that are multiplied. There are 4 and 5 shown in both arrays.
- You can change the order of the factors and the **product** does not change. The product is the result of multiplying factors, and the product is 20 in both models.

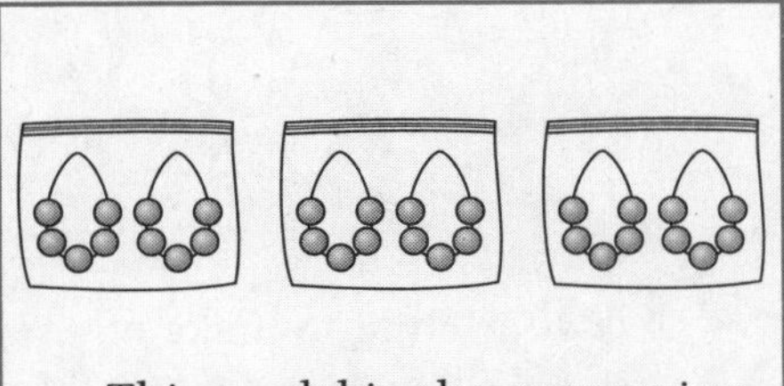

- This model is about grouping.
- There are 5 beads on each bracelet, 2 bracelets in each bag, and 3 bags.
- You need to find $5 \times 2 \times 3$ to find the total number of beads.
- Here are two ways to group the factors:
  $(5 \times 2) \times 3 \rightarrow 10 \times 3 = 30$
  $5 \times (2 \times 3) \rightarrow 5 \times 6 = 30$
  There are a total of 30 beads.

- This model is about renaming a factor to find the product.
  The model on the left shows 3×6.
  The model on the right shows that the factor 6 is renamed as $(5 + 1)$.
- You can find the product of 3×6 by finding $3 \times (5 + 1)$.
  $3 \times (5 + 1) \rightarrow (3 \times 5) + (3 \times 1) \rightarrow 15 + 3 = 18$

Invite your child to share what he or she knows about multiplication properties by doing the following activity together.

Multiplication Properties Activity

Materials: 50 identical objects, such as pennies or beans

With your child, arrange the objects to show that the product of 4×2 and 2×4 is the same.

- Ask your child to make other arrangements, such as 6×3 and 3×6, or 2×9 and 9×2.

Next, have your child arrange the objects to show renaming a factor.

- Arrange the objects in 5 rows with 9 objects in each row.
- Separate the columns: 5 rows with 3 objects in each row
  5 rows with 6 objects in each row
- Ask your child to write an expression to show renaming. The expression will be $5 \times 9 = 5 \times (3 + 6)$ or $(5 \times 3) + (5 \times 6)$.
- Ask your child to experiment with different ways to rename 9 in the previous problem, such as $(4 + 5)$, or $(2 + 7)$. Which way makes it easier to multiply?

Use Multiplication Properties

Name: ______________________

Prerequisite: Multiply Two Numbers in Different Ways

Study the example showing the results of multiplying two numbers in different ways. Then solve problems 1–6.

Example

Ms. Simon is planning a camping trip for her youth group. In one plan, there will be 4 tents with 3 girls in each tent. In another plan, there will be 3 tents with 4 girls in each tent. How many girls are going on the camping trip?

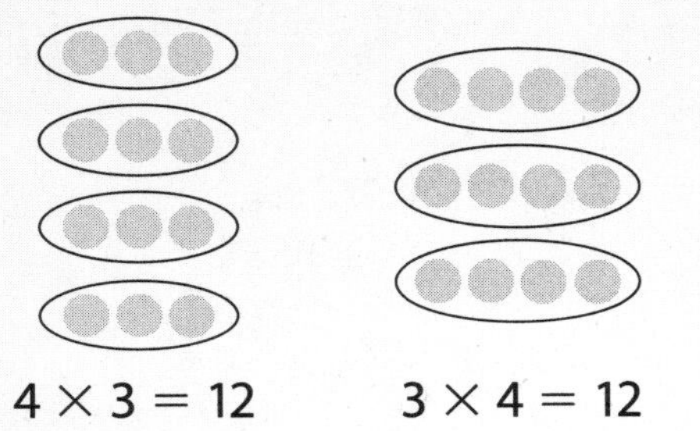

$4 \times 3 = 12$ $3 \times 4 = 12$

Both plans show that 12 girls are going on the camping trip.

1 Why are the factors in both equations the same in the example?

____

____

____

2 How are the factors in the two equations in the example different? Explain why they are different.

____

____

____

Vocabulary

factor a number that is multiplied.

product the result of multiplication.

equation a mathematical statement that uses an equal sign (=) to show that two expressions have the same value.

Solve.

3 An art teacher displays 15 clay sculptures in 3 rows with 5 in each row. What is another way the teacher could display the sculptures in rows with an equal number in each row? Use equations to explain your answer.

____

____

____

4 The array shows $2 \times 5 = 10$. Draw an array that shows $5 \times 2 = 10$.

5 If you know that $3 \times 8 = 24$, what other multiplication fact do you know?

____

6 A store sells party hats in packs of 4 and whistles in packs of 6. Ana needs 24 hats and 24 whistles. She buys 6 packs of party hats. How many packs of whistles does she buy? Explain your answer.

____

____

____

Name: ______________________

Use Order to Multiply

Study the example showing how to use order to multiply. Then solve problems 1–5.

Example

Erik went on 5 rides each day for 4 days at the county fair. Jillian went on 4 rides each day for 5 days at the fair. Without multiplying, explain how you know they rode the same number of rides.

The expression 4×5 represents Erik's rides.
The expression 5×4 represents Jillian's rides.

The factors in each expression are the same, but their order is different. If the factors are the same, the product is the same because changing the order of the factors does not change the product.

1 Jess bought 4 large posters for $9 each. Eva bought 9 small posters, each for the same price. Jess and Eva spent the same amount. How much did Eva spend on each poster? Explain how you know.

____

____

____

2 Nick put 5 balls each in 7 bins. Henry put 7 balls each in 5 bins. How many balls each did each student put in the bins?

____

Vocabulary

commutative property of multiplication changing the order of the factors does not change the product.

Solve.

3 Randee is arranging icons on her smart phone. She makes 5 rows with 4 icons in each row. Her friend Leah has a different type of smart phone. Her phone has the same number of icons as Randee, but hers are in 4 rows. Tell whether each statement about the icons is *True* or *False*.

a. There are 4 icons in each row on Leah's phone. ☐ True ☐ False

b. There are 5 icons in each row on Leah's phone. ☐ True ☐ False

c. There are 20 icons on each phone. ☐ True ☐ False

d. There are 24 icons on each phone. ☐ True ☐ False

4 A coach made 3 swim teams with 6 students on each team. He also made 6 relay teams with 3 students on each team. Did the coach put more students on the swim team or on the relay team? Explain.

____

____

____

5 Lana put all 56 rocks in her collection in a box with 8 rows. The same number of rocks is in each row. Then she rearranged her rocks into 7 rows with the same number of rocks in each row. How many rocks are in each of her rearranged rows?

____

Name: ______________________

Use Grouping to Multiply

Study the example showing how to use grouping to multiply. Then solve problems 1–6.

Example

Nate bought 5 boxes of comic books. Each box has 6 sleeves. There are 3 comic books in each sleeve. How many comic books did Nate buy in all?

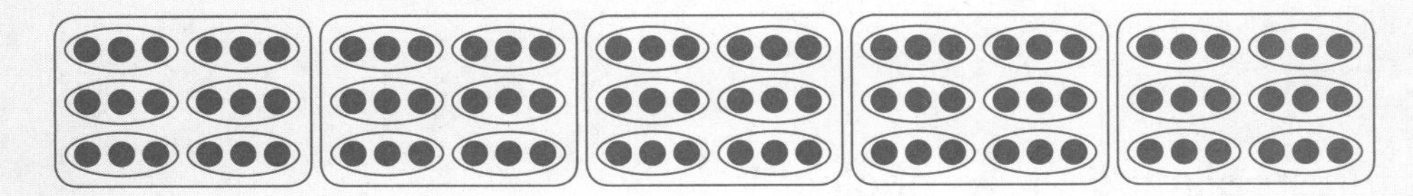

Write an expression with parentheses to group the factors. Then solve the problem.

$(5 \times 6) \times 3 \longrightarrow 30 \times 3 = 90$

Nate bought 90 comics in all.

1 Show two different ways to group the factors in the following problem. Then find the product using each grouping method.

$2 \times 6 \times 3$

2 Eight schools in a district are sending students to an environmental conference. Each school is sending 2 students from each of 5 grades. How many students are attending the conference?

Show your work.

Solution: ______________

Vocabulary

associative property of multiplication changing the grouping of three or more factors does not change the product.

Solve.

3 At a hobby shop, there are 4 sections of models. There are 3 shelves in each section and 5 models on each shelf. What is the total number of models? Group the factors with parentheses to solve.

Show your work.

Solution: ____________

4 Rangers in 3 state forests planted 6 rows of pine trees with 4 pine trees in each row. How many pine trees did the rangers plant in all?

____

5 Two groups of students are going on a field trip to the observatory. There are 7 students in each group. Tickets cost $6 each. What is the total cost of the tickets? Show three ways to solve the problem. (Remember that you can write the factors in any order.)

Show your work. Use parentheses.

Solution: ____________

6 Maya posted flyers about recycling in 3 buildings. She posted flyers on 3 floors of the buildings, and she posted 8 flyers on each floor. How many poster did Maya post?

____

Name: ____________________

Rename Numbers to Multiply

Study the example showing how to rename numbers to multiply. Then solve problems 1–5.

Example

Raoul gave 4 pencils each to 6 of his friends. How many pencils did he give to his friends in all? Rename one of the numbers to find the answer.

x x x x → x x x x x
x x x x → x x x x x
x x x x → x x x x x
x x x x → x x x x x
x x x x → x x x x x
x x x x → x x x x x

6 groups of 4 → 6 groups of 5

Raoul used subtraction to rename 4 as $5 - 1$.

$6 \times 4 \rightarrow 6(5 - 1) \rightarrow (6 \times 5) - (6 \times 1) \rightarrow 30 - 6 = 24$

Raoul gave his friends 24 pencils in all.

1 Lina drew this model to help find 6×8. Show the math equations she used to find the product.

x x x x x   x x x
x x x x x   x x x
x x x x x   x x x
x x x x x   x x x
x x x x x   x x x
x x x x x   x x x

____

____

2 Nina wants to find the answer to 5×7. She knows the answer to 5×2. Write an expression to show the next step for finding the answer.

____

Vocabulary

distributive property when one of the factors of a product is written as a sum, multiplying each addend by the other factor before adding does not change the product.

Solve.

3 Victor sent 7 postcards each to 9 friends. How many total postcards did Victor send? Rename one of the numbers to find the answer. Show two different ways to find the answer.

Show your work.

Solution: ______________________

4 Tell whether you can use the expression to find the answer to $3(2 + 6)$. Choose *Yes* or *No*.

a. $6 + 18$ ☐ Yes ☐ No

b. $6 + 6$ ☐ Yes ☐ No

c. $(3 \times 2) + (3 \times 6)$ ☐ Yes ☐ No

d. $6 + (3 \times 6)$ ☐ Yes ☐ No

5 Alberto wants to find the product of 7 and 4. He knows the product of 7 and 5. Draw a model that would help Alberto. Show the equations that can be used find the product.

Show your work.

Solution: ______________________

____

Name: ______________________

Use Multiplication Properties

Solve the problems.

1 Rami is making an app with 12 buttons arranged as an array. There must be at least 2 rows, and there must be at least 2 buttons in each row. Tell whether each array or expression could show the buttons on the app. Choose *Yes* or *No*.

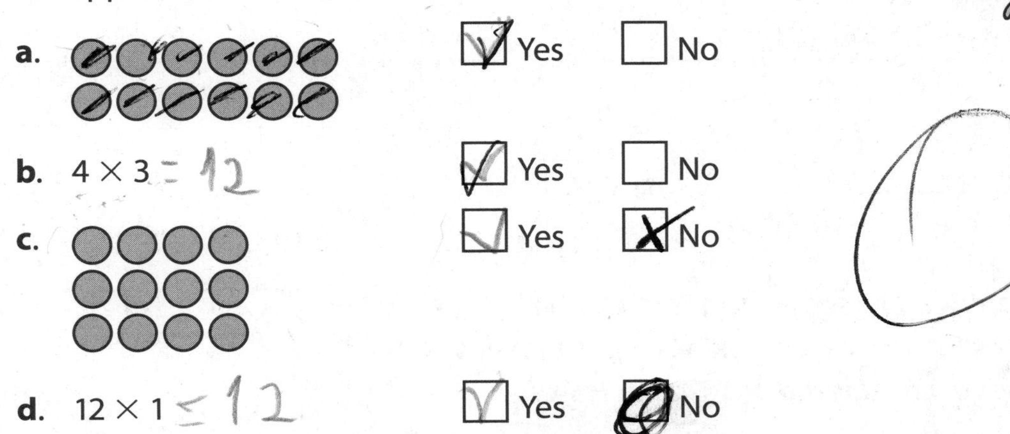

a. ☐ Yes ☐ No

b. 4 × 3 ☐ Yes ☐ No

c. ☐ Yes ☐ No

d. 12 × 1 ☐ Yes ☐ No

2 At an ocean lab, there are 3 rooms of tide pools with 9 tide pools in each room. There are 2 starfish in each tide pool. Explain how you can use either grouping or ordering with grouping to find the total number of starfish in the lab. Then show two different ways to find the answer.

Which two factors can you group to make the multiplication easier?

____

____

____

____

____

____

____

Solve.

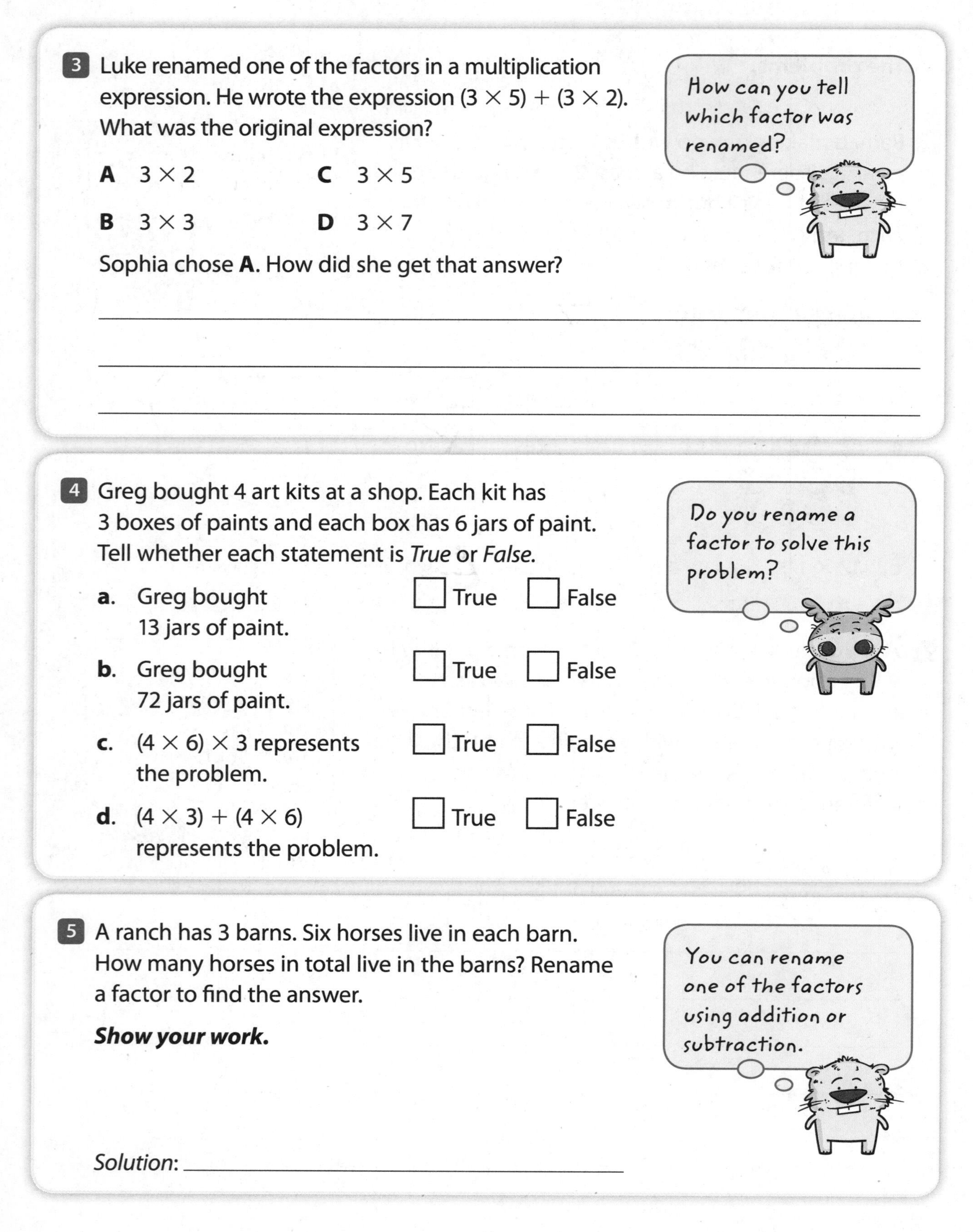

3 Luke renamed one of the factors in a multiplication expression. He wrote the expression $(3 \times 5) + (3 \times 2)$. What was the original expression?

A 3×2 **C** 3×5

B 3×3 **D** 3×7

Sophia chose **A**. How did she get that answer?

____

____

____

4 Greg bought 4 art kits at a shop. Each kit has 3 boxes of paints and each box has 6 jars of paint. Tell whether each statement is *True* or *False*.

a. Greg bought 13 jars of paint. ☐ True ☐ False

b. Greg bought 72 jars of paint. ☐ True ☐ False

c. $(4 \times 6) \times 3$ represents the problem. ☐ True ☐ False

d. $(4 \times 3) + (4 \times 6)$ represents the problem. ☐ True ☐ False

5 A ranch has 3 barns. Six horses live in each barn. How many horses in total live in the barns? Rename a factor to find the answer.

Show your work.

Solution: ______________________________

Dear Family,

This week your child is learning about multiplication and division in word problems.

Your child might see a problem like this:

Market Street sells bags of 8 apples. Mark needs 5 times that amount. How many apples does Mark need?

You can use a bar model to help understand the problem.

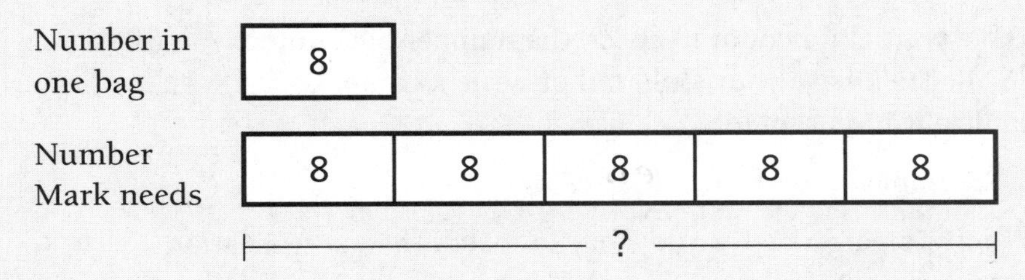

Then you can use the bar model to write an equation to help understand the problem.

$5 \times$ number of apples in one bag $=$ total apples needed

$5 \times 8 = \square$

Solve the equation.

$5 \times 8 = 40$

The answer to the problem is that Mark needs 40 apples.

Invite your child to share what he or she knows about multiplication and division in word problems by doing the following activity together.

Multiplication and Division in Word Problems Activity

Do an activity with your child to practice multiplication in word problems.

Materials: number cube, 40 counters such as pennies, beans, or paper clips

- Have your child roll the number cube first. Your child takes that number of counters and records the number.

  Example: Your child rolls a 4 and takes 4 counters.

- Then you roll the number cube. This number tells you how many times the number of your child's counters you take.

  Example: You roll a 3. You take 3 times as many counters as your child. You take 12 counters.

- Have your child count to check the number of counters you get in all. Then have your child tell or write a comparison multiplication sentence.

  Example: $3 \times 4 = 12$

- Finally, create a real-world story to match the multiplication sentence.

Tess has 4 seashells. I have 3 times as many seashells as Tess. I have 12 seashells.

Multiplication and Division in Word Problems

Name: ____________________

Prerequisite: Model Multiplication

Study the example showing how to use a model to solve a multiplication problem. Then solve problems 1–6.

Example

Lauren worked 4 hours last week. She worked 3 times as many hours this week as last week. How many hours did Lauren work this week?

Last week [4]

This week [4][4][4]

|—— 12 ——|

12 is 3 times as many as 4.

$12 = 3 \times 4$

Lauren worked 12 hours this week.

1 Nina picked 8 tomatoes last month. She picked 4 times as many tomatoes this month. How many tomatoes did Nina pick this month?

Label the bar model and complete the sentences.

Last month [ ]

This month [ ][ ][ ][ ]

_______ is _______ times as many as _______ .

_______ = _______ × _______

Nina picked _______ tomatoes this month.

2 Ben has 6 marbles. Tom has 3 times as many marbles as Ben. How many marbles does Tom have?

6 6 6

0 6 12 18

_______ × _______ = 18

Tom has _______ marbles.

Vocabulary

multiplication an operation used to find the total number of items in equal-sized groups.

Solve.

3 Yesterday Ruth scored 2 points at the game. Today she scored 8 times as many points as she did yesterday. How many points did Ruth score today?

Show your work.

Solution: ______________________________

4 Matt planted 5 times as many flowers on Sunday as he planted on Saturday. Matt planted 7 flowers on Saturday. How many flowers did Matt plant on Sunday?

Show your work.

Solution: ______________________________

5 Mr. Ash has 7 students in art class. Mr. Trent has double the number of students in his class as Mr. Ash. How many students does Mr. Trent have in his class?

Show your work.

Solution: ______________________________

6 Which is more: 2 times as many as a number or 5 times as many as the same number? Explain. Choose any number to show how you know.

____

____

____

____

Name: ____________________

Use Multiplication in Word Problems

Study the example showing one way to use multiplication to solve a word problem. Then solve problems 1–5.

Example

Sue swam 4 laps in a pool. Andy swam 5 times as many laps as Sue. How many laps did Andy swim?

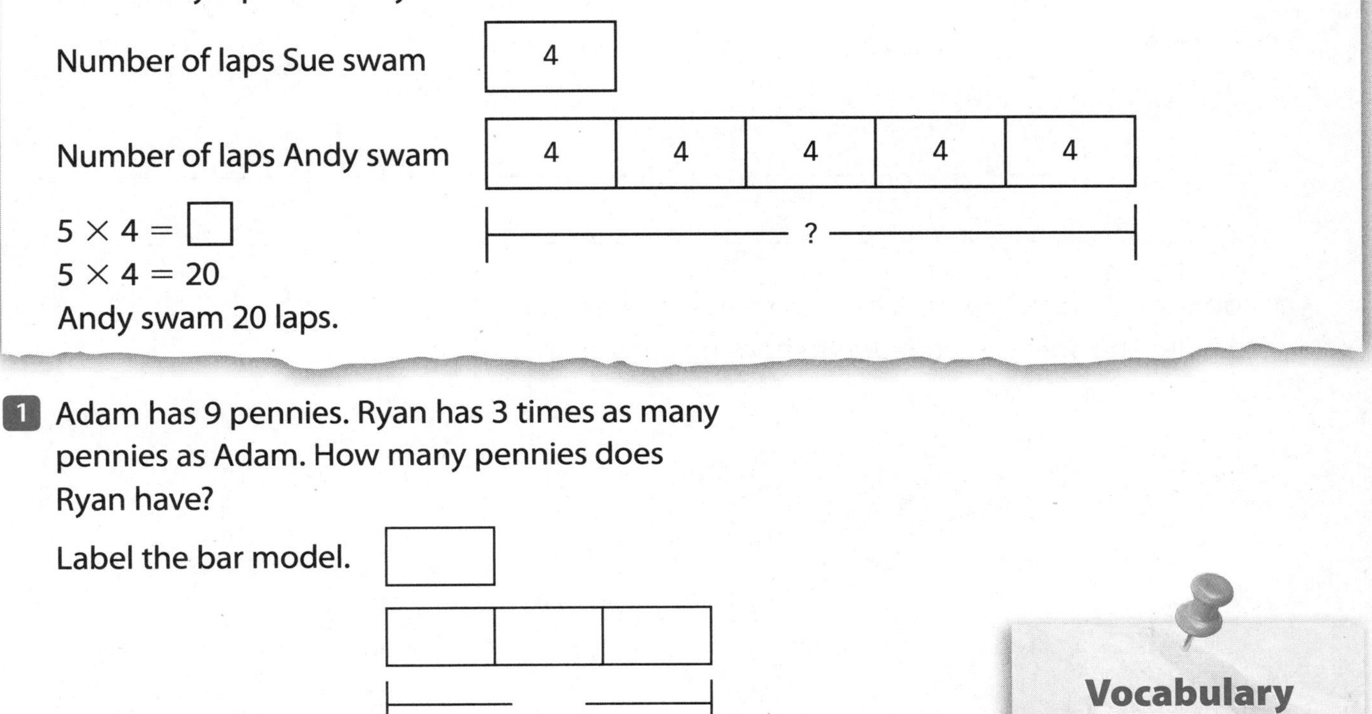

$5 \times 4 = \square$

$5 \times 4 = 20$

Andy swam 20 laps.

1 Adam has 9 pennies. Ryan has 3 times as many pennies as Adam. How many pennies does Ryan have?

Label the bar model.

Write an equation.

Use $\square$ for the unknown. ____ × ____ = ____

Solve the equation. ______________

Write the answer. Ryan has ____ pennies.

2 Jade picked 5 pounds of berries. She needs 3 times that amount to make jam. How many pounds of berries does Jade need to make jam?

Skip count to find the amount Jade needs:

5, ______, ______.

Jade needs ______________________________.

Vocabulary

unknown a missing number in an equation.

$\square = 5 \times 4$

$\square$ is the unknown.

$6 \times 7 = P$

P is the unknown.

equation a mathematical sentence that uses an equal sign (=) to show that two expressions have the same value.

$5 \times 4 = 20$

Solve.

3 Look at how a student solved the problem below.

> A cook used 12 eggs at lunch. He used 3 times as many eggs at breakfast. How many eggs did the cook use at breakfast?
>
> Skip count: 12, 24, 36, 48
> The cook used 48 eggs at breakfast.

What did the student do wrong?

___

___

4 Look at problem 3. Draw a bar model. Use the model to write and solve an equation to find the correct answer.

Solution: The cook used ________________ at breakfast.

5 Which problems can be solved using the equation $8 \times 2 = A$? Circle the letter of all that apply.

A In June, Ali read 8 books. In July, she read half as many books. How many books did Ali read in July?

B Cal is twice as old as his sister. Cal's sister is 8 years old. How old is Cal?

C A muffin costs $2. Dylan bought 8 muffins. How much did Dylan spend on muffins?

D Jordan has 8 apples and 2 oranges. How many pieces of fruit does she have altogether?

Name: ____________________

Use Division in Word Problems

Study the example showing a way to use division to solve a word problem. Then solve problems 1–5.

Example

The Tigers scored 36 points. They scored 4 times as many points as the Lions. How many points did the Lions score?

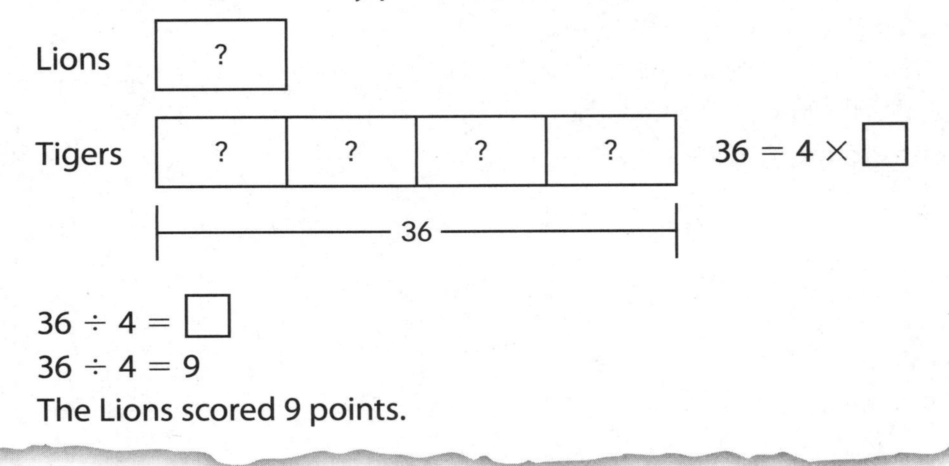

$36 \div 4 = \square$

$36 \div 4 = 9$

The Lions scored 9 points.

1 Charlie and Gabe collected cans to recycle. Charlie collected 5 times as many cans as Gabe. Charlie collected 50 cans. Draw a bar model you could use to compare the number of cans each boy collected.

2 Look at the model you drew in problem 1. Write and solve an equation to show how many cans Gabe collected.

Show your work.

Solution: ____________________

Vocabulary

division an operation used to separate a number of items into equal-sized groups.

equation a mathematical sentence that uses an equal sign (=) to show that two expressions have the same value.

$36 \div 4 = 9$

Solve.

3 Choose *Yes* or *No* to tell whether each equation is solved correctly.

a.	$6 = 2 \times \square$	$\square = 12$	☐ Yes	☐ No
b.	$7 \times H = 28$	$H = 4$	☐ Yes	☐ No
c.	$2 = p \div 5$	$p = 10$	☐ Yes	☐ No

4 James and Chris are in the school play. James has 42 lines to memorize. That is 6 times as many lines as Chris. Write and solve an equation to find the number of lines Chris has to memorize.

Show your work.

Solution: ______________________

5 Choose numbers from the tiles below to fill in the bar model. Then write and solve an equation using the model.

24 12 8 6 4 3 2 1

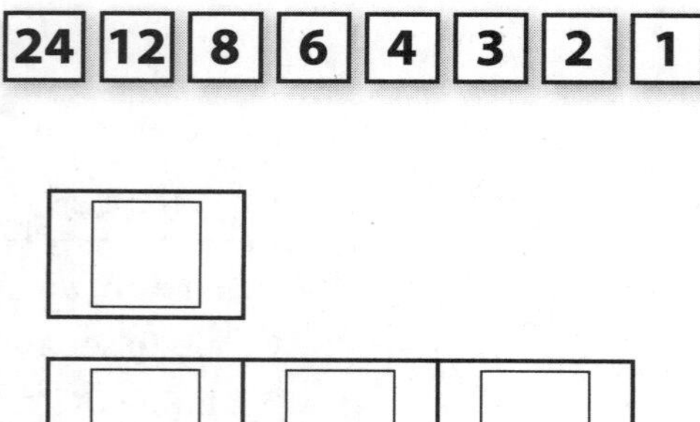

Equation: ______________________

Solution: ______________________

Name: ______________________________

Multiplication and Division in Word Problems

Solve the problems.

1 Lin and Karla are planning a party. Lin spent $20 on invitations and decorations. Karla spent 4 times that amount on food and entertainment. How much did they spend altogether on the party?

A $20

B $80

C $100

D $120

Do you need to use more than one operation to find the answer?

2 Write and solve an equation for each problem below.

Darcy earned $5. Samantha earned $30. Samantha earned ______ times as much as Darcy.

Equation: ______________________________

Solution: ______________________________

Carey teaches twice as many fitness classes as Fran. If Fran teaches 7 classes, how many classes does Carey teach?

Equation: ______________________________

Solution: ______________________________

Joelle practices piano for 3 times as many minutes a day as Tran. Tran practices for 20 minutes a day. How many minutes a day does Joelle practice?

Equation: ______________________________

Solution: ______________________________

You can write either a multiplication equation or a division equation for each problem.

Solve.

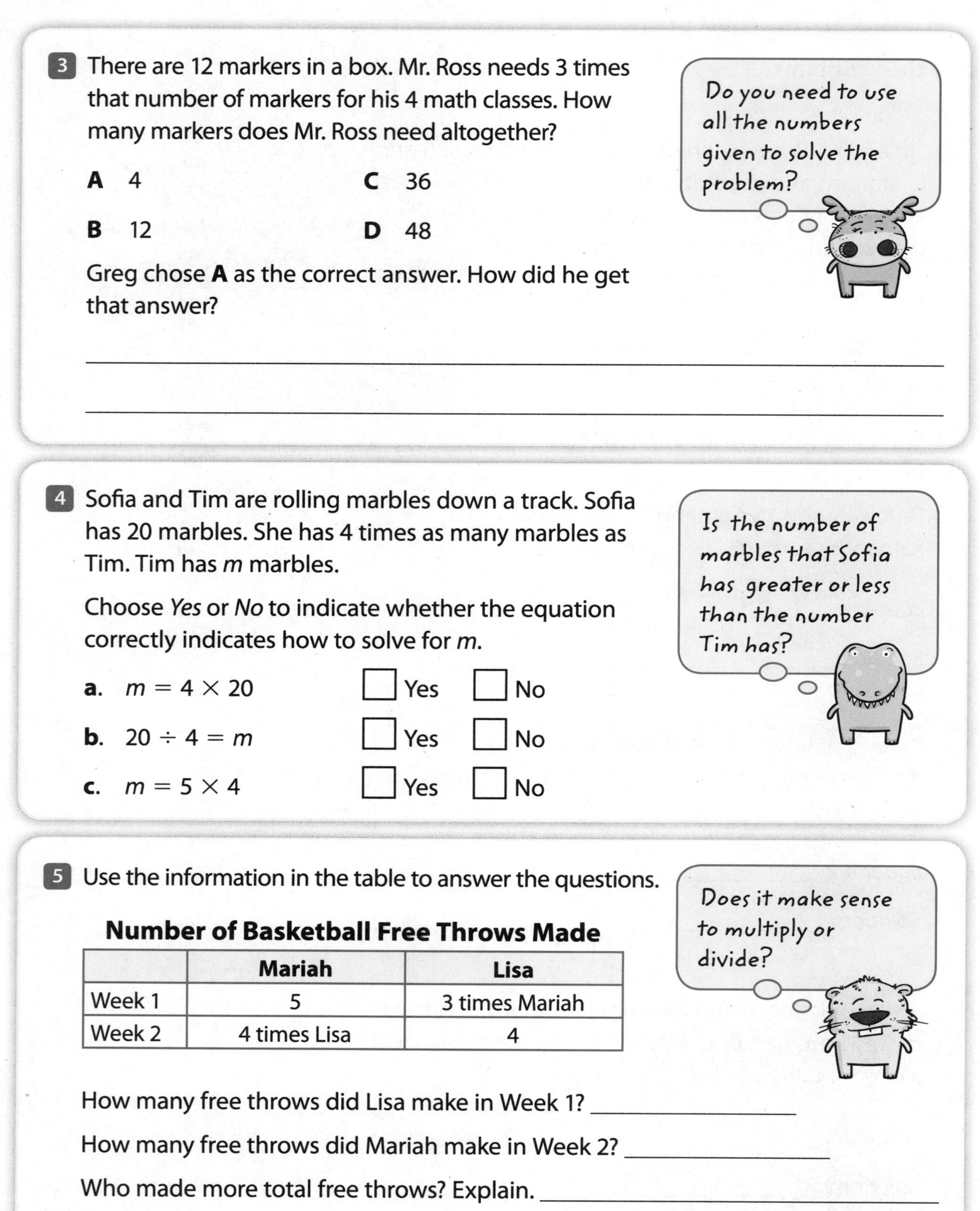

3 There are 12 markers in a box. Mr. Ross needs 3 times that number of markers for his 4 math classes. How many markers does Mr. Ross need altogether?

A 4

B 12

C 36

D 48

Greg chose **A** as the correct answer. How did he get that answer?

____

____

4 Sofia and Tim are rolling marbles down a track. Sofia has 20 marbles. She has 4 times as many marbles as Tim. Tim has *m* marbles.

Choose *Yes* or *No* to indicate whether the equation correctly indicates how to solve for *m*.

a. $m = 4 \times 20$ ☐ Yes ☐ No

b. $20 \div 4 = m$ ☐ Yes ☐ No

c. $m = 5 \times 4$ ☐ Yes ☐ No

5 Use the information in the table to answer the questions.

Number of Basketball Free Throws Made

	Mariah	Lisa
Week 1	5	3 times Mariah
Week 2	4 times Lisa	4

How many free throws did Lisa make in Week 1? ____________

How many free throws did Mariah make in Week 2? ____________

Who made more total free throws? Explain. ____________

____

Dear Family,

This week your child is learning about multiples and factors.

factor pair: two numbers that are multiplied together to give a product.

multiple: the product of the number and any other whole number (0, 4, 8, 12, etc., are multiples of 4).

composite number: a number that has more than one pair of factors.

Your child might see a problem like this:

> Monica is pasting 40 stars in rows on the wall. She wants to put the same number of stars in each row. Find all the ways she can arrange the stars.

One way to paste the stars is 5 rows of 8.
Another way is 8 rows of 5.
5 and 8 are a **factor pair**.

Other ways to paste the stars are:
10 rows of 4 or 4 rows of 10
2 rows of 20 or 20 rows of 2
1 row of 40 or 40 rows of 1

40 is a **composite number**. Factor pairs of 40 are:
5 and 8, 10 and 4, 2 and 20, 1 and 40.

40 is a **multiple** of 1, 2, 4, 5, 8, and 10.

Invite your child to share what he or she knows about multiples and factors by doing the following activity together.

Factors Activity

Do an activity with your child to practice finding factors of a number.

Materials: 2 number cubes

- One player rolls both number cubes and uses the numbers on the cubes to create a 2-digit number.
- The other player reverses the order of the digits to create another 2-digit number.

  Example:

Player 1: 21 Player 2: 12

- Each player finds all the factor pairs of his or her number.

  Example:
  Player 1: Factor pairs of 21 are 1 and 21, 3 and 7.
  Player 2: Factor pairs of 12 are 1 and 12, 2 and 6, 3 and 4.

- The player with the most factor pairs is the winner of the round.
- Play 5 rounds.

Multiples and Factors

Name: ____________________

Prerequisite: Use Fact Families

Study the example showing multiplication and division facts in a fact family. Then solve problems 1–6.

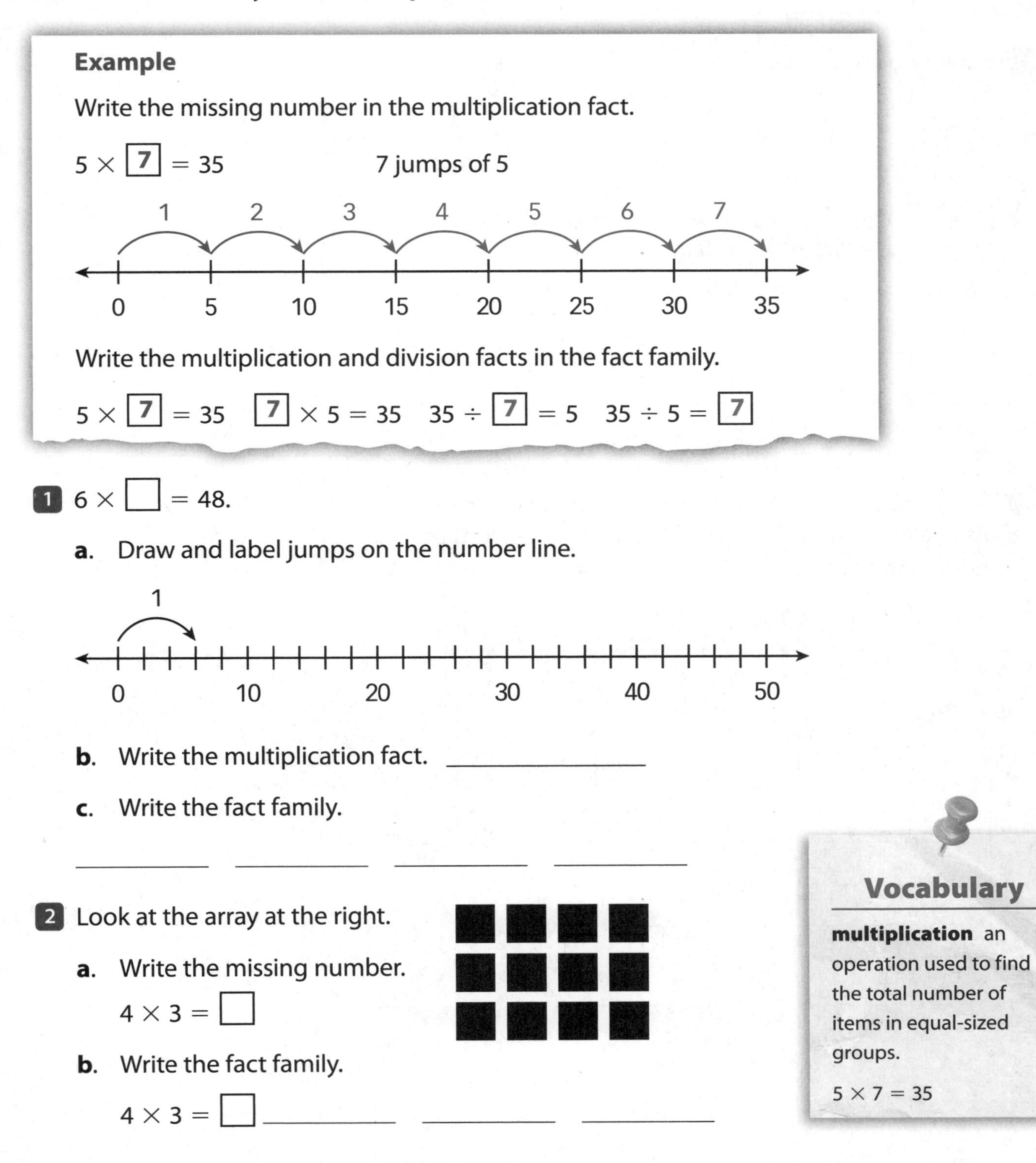

Example

Write the missing number in the multiplication fact.

$5 \times \boxed{7} = 35$ 7 jumps of 5

Write the multiplication and division facts in the fact family.

$5 \times \boxed{7} = 35$ $\boxed{7} \times 5 = 35$ $35 \div \boxed{7} = 5$ $35 \div 5 = \boxed{7}$

1 $6 \times \square = 48.$

a. Draw and label jumps on the number line.

b. Write the multiplication fact. ____________

c. Write the fact family.

__________ __________ __________ __________

2 Look at the array at the right.

a. Write the missing number.

$4 \times 3 = \square$

b. Write the fact family.

$4 \times 3 = \square$ __________ __________ __________

Vocabulary

multiplication an operation used to find the total number of items in equal-sized groups.

$5 \times 7 = 35$

Solve.

3 Write the multiplication and division facts for the fact family with the numbers 5, 6, and 30.

_______________ _______________

_______________ _______________

4 What two multiplication facts can you use to solve

$\square \div 9 = 7$?

_______________ _______________

5 Look at the multiplication and division facts below. Are they a fact family? Explain.

$4 \times 6 = 24 \quad 24 = 3 \times 8 \quad 24 \div 6 = 4 \quad 8 = 24 \div 3$

____

____

____

6 Complete each fact family. Use the numbers in the tiles below to fill in each box. You may use some tiles more than once.

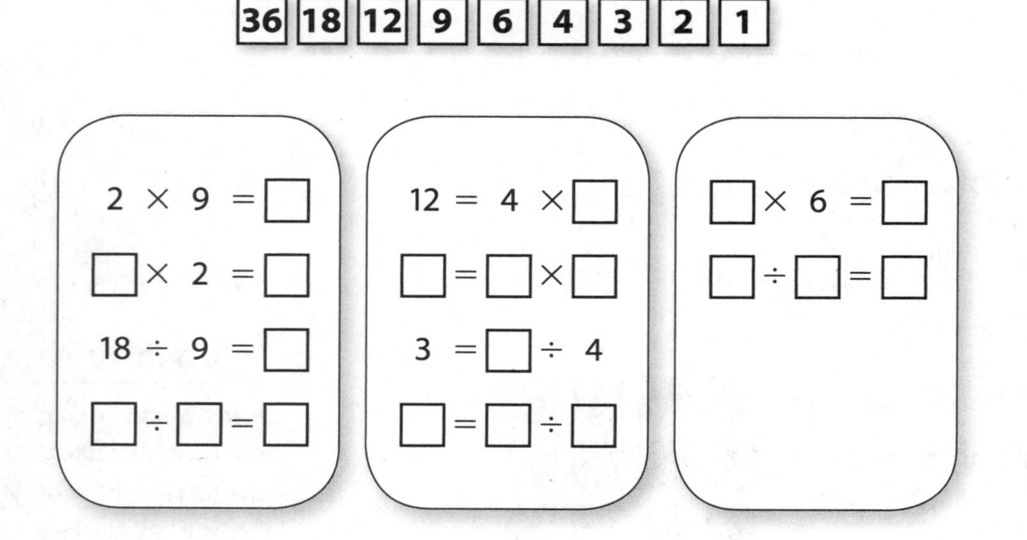

Name: ______________________

Use Multiples

Study the example showing how to use multiples to solve a word problem. Then solve problems 1–6.

Example

Markers come in boxes of 5. Paul needs 40 markers for students in the art club. Can Paul buy exactly 40 markers in boxes of 5? How many boxes does he need to buy?

Find multiples of 5.

$5 \times 1 = \mathbf{5}$	$5 \times 4 = \mathbf{20}$	$5 \times 7 = \mathbf{35}$
$5 \times 2 = \mathbf{10}$	$5 \times 5 = \mathbf{25}$	$5 \times 8 = \mathbf{40}$ (circled)
$5 \times 3 = \mathbf{15}$	$5 \times 6 = \mathbf{30}$	$5 \times 9 = \mathbf{45}$

40 is a multiple of 5.
Paul can buy exactly 40 markers in boxes of 5.
Paul needs to buy 8 boxes.

1 Skip count by 4s to find multiples of 4. Circle the multiples on the number line.

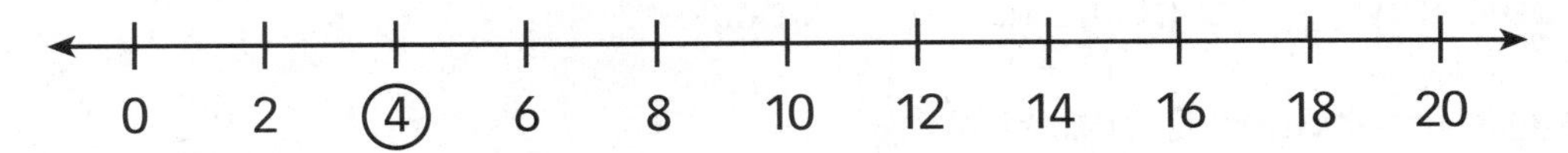

2 Complete the multiplication facts to find more multiples of 4.

$4 \times 6 =$ _____ $\qquad$ $4 \times$ _____ $=$ _____

$4 \times$ _____ $=$ _____ $\qquad$ $4 \times$ _____ $=$ _____

$4 \times$ _____ $=$ _____ $\qquad$ $4 \times$ _____ $=$ _____

3 Look at problems 1 and 2. Are these the only multiples of 4? Use words and numbers to explain.

____

____

____

Vocabulary

multiple the product of a number and any other whole number, for example, 3, 6, 9, 12, and 15 are multiples of 3.

Solve.

4 Max ordered 72 mugs. Mugs are packed 8 to a box. How many boxes of mugs did Max order?

Choose *Yes* or *No* to indicate whether the equation or statement could be used to solve the problem above.

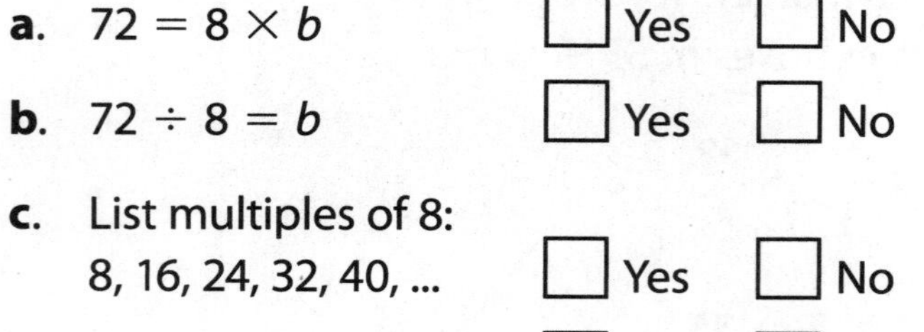

a. $72 = 8 \times b$ ☐ Yes ☐ No

b. $72 \div 8 = b$ ☐ Yes ☐ No

c. List multiples of 8: 8, 16, 24, 32, 40, ... ☐ Yes ☐ No

d. $b = 72 + 8$ ☐ Yes ☐ No

5 Cupcakes are packed 6 to a box. If Abby only buys full boxes of cupcakes, give two possible numbers of cupcakes that she could buy.

Show your work.

Solution: Abby could buy _____ cupcakes or _____ cupcakes.

6 Strawberries are sold in 1-pound, 2-pound, and 5-pound boxes. Stacy wants to buy exactly 10 pounds of strawberries. What are two ways that Stacy could buy exactly 10 pounds of strawberries? Tell which sizes of boxes she could buy and how many of each size box.

Show your work.

Solution: ____

____

Name: ____________________

Find Factors and Factor Pairs

Study the example problem about factors and factor pairs. Then solve problems 1–6.

Example

Mr. Kennedy is arranging the 16 chairs in his classroom for a presentation. He wants to put the chairs in rows with an equal number of chairs in each row. Find all the ways he can arrange the chairs.

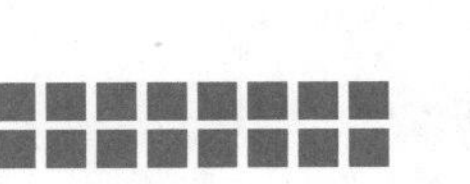

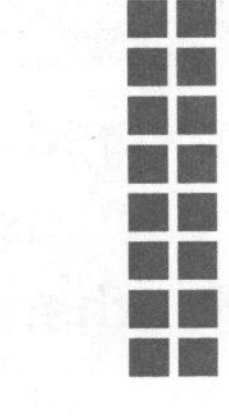

1 row of 16 chairs	2 rows of 8 chairs	4 rows of 4 chairs	8 rows of 2 chairs	16 rows of 1 chair
$1 \times 16 = 16$	$2 \times 8 = 16$	$4 \times 4 = 16$	$8 \times 2 = 16$	$16 \times 1 = 16$

Factors of 16: 1, 2, 4, 8, 16.
Factor pairs: 1 and 16, 2 and 8, 4 and 4.
Mr. Kennedy can arrange the chairs in 5 ways.

1 Complete the list to show the factors of 12.

1, _____, 3, _____, 6, _____

2 Write the factor pairs of 12.

1 and _____, _____ and _____, _____ and _____

3 The 20 students in Amanda's class each carved a wooden plate to display on the wall. They want each row to have the same number of plates. Find all the ways to display the plates.

Show your work.

Solution: ______________________________

____

Vocabulary

factor pair two numbers that are multiplied together to give a product.

$2 \times 4 = 8$, so 2 and 4 are a factor pair of 8.

Solve.

4 Tell whether each sentence about the factors of 18 is *True* or *False*.

a. All the factors of 18 are 2, 3, 6, 9, 18. ☐ True ☐ False

b. 1 and 18 are a factor pair. ☐ True ☐ False

c. 180 is a factor because $10 \times 18 = 180$. ☐ True ☐ False

d. An array showing the factor pair of 3 and 6 would have 3 rows of 6 objects. ☐ True ☐ False

5 Carlos arranged his building blocks into 2 rows of 12 blocks. Liz arranged her blocks into 6 rows of 4 blocks. If they each use the same number of blocks, what two other ways could they arrange their blocks?

Show your work.

Solution: ______________________________

____

6 Jonah has 100 flowers to arrange into vases. He wants to put the same number of flowers in each vase. List the factor pairs of 100. Then complete the table to show the different ways to arrange the flowers.

Factor pairs of 100: ______________________________

____

Number of vases									
Number of flowers in each vase									

Name: ______________________

Identify Prime and Composite Numbers

Study the example showing how to identify prime and composite numbers. Then solve problems 1–6.

Example

Ms. Morris teaches a morning class with 13 students and an afternoon class with 14 students. Which class has a prime number of students?

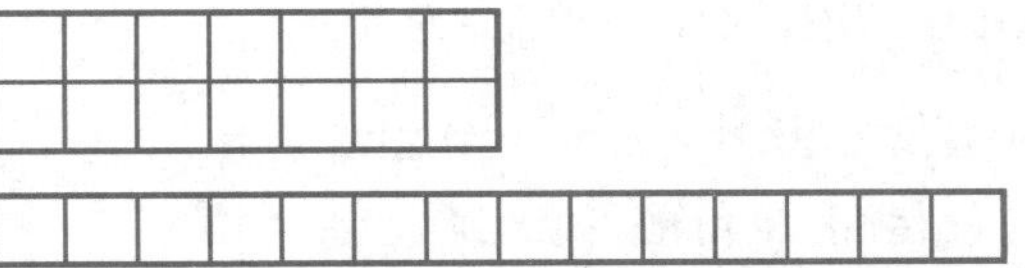

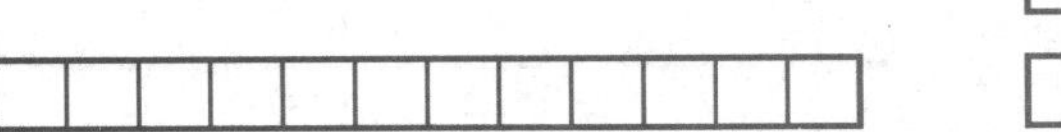

13 has one factor pair: 1 and 13
13 is a prime number.

14 has more than one factor pair: 2 and 7, 1 and 14
14 is a composite number.

The morning class has a prime number of students.

1 Is the number 2 prime or composite? Explain.

____

____

2 Kevin ran 23 laps around the track. Is the number 23 prime or composite? Explain.

____

____

3 Mae has more than 3 bracelets. She has an even number of bracelets. Is the number of bracelets a prime number or a composite number? Explain.

____

____

____

____

____

Vocabulary

prime number a number that has only one pair of factors: itself and 1.

5 is a prime number; its factors are 5 and 1.

composite number a number that has more than one pair of factors.

8 is a composite number; it has the factors 1, 2, 4, and 8.

Solve.

4 Tell whether each sentence is *True* or *False*.

a. The number 9 is prime. ☐ True ☐ False

b. 2 is the only even prime number. ☐ True ☐ False

c. All the odd numbers between 1 and 10 are prime. ☐ True ☐ False

d. Some composite numbers have only two factors. ☐ True ☐ False

5 The area of a garden is 5 square feet.

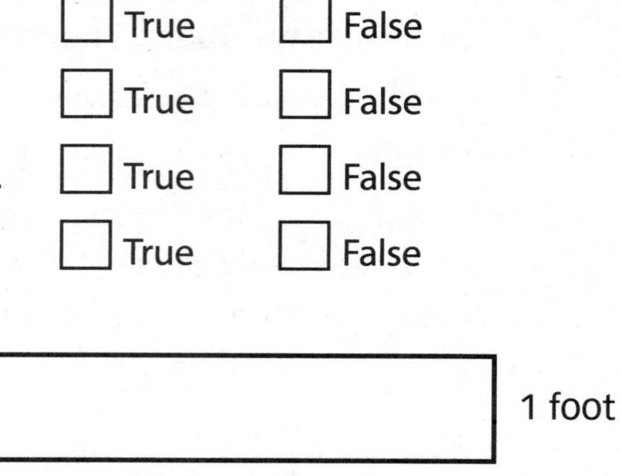

The dimensions of the garden are 1 foot and 5 feet. 1 and 5 are factors of the number 5.

a. Is the number 5 a prime number? ____________

b. If the area of a garden is 11 square feet, what could be the dimensions of the garden?

____

6 Jordan and Mitchell are planning a graduation party with 45 guests. They want to seat an equal number of guests at each table. Each table should have more than one guest. Answer the questions below.

a. List the different ways the guests and tables could be arranged. Tell how many tables are needed for each group of guests.

____

____

b. Jordan and Mitchell forgot to include themselves in the seating. They still want to have an equal number of guests at each table. List the ways the guests and tables could be arranged now.

____

____

Name: ____________________

Multiples and Factors

Solve the problems.

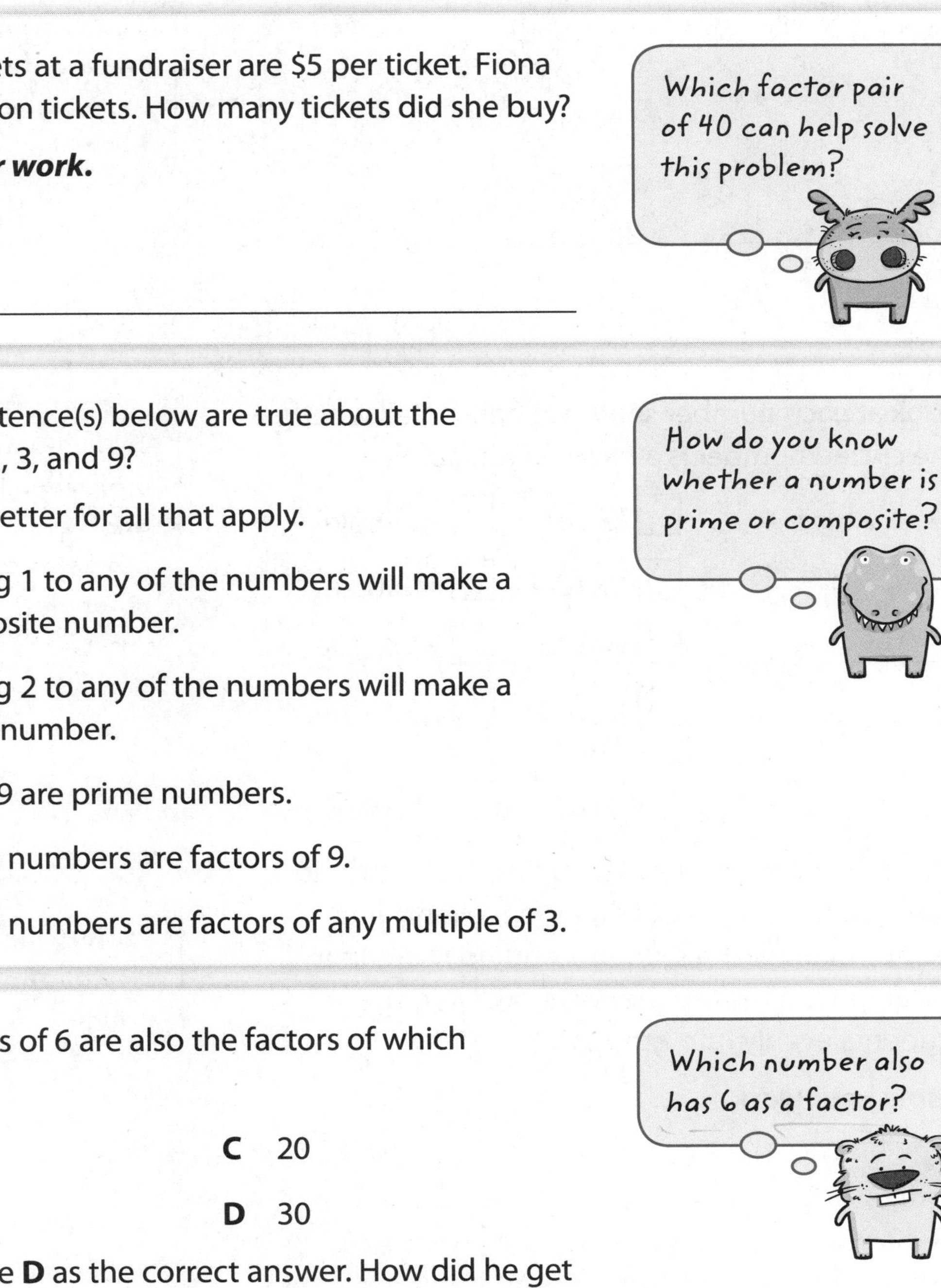

1 Raffle tickets at a fundraiser are $5 per ticket. Fiona spent $40 on tickets. How many tickets did she buy?

Show your work.

Solution: ____________________

Which factor pair of 40 can help solve this problem?

2 Which sentence(s) below are true about the numbers 1, 3, and 9?

Circle the letter for all that apply.

A Adding 1 to any of the numbers will make a composite number.

B Adding 2 to any of the numbers will make a prime number.

C 3 and 9 are prime numbers.

D All the numbers are factors of 9.

E All the numbers are factors of any multiple of 3.

How do you know whether a number is prime or composite?

3 The factors of 6 are also the factors of which number?

A 5

B 10

C 20

D 30

Mike chose **D** as the correct answer. How did he get that answer?

____

____

Solve.

4 If n = any number, what is one factor pair that you know n has?

All numbers have 1 as a factor. What is the greatest factor any number can have?

Solution: ______________________________

____

5 Look at each number sentence below. Tell whether the circled number is a *factor* or *multiple*.

a. $1 \times (4) = 4$ ☐ factor ☐ multiple

b. $4 \times 1 = (4)$ ☐ factor ☐ multiple

c. $(5) \times 1 = 5$ ☐ factor ☐ multiple

d. $(5) = 5 \times 1$ ☐ factor ☐ multiple

Is the number multiplied by another number or is it a product of two numbers?

6 There are 56 fourth graders going on a field trip. The teacher wants to divide them evenly into groups of at least 4 students and no more than 8 students. What are the ways to divide the students evenly into groups?

Show your work.

How can you use the factor pairs of 56 to find all the possible groups?

Solution: ______________________________

Dear Family,

Your child might see a number pattern like the one below. He or she is learning how to find the next numbers in the pattern.

3, 6, 9, 12, ______, ______

The rule in the number pattern is "add 3." So the next numbers are 15, 18.

Your child will identify the pattern's rule and extend the pattern. In the pattern below, the rule is that each shape has 1 more side than the shape before it.

Your child is also learning how to write pattern rules as an equation and to use the equation to complete a table. For example:

If you buy 1 piece of pizza, you get 2 free cookies. How many cookies do you get if you buy 3 pieces of pizza?

The number of Cookies you get equals 2 times the number of Pieces of pizza that you buy.

$$C = 2 \times P$$

Number of Pieces, *P*	Number of Cookies, *C*
1	2
2	4
3	6

Invite your child to share what he or she knows about patterns by doing the following activity together.

Number Pattern Activity

Do an activity with your child to practice finding patterns in numbers.

- Look at the number pattern below with your child.

11, 22, 33, 44, 55, 66, 77, 88, 99, . . .

- Work together to identify the rule for the pattern (add 11).
- Talk about other patterns you notice in the numbers.

  Examples:

  The numbers alternate between odd and even: the first number is odd, the second number is even, and so on.

  The tens and ones digits are the same in each number.

  The tens and ones digits each go up by 1 in the next number in the pattern.

- Next, look at another number pattern and work together to identify the rule for the pattern.

12, 23, 34, 45, 56, 67, 78, 89, . . .

- Talk about other patterns you notice in the numbers. Discuss how this pattern and the first pattern are alike and different.
- Challenge your child to write an equation that demonstrates the rule for the following problem: Each child eats 4 pieces of fruit. (The number of pieces of fruit is 4 times the number of children, or $F = 4C$.)
- Then, ask him or her to use the equation to tell you how many pieces of fruit 8, 9, and 10 children eat.

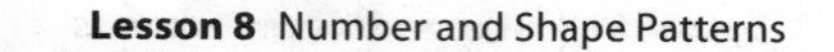

Number and Shape Patterns

Name: ____________________

Prerequisite: Identify Number Patterns

Study the example showing a number pattern. Then solve problems 1–5.

Example

Leo noticed a pattern in the addition table.
What pattern did Leo notice?
What is the rule for the pattern?
What is the next number in the pattern?

Pattern: 0, 2, 4, 6, 8
Rule: add 2

Use the rule to find the next number in the pattern:
$8 + 2 = 10$

10 is the next number in the pattern.

	0	**1**	**2**	**3**	**4**	**5**
0	0	1	2	3	4	5
1	1	2	3	4	5	6
2	2	3	4	5	6	7
3	3	4	5	6	7	8
4	4	5	6	7	8	9
5	5	6	7	8	9	?

1 Use the number line below to answer the questions.

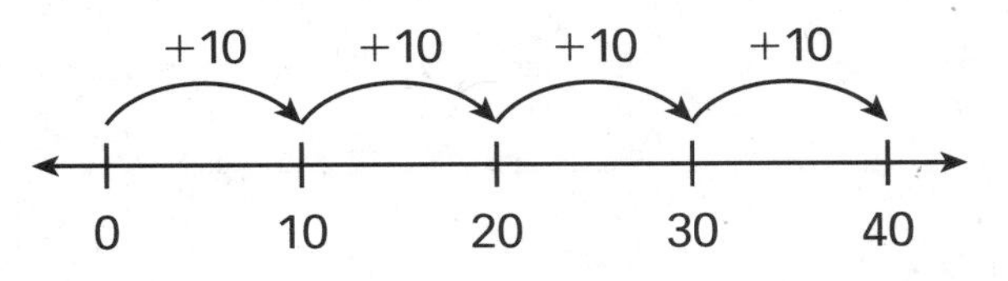

a. What pattern of numbers do you see on the number line?

0, ____, 20, ____, 40

b. What is the rule for the pattern? add ____

2 Use the number line below to answer the questions.

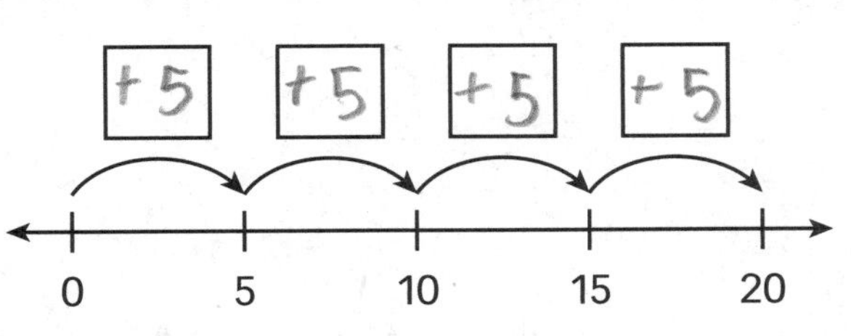

a. What pattern of numbers do you see on the number line?

____, ____, ____, ____, 20

b. Label the number line to show the rule for the pattern.

Vocabulary

number pattern a series of numbers that follow a rule to repeat or change.

rule a procedure to follow to go from one number or shape to the next in a pattern.

Solve.

3 Fill in the missing numbers to show patterns with addends and sums.

Addend	Addend	Sum
100	10	110
90	20	
80		110
	40	110
60		

4 Look at problem 3.

a. What pattern do you see in the first Addend column?

____

____

b. What pattern do you see in the second Addend column?

____

____

c. When the sum remains the same, what do you notice about the two addends?

____

____

5 What is the same and what is different about the two patterns below?

Pattern A: 5, 10, 15, 20, 25, 30

Pattern B: 30, 25, 20, 15, 10, 5

Same: ______________________________

Different: ______________________________

Name: Avril

Use Number Patterns

Study the example showing how to use a pattern on a number line to solve a word problem. Then solve problems 1–8.

Example

Riley wants to save $10 from her weekly babysitting job for the next 4 weeks. She has $50 in savings now. How much will Riley have in savings at the end of 4 weeks?

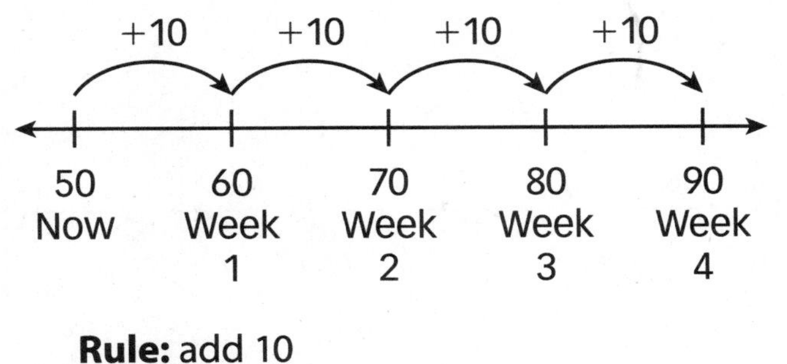

Rule: add 10

Pattern: 50, 60, 70, 80, 90

Riley will have $90 in savings at the end of 4 weeks.

Eduardo practices the flute each weekday. Each day this week, he wants to practice 5 minutes more than the day before. Eduardo practices for 20 minutes on Monday. How many minutes will Eduardo practice on Friday?

1 Complete the table to show how many minutes Eduardo will practice each day this week.

Day	Monday	Tuesday	Wednesday	Thursday	Friday
Number of Minutes	20				

+5 +5 +5 +5

2 Complete the sentence.

Eduardo will practice for _______________ on Friday.

Solve.

3 Use the table below to answer the questions.

	Monday	Tuesday	Wednesday	Thursday	Friday
Jeff	1	2	3	4	5
Eric	2	4	6	8	10

a. What is the rule for the pattern in Jeff's row? _______

b. What is the rule for the pattern in Eric's row? _______

c. Look at both Jeff's and Eric's numbers from day to day. What pattern do you see?

____

____

d. If Saturday were shown in the table, what would be the numbers in Jeff's row and in Eric's row?

____

Eve's soccer team has 48 water bottles in the locker room. Each of the 12 players takes a water bottle before a game.

4 Complete the table to show how many water bottles are left in the locker room at the end of each of the first three games.

Game		1	2	3
Number of Bottles	48			

5 Use words and numbers to explain how you found the number of bottles left after Game 1.

____

____

6 What is the rule for the pattern? ______________________________

7 What number would come after 12 in the pattern? ______________________________

8 What does this number mean? ______________________________

Name: ____________________

Identify Patterns with Equations

Study the example showing how to write and use equations to find the value of a variable. Then solve problems 1–7

Example

Lia has a special in her pizza shop. Customers get 2 free cans of juice with each pizza they buy. If you buy 3 pizzas, how many cans of juice will you get?

This problem can be written as an equation.
The number of **P**izzas you buy times 2 equals the number of **C**ans you get.

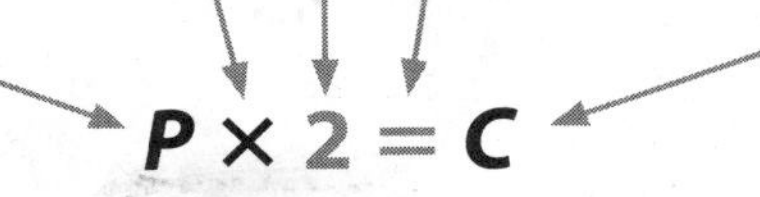

$$P \times 2 = C$$

The situation can also be written in a chart.

Number of Pizzas, *P*	Number of Cans, *C*
1	2
2	4
3	6

You get 6 cans of juice.

1 Use the equation $P \times 2 = C$.

What does P stand for? ____________________

What does C stand for? ____________________

What does $P \times 2$ tell you? ____________________

2 You buy 8 pizzas. How many cans of juice do you get?
Write the equation. Then answer the question.

____

3 You buy 10 pizzas. How many cans of juice do you get?
Write the equation. Then answer the question.

____

Solve.

Use the information below for problems 4 and 5.

Lia has a new special. If customers buy 1 pizza, they get 3 free cans of juice.

4 Fill in the blank to complete the equation.

$P \times \square = C$

5 Use the equation to complete the table.

P	*C*
5	
6	
7	
8	
9	

6 Xavier bakes 3 cookies for each guest plus 5 extra cookies. Explain how to write the equation that describes this relationship.

____

____

____

Use the equation to complete the table below.

4 guests	6 guests	8 guests

7 Use the equation $B = (4 \times A) - 2$ to complete the table.

A	*B*
1	2
2	
3	
4	

Name: ______________________

Number and Shape Patterns

Solve the problems.

1 How are the two number patterns below different?

Pattern A: 11, 22, 44, 88

Pattern B: 11, 22, 33, 44

____

____

____

____

____

____

2 Describe a rule you see in the shape pattern below.

B E C F D H G L

Look at how the letters are formed. What do some letters have in common? What do other letters have in common?

____

____

____

____

____

3 Use the letters T, P, J, and I to continue the pattern in problem 2.

How can you use the rule to find the next letter in the pattern?

____

____

____

Solve.

4 Complete the pattern below. The pattern follows the rule "add 2, subtract 1."

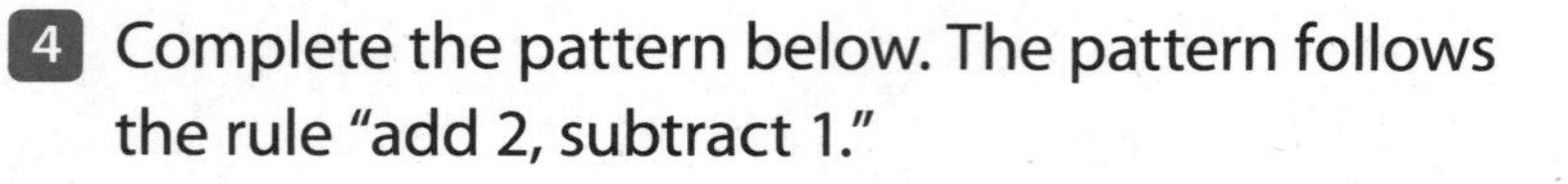

1, 3, 2, 4, 3, 5, 4, 6, 5, ___, ___, ___, ___

Circle one number in each sentence below that makes the sentence true about the pattern.

a. The number in the 15th spot is 7 8 9.

b. The difference between the numbers in every other spot is 1 2.

5 Circle the letter of the table that shows values from the following equation:

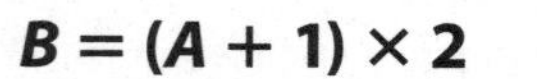

$B = (A + 1) \times 2$

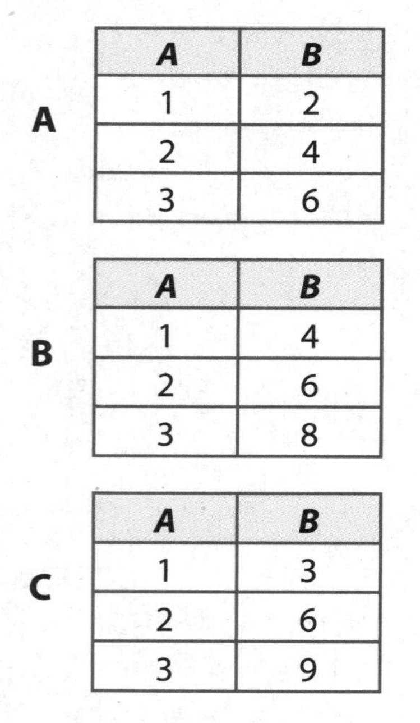

A

A	*B*
1	2
2	4
3	6

B

A	*B*
1	4
2	6
3	8

C

A	*B*
1	3
2	6
3	9

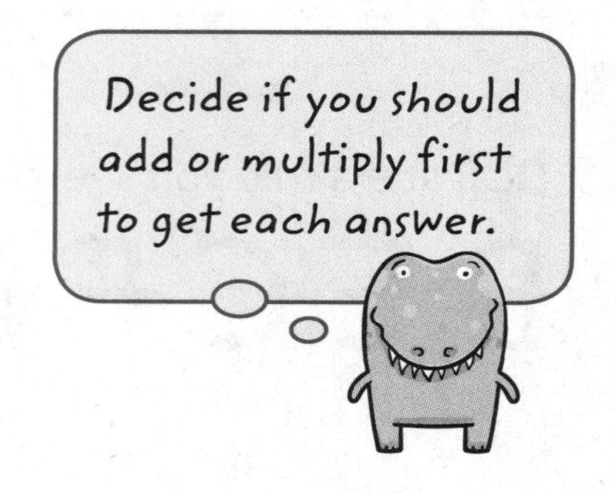

Model Multi-Step Problems

Name: ______________________

Prerequisite: Model Two-Step Problems

Study the example showing how to model a two-step word problem. Then solve problems 1–9.

Example

Mr. Norman's fourth grade class held a pancake breakfast fundraiser. They bought 4 cartons of eggs to use for the pancakes. Each carton has 12 eggs. They have 7 eggs left over. How many eggs were used?

4 groups of 12 is 48.
$4 \times 12 = 48$
7 eggs are left over.

48			
12	12	12	12
?			7

Subtract 7 from 48 to find how many eggs were used.
$48 - 7 = 41$
41 eggs were used.

1 Fiona has 6 garden boxes. She wants to plant 3 vegetable seeds and 3 flower seeds in each garden box. How many seeds does Fiona need in all? Draw a picture to model the problem. Then solve the problem.

Solution: Fiona needs _______ seeds in all.

2 Zander bought 3 hats for $7 each and 2 shirts for $9 each. How much did Zander spend? Draw and label jumps on the number line below to show how much Zander spent.

Zander spent _______.

Solve.

Nadia bought 4 bags of popcorn at the movies. She shared the popcorn with her 7 friends. Each bag held 6 cups of popcorn. If everyone had an equal amount, how many cups of popcorn did each person have?

3 Complete the bar model below to solve the problem.

4 What do the parts of the top bar represent?

____

5 What do the parts of the bottom bar represent?

____

6 Why are there more than 7 parts in the bottom bar?

____

7 Explain how to find the number of cups of popcorn each person had. ______________________________

____

____

Tom buys 5 packs of juice boxes for the class picnic. Each pack has 6 juice boxes.

8 At the picnic, 18 students take a juice box. How many juice boxes are left?

Show your work.

Solution: ______________________________

Name: ____________________

Write Equations

Study the example showing how to model a multi-step problem and write an equation. Then solve problems 1–4.

Example

The table shows Eli's after-school activities. Write an equation to show how many hours a week Eli spends doing activities.

Activity	How long?	How often?
Volunteer at the library	2 hours	2 times a week
Work at the skate shop	2 hours	4 times a week
Swim practice	1 hour	5 times a week

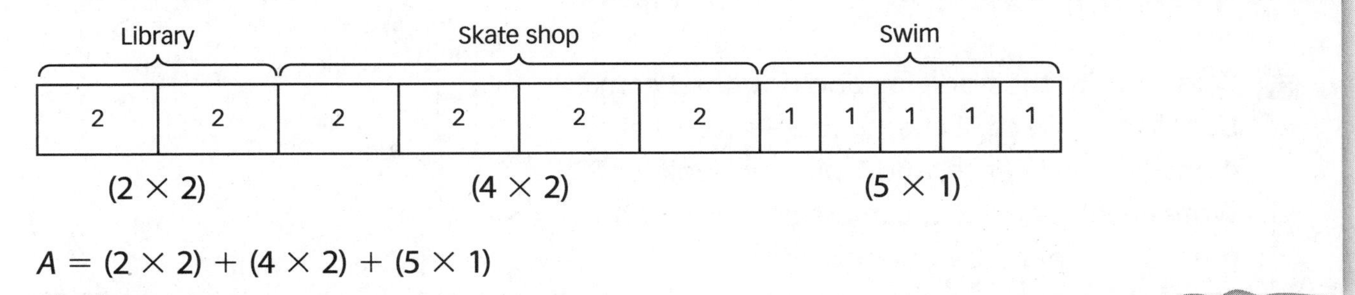

$A = (2 \times 2) + (4 \times 2) + (5 \times 1)$

Mia volunteered at the animal shelter on 7 weekends. On Saturdays, she volunteered for 3 hours. On Sundays, she volunteered for 2 hours.

1 Write an equation to find how many hours Mia volunteered.

a. Complete the bar model.

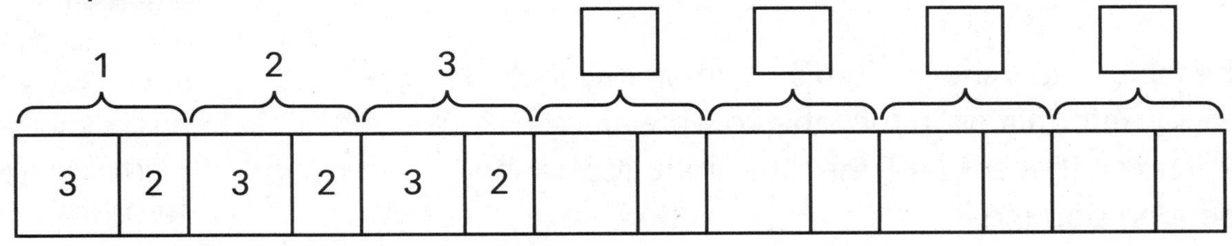

b. What do the numbers above the bar represent?

____

c. What do the numbers in each part of the bar represent? ____________________

d. Write an equation. ____________________

Solve.

2 A bike rental is $20 for a day and $3 for an hour. Caroline rented a bike for 2 days and 2 hours. Which equation could you use to find how much money, M, Caroline spent? Circle the letter for all that apply.

A $M = (2 \times 20) + (2 \times 3)$

B $M = (3 \times 20) + (2 \times 2)$

C $M = (20 \times 2) \times (3 \times 2)$

D $M = (20 \times 2) + (3 \times 2)$

3 Zara went to the book fair and bought 3 comic books for $5 each, 2 chapter books for $9 each, 4 posters for $2 each, and 1 picture book for $7. Write an equation that can be used to find how much Zara spent at the book fair.

Show your work.

Solution: ______________________________

4 The table below shows clothing sales at a school fair. Use the information in the table to write an expression that equals T, the total amount of money spent on clothing.

Item	Price	Number sold
T-shirts	$12	100
Sweatshirts	$20	50

Solution: ______________________________

Vocabula

equation a mathematical sen… that uses an equal… (=) to show that tv… expressions have … same value.

$R = (6 \times 3) + 4$

expression a g… one or more nur… unknowns and operations that represents a quantity.

$5 \times h$

Name: ______________________

Model Multi-Step Problems

Solve the problems.

1 Phillip earns $15 an hour at his tutoring job and $10 an hour babysitting. Last week, he worked 10 hours tutoring and 4 hours babysitting. Which equation shows how much Phillip earned, E?

A $E = (15 \times 10) + (10 \times 4)$

B $E = (15 + 10) \times (10 + 4)$

C $E = (15 \times 10) \times (10 \times 4)$

D $E = (15 \times 4) + (10 \times 10)$

2 The table below shows a cell phone plan.

	Cost per month
Phone	$22 each
Unlimited texting	$30 for a family
Unlimited data	$80 for a family
Insurance	$3 for each phone

Lola's family has 4 cell phones. They want to have insurance on each phone. They also want to have texting and data on each phone. Write an equation to show the monthly cost for Lola's family.

Show your work.

Solution: ____

____

Solve.

3 There are 6 friends sharing 3 pizzas. Each pizza is cut into 8 slices. Which equation could be used to find the total number of slices, P, each friend will get?

A $(6 \times 3) \div 8 = P$

B $(3 \times 8) \div 6 = P$

C $8 \times (6 \div 3) = P$

D $(8 \times 6) \div 3 = P$

Sadie chose **B** as the correct answer. How did she get that answer?

____

____

____

____

____

____

4 Margaret received \$20 each from 3 relatives and \$50 from her parents at graduation. She spent \$30. She saved half of the remaining money and donated the other half. Which equation(s) could you use to find how much money, S, she saved? Circle the letter of all that apply.

A $S = (3 \times 20 - 50) - 30 \div 2$

B $S = (3 \times 20 + 50) - 30 \div 2$

C $S = (20 + 20 + 20 + 50 - 30) \div 2$

D $S = (3 \times 20 - 50 + 30) \div 2$

E $S = (3 \times 20 + 50 - 30) \div 2$

Solve Multi-Step Problems

Name: ______________________

Prerequisite: Solve Two-Step Problems

Study the example showing how to use a model to solve a two-step word problem. Then solve problems 1–5.

Example

Brian and his friends are doing a 200-piece jigsaw puzzle. Each of the 6 friends has placed 12 puzzle pieces. How many pieces have not been placed?

200	
6×12	p

$(6 \times 12) + p = 200$

$72 + p = 200$

$p = 200 - 72$

$p = 128$

128 pieces have not been placed.

1 Use estimation to check whether 128 is a reasonable answer in the example above.

$p = 200 - 72$

Round to the nearest ten. $p =$ _____ $-$ _____

Subtract the rounded numbers. _____ $=$ _____ $-$ _____

_______ is close to 128 so 128 is a reasonable answer.

2 There are 8 students at each of 4 round tables in the cafeteria. There are 64 students at long tables. Use the bar model to write and solve an equation to find how many students there are in the cafeteria.

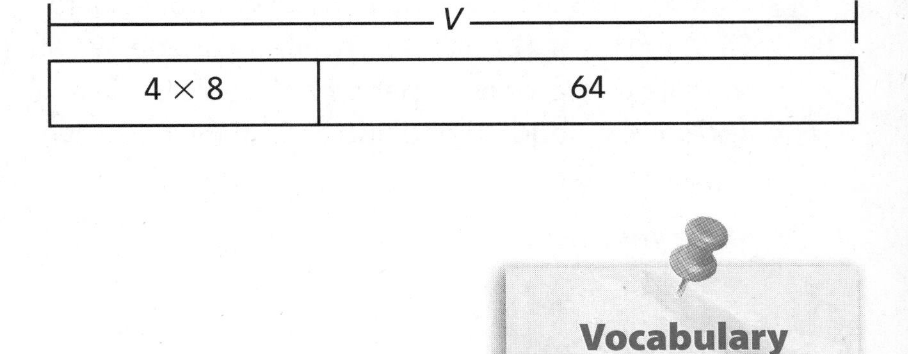

Show your work.

Solution: There are ______________ in the cafeteria.

Vocabulary

reasonable something that makes sense when the given facts are taken into account.

Solve.

3 The table below shows the cost of admission tickets at a museum. Write and solve an equation to find the cost of tickets for 1 child and 2 adults.

	Child	Adult
Cost of ticket	$6	$11

Show your work.

Solution: ______________________________

4 Liz is training for a swim meet. Her goal is to swim 100 laps. She swam 12 laps in the pool on each of 3 days. Write and solve an equation to find how many more laps Liz needs to swim to reach her goal.

Show your work.

Solution: ______________________________

5 Paperbacks sell for $2 and hardcover books sell for $4 at the library book sale. The library made $98 at the sale. There were 25 paperback books sold. Write and solve an equation to find how many hardcover books were sold.

Show your work.

Solution: ______________________________

Vocabulary

equation a number sentence that shows two expressions have equal value.

$R = 6 \times 3$

Name: ____________________

Solve Multi-Step Problems

Study the example showing how to model a multi-step problem with a remainder. Then solve problems 1–5.

Example

Mrs. Murray has 12 students in one science class and 14 students in another. She wants to combine both classes to do group work. Each table in the science room can seat 4 students. How many tables does Mrs. Murray need?

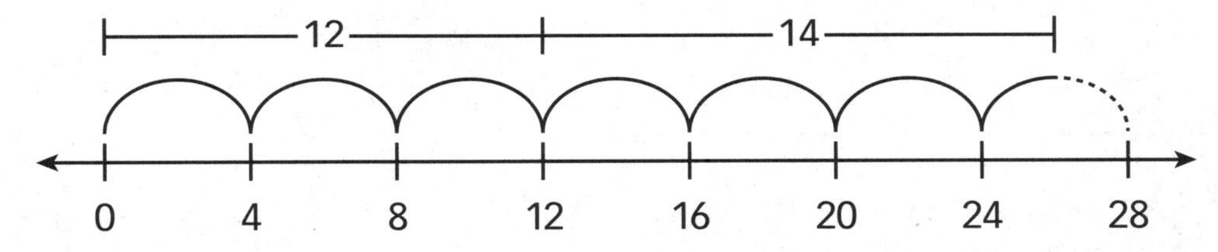

Let T equal the number of tables needed.

$T = (12 + 14) \div 4$
$= 26 \div 4$
$= 6 \text{ R}2$

6 R2 means:
- 6 tables with 4 students each
- 2 more students need another table

Mrs. Murray needs 7 tables.

1 Check the solution to the equation in the example.

_______ tables × _______ students per table +

_______ students = _______ total students

2 Leticia earns $8 each time she rakes the yard. She has earned $24 so far. Write and solve an equation to show how many more times Leticia needs to rake the yard to earn enough to buy a music player that costs $45.

Show your work.

Solution: ______________________________

____

remainder the amount left over that will not divide equally into the given number of groups.

$26 \div 4 = 6 \text{ R}2$

equation a mathematical sentence that uses an equal sign (=) to show that two expressions have the same value.

Solve.

3 Meghan found 15 pieces of sea glass on the beach. The next day she found 4 more pieces than she found the day before. Write and solve an equation to find how many pieces of sea glass she found altogether.

Show your work.

Solution: ______________________________

4 The table shows ticket prices at a movie theater. Ticket sales to an afternoon show were $146. There were 10 child tickets sold. Write and solve an equation to find how many adult tickets were sold.

	Child	**Adult**
Ticket price	$5	$12

Show your work.

Solution: ______________________________

5 Ticket prices for 3-D movies are $10 for a child and $15 for an adult. One adult spent $55 to take a group of children to the movies. Write and solve an equation to find how many children went to the movies.

Show your work.

Solution: ______________________________

Name: ___________________________

Solve Multi-Step Problems

Solve the problems.

1 Jensen bought 10 boxes of granola bars. Each box has 8 bars. He wants to share the bars with 6 soccer teams. Which equation can be used to find how many bars each team gets?

A $b = (8 \times 10) - 6$

B $b = (10 + 6) \div 8$

C $b = (6 + 8) \div 10$

D $b = (10 \times 8) \div 6$

2 Solve the equation in problem 1 to find how many granola bars each team gets. Are bars left over?

Show your work.

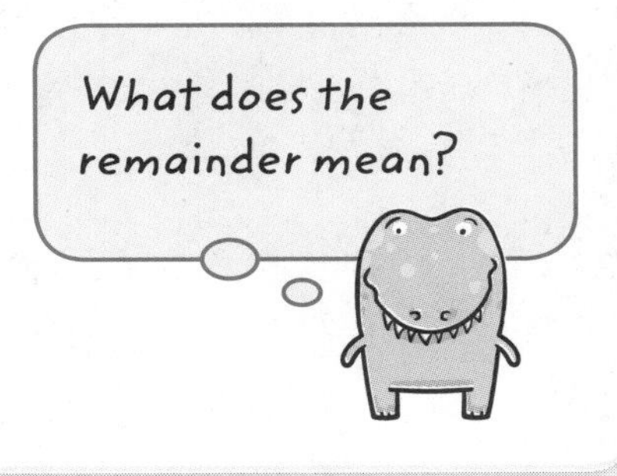

Solution: ___________________________

3 The community center used 4 recycling bins one week, twice as many the next week, 7 bins the third week, and 5 bins the last week of the month. Which equation shows how many bins were used for the month?

A $4 + (2 \times 7) + 7 + 5 = 30$

B $4 + (2 \times 4) + 7 + 5 = 24$

C $(1 \times 4) + (2 \times 4) + (3 \times 7) + 5 = 34$

D $4 + (4 \div 2) + 7 + 5 = 18$

Mia chose **A** as the correct answer. How did she get that answer?

____

____

Solve.

4 The table shows the results of a bake sale. The cost of renting tables for the bake sale was $100.

Write and solve an equation to show how much money the bake sale made.

Baked item	Number sold	Price
Cookies	90	$1 each
Brownies	75	$1 each
Crispy treats	60	$2 each
Cupcakes	50	$3 each

Show your work.

Solution: ______________________________

5 Look at the table in problem 4. If 10 fewer cookies and 10 more cupcakes were sold, how much would the bake sale have made?

Which numbers in the equation you wrote in problem 4 do you need to change?

Show your work.

Solution: ______________________________

Unit 2 Game

Name: ______________________

Factor Finder

What you need: Recording Sheet, Game Board, 2 sets of digit cards (1–9), 40 counters (2 different colors)

Directions

Name: ______________________

Factor Finder Recording Sheet

Two-Digit Numbers

☐0 ☐1 ☐2 ☐3 ☐4 [3]5 ☐6 ☐7 ☐8 ☐9

Emma	Jacob
Player A Name	Player B Name
1. Two-digit number: 35 Factors: 1, 35, 5, 7	1. Two-digit number: 18 Factors: 1, 18, 2, 9, 3, 6
2. Two-digit number: ______ Factors: ______________	2. Two-digit number: ______ Factors: ______________

- Mix the digit cards and place them facedown in a stack.
- Player A picks a card and writes the digit on that card in the list at the top of the Recording Sheet to make a two-digit number.
- Player A writes that two-digit number and all the factors for that two-digit number on the Recording Sheet.
- Player A places counters on the Game Board to cover the factors for that two-digit number. Not all factors are on the Game Board, and some factors appear more than once. Cover a factor only once.
- Player B takes a turn, following the same steps as Player A. Player B uses different color counters on the Game Board.
- The first player to have 5 counters in a row on the Game Board wins.
- If no player has 5 counters in a row, the player with the most counters on the board after 5 rounds wins the game.

I picked 3 and made the two-digit number 35. The factors of 35 are 1, 35, 5, and 7.
I put counters on the 5 and 7 on the Game Board because they are both factors of 35.

Name: ______________________

Factor Finder Recording Sheet

Two-Digit Numbers

☐0 ☐1 ☐2 ☐3 ☐4 ☐5 ☐6 ☐7 ☐8 ☐9

____
Player A Name

1. Two-digit number: ________
   Factors: ______________________
2. Two-digit number: ________
   Factors: ______________________
3. Two-digit number: ________
   Factors: ______________________
4. Two-digit number: ________
   Factors: ______________________
5. Two-digit number: ________
   Factors: ______________________

____
Player B Name

1. Two-digit number: ________
   Factors: ______________________
2. Two-digit number: ________
   Factors: ______________________
3. Two-digit number: ________
   Factors: ______________________
4. Two-digit number: ________
   Factors: ______________________
5. Two-digit number: ________
   Factors: ______________________

Name: ______________________

Factor Finder Game Board

2	8	7	6	5
3	6	5	8	11
12	2	10	4	12
6	9	8	3	4
5	4	3	9	2

Digit Cards (1–9)

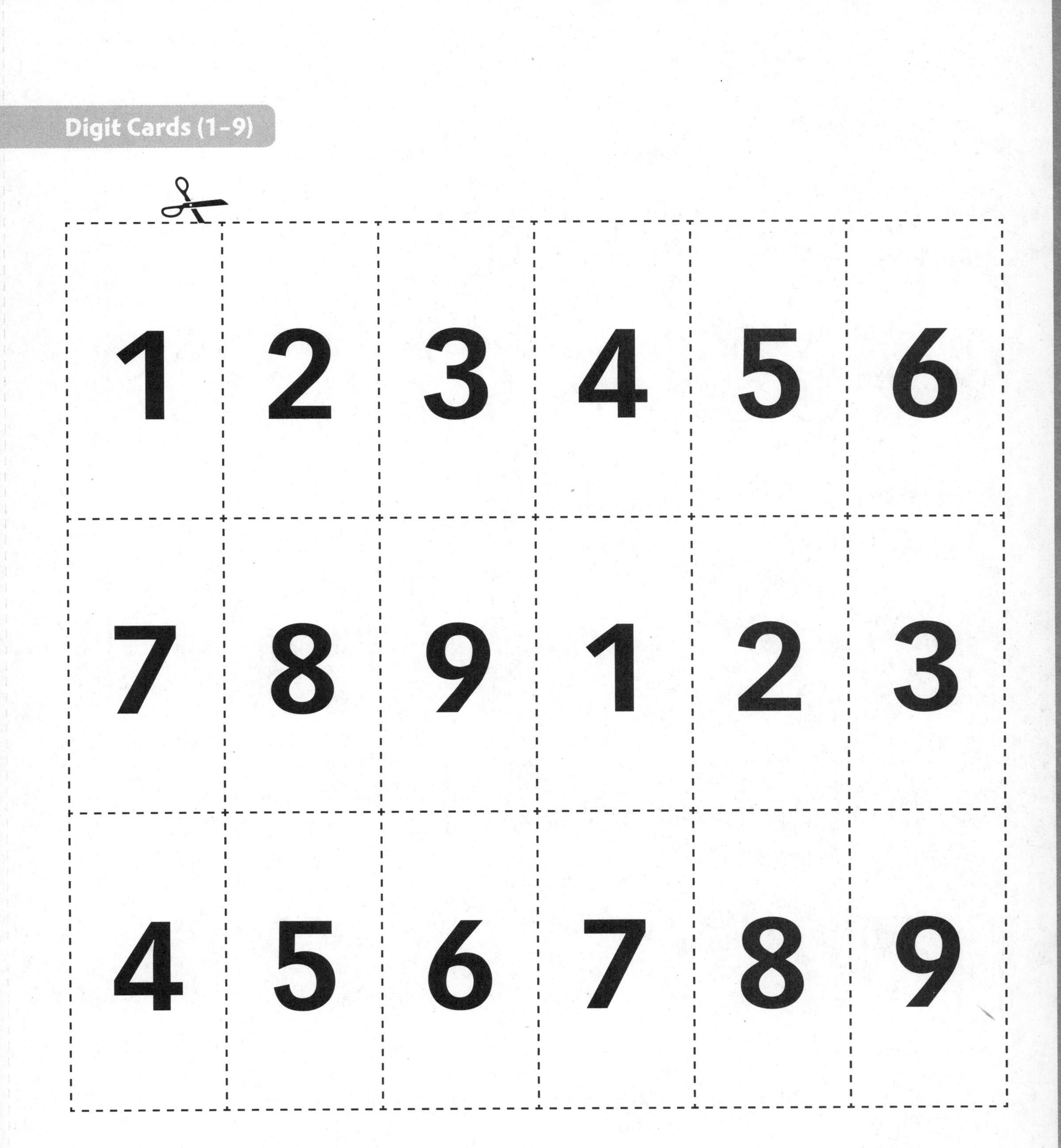

Unit 2 Practice

Name: ____________________

Algebraic Thinking

In this unit you learned to:	Lesson
multiply and divide to solve comparison problems, for example: 28 is 4 times as many as 7.	5A, 6
use multiplication properties to solve problems, for example: $4 \times 6 = 4 \times (5 + 1)$.	5B
identify factor pairs for a number, for example: 4 and 5 are a factor pair for 20.	7
identify multiples of a number, for example: 42 is a multiple of 6.	7
identify prime and composite numbers, for example: 16 is composite.	7
generate and describe patterns, for example: every other number is odd in 3, 10, 17, 24, … .	8
model and solve multi-step word problems using equations, for example: $(6 \times 3) - 11 + 2 = 9$.	9, 10

Use these skills to solve problems 1–4.

1 Extend the pattern below by drawing a shape on each blank. Use each shape in the box once.

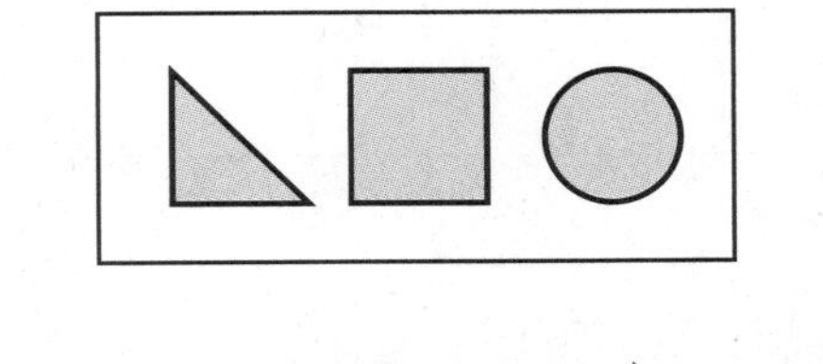

____ ____ ____

2 Gwen, Alex, and Manny are playing a game as a team. Gwen has scored 2 times as many points as Manny. Alex has scored 7 more points than Manny. Manny has scored 15 points. Which equation shows how many points their team has scored altogether?

A $T = 15 + (2 \times 7) + (15 + 7)$

B $T = 15 + (2 + 15) + (2 \times 7)$

C $T = 15 + (2 \times 15) + (15 + 7)$

D $T = 15 + (2 + 7) + (15 \times 7)$

Solve.

3 Extend the number pattern below. Then write the number that would be the 100th number in the pattern. Explain how you figured out what the number would be.

5, 10, 15, 20, 25, 30, ______, ______, ______, . . . , ______ (100th)

____

____

____

4 Ken is building an outdoor walking path with pavers. Pavers are sold \$8 for 10 pavers or \$1 per paver.

Part A

The walking path needs 52 pavers. What is the least amount that 52 pavers cost?

Show your work.

Solution: ____

Part B

How much more would it cost to buy 52 pavers individually?

Show your work.

Solution: ____

Part C

What is the greatest number of pavers Ken can buy for \$60?

Show your work.

Solution: ____

Unit 2 Performance Task

Name: ______________________

Answer the questions and show all your work on separate paper.

The Pet Club is raising money for the local animal shelter. The club members want to make fundraising posters that tell how a donation helps the animals in the shelter. Each poster will have a statement like the following:

A donation of $_______ helps _______ cats, _______ small dogs, and _______ large dogs for one day.

The chart below shows the amount that the shelter spends caring for animals.

Animal	Cost per Day
Cat	$3
Small dog	$4
Large dog	$5

Decide on three different donation amounts for the posters. Complete a statement for each donation amount. Write how many of each kind of animal the donation helps. Explain how you decided which numbers to use in your three statements.

Checklist

Did you . . .

- ☐ check your calculations?
- ☐ write three statements?
- ☐ explain how you chose the numbers you used?

Reflect on the Process Standards

After you complete the task, choose one of the following questions to answer.

1. **Persevere** How did you use the information in the table to help you decide on donation amounts?

2. **Reason Mathematically** How do factors and multiples help you solve this problem?

Performance Task Tips

Word Bank Here are some words that you might use in your answer.

multiply	each	expression
product	factor	equation
total	multiple	equals

Models Here are some models that you might use to find the solution.

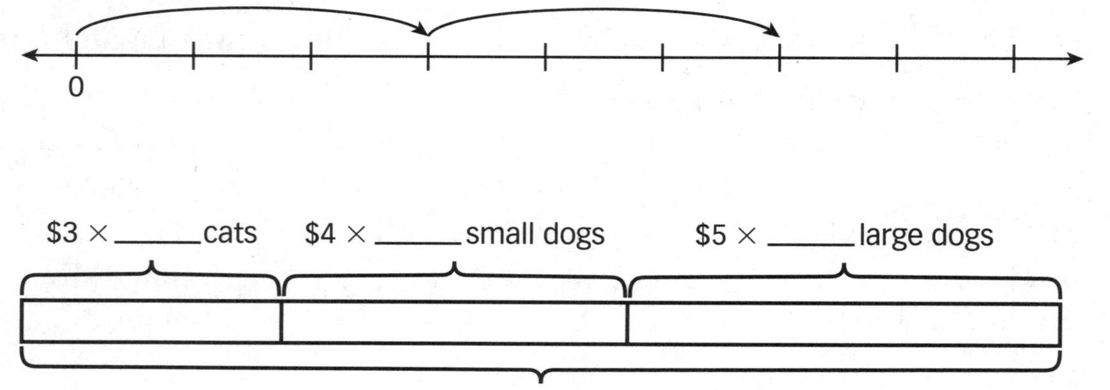

Sentence Starters Here are some sentence starters that might help you write an explanation.

The cost per day for ________________ is ________________

Multiples of __________ are ______________________________

An expression that represents the number of ______________________ is ______________________

An equation that represents a donation of $__________ is ____________________________________

Unit 2 Vocabulary

Name: ____________________

My Examples

multiplication

an operation used to find the total number of items in equal-sized groups

product

the result of multiplication

factors

numbers that are multiplied together to get a product

factor pair

two numbers that are multiplied together to give a product

My Examples

multiple

the product of a number and any other whole number; for example, 3, 6, 9, 12, and 15 are multiples of 3

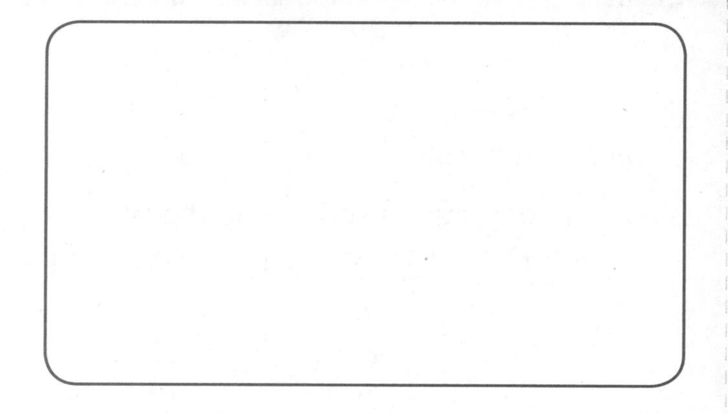

division

an operation used to separate a number of items into equal-sized groups

remainder

the amount left over that will not divide equally into the given number of groups

reasonable

something that makes sense when the given facts are taken into account

My Examples

symbol

an object used to stand for an unknown number in an equation

unknown

a missing number in an equation

equation

a mathematical sentence that uses an equal sign (=) to show that two expressions have the same value

expression

a group of one or more numbers, unknowns, and operations that represents a quantity, for example, $5 \times h$

My Examples

composite number

a number that has more than one pair of factors

prime number

a number that has only one pair of factors: itself and 1

shape pattern

a series of shapes that follow a rule to repeat or change

number pattern

a series of numbers that follow a rule to repeat or change

rule

a procedure to follow to go from one number or shape to the next in a pattern

My Examples

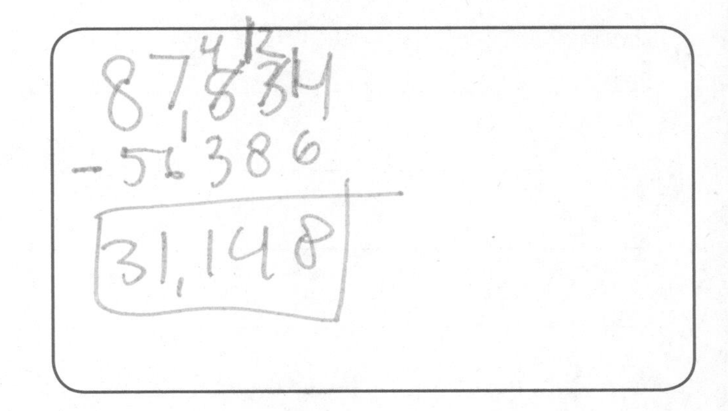

My Words

My Words	My Examples

Dear Family,

This week your child is learning to multiply whole numbers.

Your child is learning to multiply two-digit numbers, such as 16×28.

One way your child can multiply two-digit numbers is by using an area model. With this strategy, your child multiplies using the place value of each digit.

The area model below shows the number 16 as $10 + 6$ along the top, and the number 28 as $20 + 8$ at the left. Your child finds the individual products, then adds the products together to find the total product of the multiplication.

	10	+ 6
20	20×10 2 tens × 1 ten = 2 hundreds **200**	20×6 2 tens × 6 = 12 tens **120**
+ 8	8×10 8 × 1 ten = 8 tens **80**	$8 \times 6 =$ **48**

$200 + 80 + 120 + 48 = 448$

$16 \times 28 = 448$

Invite your child to share what he or she knows about multiplying whole numbers by doing the following activity together.

Multiplying Whole Numbers Activity

Do an activity with your child to practice multiplying two-digit numbers.

Materials: timer or watch with a second hand

- Together with your child, think of things that can be counted in one minute, such as the number of times you clap your hands or the number of steps you walk.
- Choose one idea. Have one person do the activity while the other person times the activity for one minute.

- The person doing the activity counts how many. Count carefully. Stop counting when the person with the timer says "Stop!"

  Example: Clap your hands for one minute, counting each clap. Count 92 hand claps.

- Have your child use that number to figure out how many could be counted in 15 minutes.

  Example: $15 \times 92 = ?$

- Have your child multiply to find the answer.
- Switch roles and repeat the activity.

Look for other real-life opportunities to practice multiplying two-digit numbers with your child.

Multiply Whole Numbers

Name: ____________________

Prerequisite: Multiply by a Multiple of 10

Study the example showing how to multiply by a multiple of 10. Then solve problems 1–7.

Example

Roy swims for 20 minutes a day, 6 days a week. How many minutes does Roy swim in a week?

Use base-ten blocks.

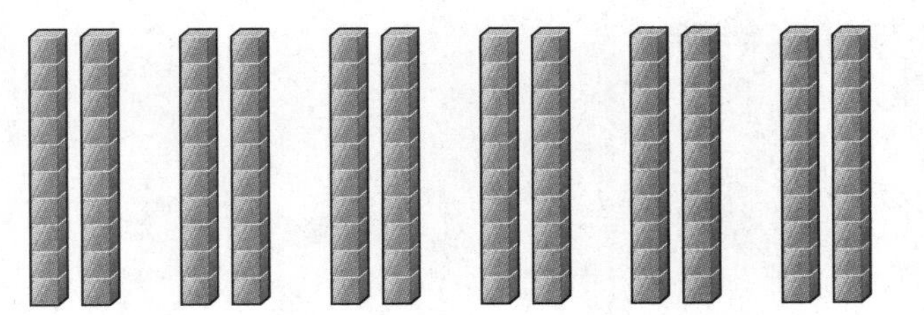

6 groups of 2 tens is
6×2 tens, or 12 tens.
12 tens $= 120$

Use factors and grouping to multiply.	6×20
Break down 20 into factors 2 and 10.	$6 \times (2 \times 10)$
Change grouping and multiply.	$(6 \times 2) \times 10$ $12 \times 10 = 120$

Roy swims 120 minutes in a week.

1 The base-ten blocks below show 4×30.

Fill in the blanks to find the product.

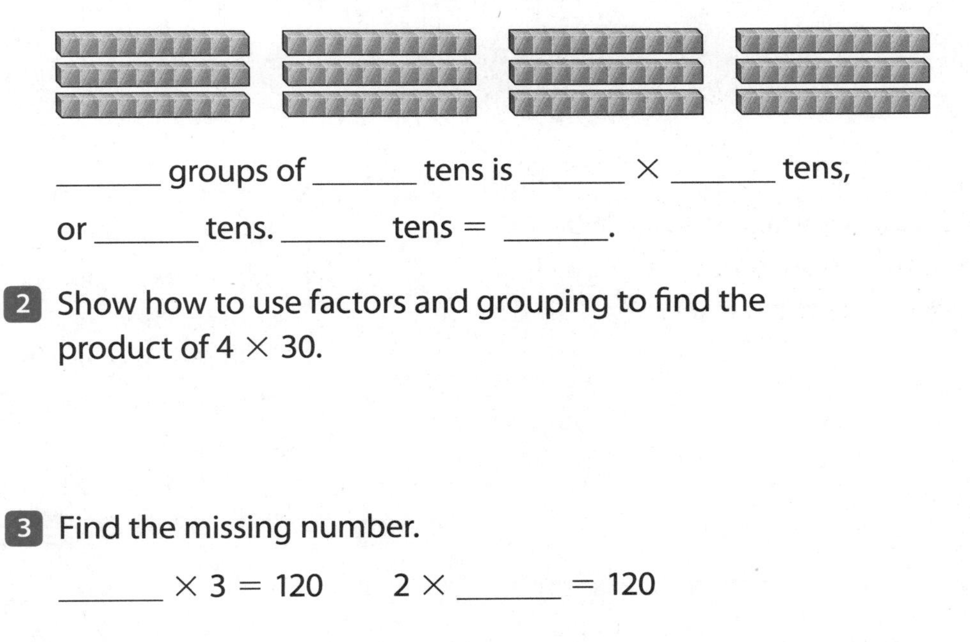

_______ groups of _______ tens is _______ $\times$ _______ tens,

or _______ tens. _______ tens = _______.

2 Show how to use factors and grouping to find the product of 4×30.

3 Find the missing number.

_______ $\times 3 = 120$ $\quad$ $2 \times$ _______ $= 120$

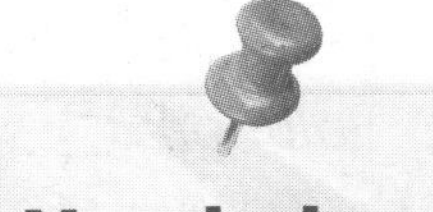

Vocabulary

factors numbers that are multiplied together to get a product.

product the result of multiplication.

$6 \times 20 = 120$

factors product

Solve.

4 Saundra has 8 folders on her computer. Each folder has 50 files. How many files are on Saundra's computer?

Show your work.

Solution: ______________________________

5 There are 5 ten-pound bags and 8 twenty-pound bags of rice on a shelf. How many pounds of rice are on the shelf?

Show your work.

Solution: ______________________________

6 Lola gets two 20-minute breaks at work each day. She works 5 days a week. How much time does she spend on break each week?

Show your work.

Solution: ______________________________

7 Andrew wants to buy 3 video games that are $50 each. He earns $80 a week. In how many weeks will he have enough money to buy the games?

Show your work.

First find the total cost of the video games. Then compare the cost to the amount he earns in a week.

Solution: ______________________________

Name: ______________________

Multiply by a One-Digit Number

Study the example showing one way to multiply by a one-digit number. Then solve problems 1–5.

Example

Jesse's family has 4 music players. Each music player can hold 8,352 songs. What is the total number of songs all 4 music players can hold?

Use an area model.

	8,000	+ 300	+ 50	+ 2
4	$4 \times 8{,}000$	4×300	4×50	4×2

$$\begin{aligned} 4 \times 8{,}352 &= (4 \times 8{,}000) + (4 \times 300) + (4 \times 50) + (4 \times 2) \\ &= 32{,}000 + 1{,}200 + 200 + 8 \\ &= 33{,}408 \end{aligned}$$

All 4 music players can hold 33,408 songs.

1 Look at the multiplication above. Use partial products to multiply $4 \times 8{,}352$. Fill in the blanks.

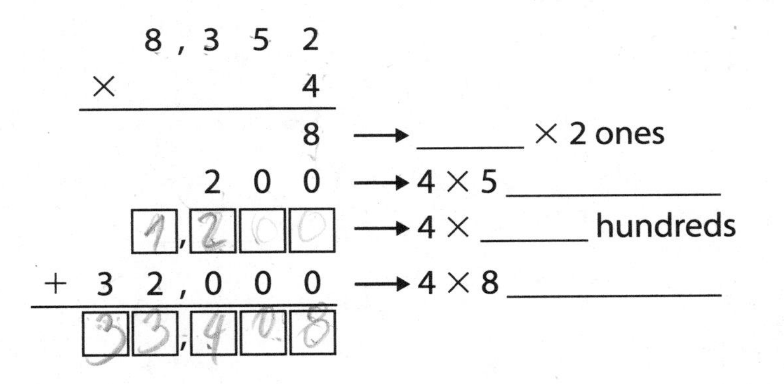

2 Show how to use partial products to multiply $5 \times 1{,}643$.

Vocabulary

multiplication an operation used to find the total number of items in equal-sized groups.

product the result of multiplication.

Solve.

3 Write $4 \times 3{,}569$ in expanded form to show the place value of each digit. Then find the product.

____

____

____

4 Lee earns $1,075 each month. How much does he earn in 6 months?

Show your work.

Solution: ______________________________

5 Look at Callie's work for solving $3 \times 9{,}423$.

a. Explain what Callie did wrong.

$$\begin{array}{r} 9{,}423 \\ \times \quad 3 \\ \hline 9 \\ 60 \\ 120 \\ +\ 2{,}700 \\ \hline 2{,}889 \end{array}$$

____

____

____

____

____

____

____

____

b. What is the correct answer for $3 \times 9{,}423$?

____

Name: ______________________

Multiply Two-Digit Numbers by Two-Digit Numbers

Study the example showing how to multiply a two-digit number by a two-digit number to solve a word problem. Then solve problems 1–6.

Example

Aaron's guitar lesson is 35 minutes a week.
He has been taking lessons for 12 weeks.
How many minutes has Aaron spent at lessons?

Use an area model to multiply 35×12.

	30	+ 5
10	10×30 1 ten $\times$ 3 tens = 3 hundreds **300**	10×5 1 ten $\times$ 5 = 5 tens **50**
+ 2	2×30 $2 \times$ 3 tens = 6 tens **60**	$2 \times 5 =$ **10**

$300 + 60 + 50 + 10 = 420$ minutes
Aaron has spent 420 minutes at lessons.

1 Look at the example above. Use partial products to multiply 35×12. Fill in the blanks.

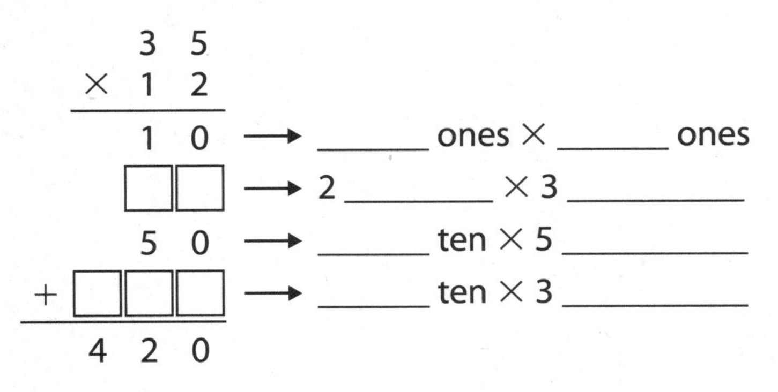

2 Show how to use an area model to multiply 71×48.

$71 \times 48 =$ ______ + ______ + ______ + ______ = ______

Solve.

3 Show how to use partial products to multiply 48×71.

$$48 \times 71 = \_\_\_\_\_\_\_\_\_\_$$

4 Tell whether each number sentence is *True* or *False*.

a. $18 \times 42 = (10 \times 40) + (10 \times 2) + (8 \times 40) + (8 \times 2)$ ☐ True ☐ False

b. $60 \times 15 = (6 \times 10) + (6 \times 5)$ ☐ True ☐ False

c. $37 \times 22 = (30 \times 20) + (30 \times 20) + (7 \times 20) + (7 \times 20)$ ☐ True ☐ False

d. $99 \times 11 = (1 \times 9) + (1 \times 90) + (10 \times 9) + (10 \times 90)$ ☐ True ☐ False

5 Mr. Greene is preparing 28 bags of materials for his art class. Each bag needs 40 glass tiles. How many glass tiles are needed?

Show your work.

Solution: ____________________

6 Stephanie has 6 classes a day at school. Each class is 52 minutes long. She goes to school 5 days a week. How much time does she spend in class each week? Show two different ways to solve this problem.

Show your work.

Solution: ____________________

Name: ______________________

Multiply Whole Numbers

Solve the problems.

1 One mile is 5,280 feet. How many feet are in 6 miles?

A 30,068 **C** 31,248

B 30,168 **D** 31,680

2 Which of the following are equal to 420×3?

Circle the letter for all that apply.

A $(3 \times 400) + (3 \times 20)$

B $420 + 420 + 420$

C $(3 \times 400) + (3 \times 2)$

D 1,260

3 The bell on a clock tower rings every 15 minutes. If the bell has rung 24 times, how many minutes have passed?

A 220 minutes

B 342 minutes

C 360 minutes

D 380 minutes

Amber chose **A** as the correct answer. How did she get that answer?

____

____

____

Solve.

4 The multiplication problem 5 × 3,000 can be written in many different ways. One way is 5 × 3 × 1,000. Write 3 more ways.

____

____

____

You can also write 3,000 as 3 × 10 × 100. What other ways can you think of?

5 A distance race is 42 kilometers. Kylie has completed 16 distance races. How many kilometers has she run?

Show your work.

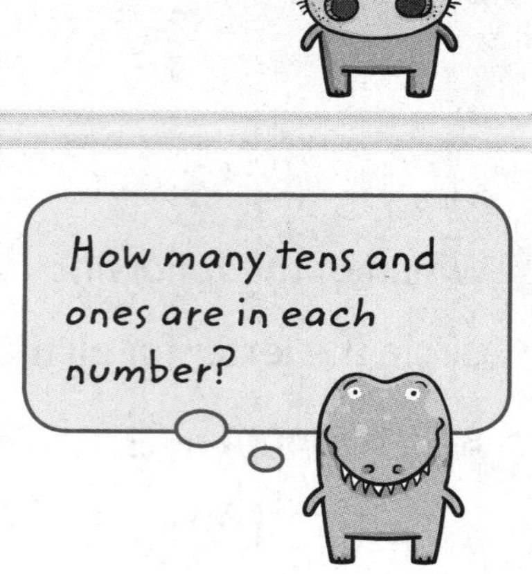

Solution: ______________________________

6 Fourth graders are taking a field trip. The cost is $15 for each student and $18 for each chaperone. There are 94 students and 16 chaperones on the field trip. What is the total cost for all students and chaperones?

Show your work.

How much does it cost for all the students? All the chaperones?

Solution: ______________________________

Dear Family,

This week your child is learning to divide whole numbers.

Here are some vocabulary words your child is using to communicate about division.

quotient: the answer to a division problem.
dividend: the number you divide in a division problem.
divisor: the number you divide by in a division problem.

Your child is learning to divide three-digit or four-digit numbers by a one-digit number. One way your child can solve a division problem is to find partial quotients. With this strategy, your child divides using place value. The division problem below shows how to divide 2,125 by 4.

```
        6
       25
      500
  4)2,125 ──> 1. How many groups of 4 in 2,000? 500
  − 2,000 ──> 2. Subtract 500 groups of 4.
      125 ──> 3. How many groups of 4 in 100? 25
    − 100 ──> 4. Subtract 25 groups of 4.
       25 ──> 5. How many groups of 4 in 25? 6
     − 24 ──> 6. Subtract 6 groups of 4.
        1
```

The sum of the partial quotients is 531. The remainder is 1.

Altogether there are $500 + 25 + 6$, or 531 groups of 4 in 2,125, with one extra left over. $2{,}125 \div 4 = 531$ R1

Invite your child to share what he or she knows about dividing whole numbers by doing the following activity together.

Dividing Whole Numbers Activity

Do an activity with your child to practice dividing a three-digit number by a one-digit number.

Materials: book with a number of pages in the hundreds

- With your child, choose a favorite book and look at the number of pages it has.
- Suppose you want to read the entire book in a week. How many pages would you need to read each day in order to finish the book in a week (7 days)?
- Have your child use division to find the answer.

  Example: The book has 157 pages.
  $157 \div 7 = 22$ R3
- You and your child can check the answer to the division problem by using multiplication. If you have a remainder, remember to add the remainder to the product.
- Decide what to do if you have a remainder. Will you read one page each day for the number of days shown by the remainder or will you read all the remaining pages on the last day?

You and your child can repeat the activity with other favorite books.

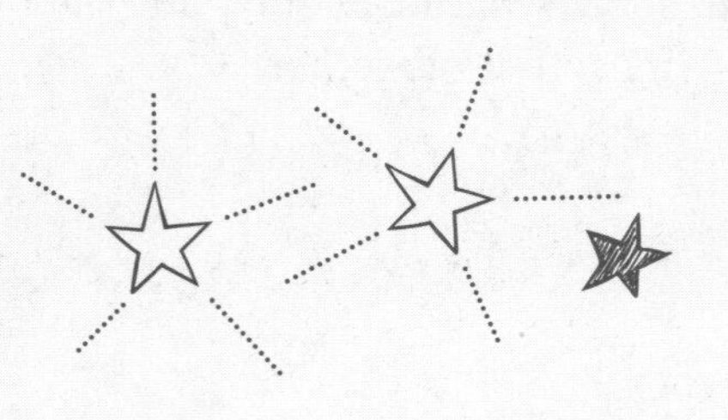

Divide Whole Numbers

Name: ____________________

Prerequisite: Relate Multiplication and Division

Study the example showing how to use multiplication to solve a division problem. Then solve problems 1–7.

Example

The Lin family spent \$800 on 4 airplane tickets. Each ticket was the same price. How much did each ticket cost?

Divide 800 by 4. $800 \div 4 = ?$

Use the related multiplication equation.
$4 \times 200 = 800$
So, $800 \div 4 = 200$

800

200	200	200	200

Each ticket cost \$200.

1 Look at the model below. Write a division equation and a related multiplication equation.

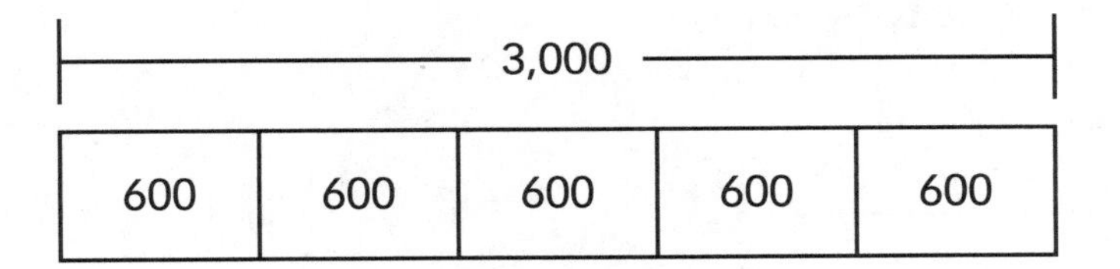

Division equation: _______ $\div 5 = 600$

Multiplication equation: _______ $\times$ _______ $=$ _______

2 Multiply.

$4 \times 700 =$ ____________

$6 \times 300 =$ ____________

$3 \times 900 =$ ____________

3 Write the missing numbers in the equation.

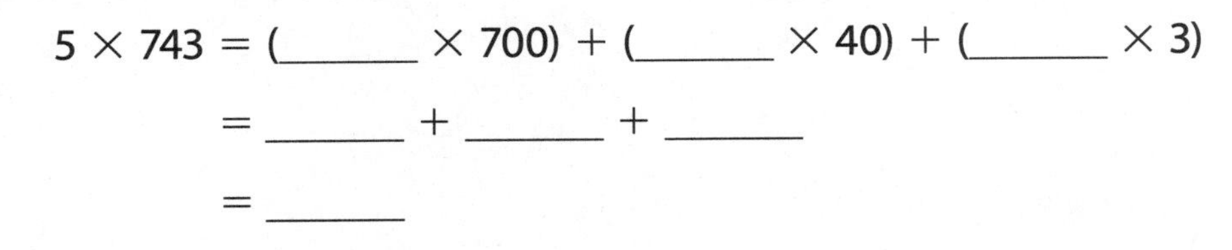

$5 \times 743 = ($_______ $\times 700) + ($_______ $\times 40) + ($_______ $\times 3)$

$=$ _______ $+$ _______ $+$ _______

$=$ _______

Solve.

4 Write numbers in the area model below to show 6×925. Then complete the equation.

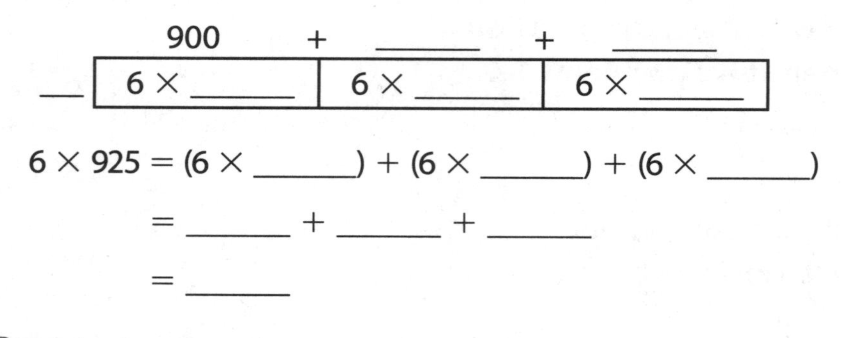

5 Multiply. $3 \times 213 = ?$

Show your work.

Solution: $3 \times 213 =$ ______

6 For each division equation below, write a related multiplication equation. The first one is done for you.

$900 \div 3 = ?$ **$3 \times 300 = 900$**

$600 \div 3 = ?$ ______________________

$30 \div 3 = ?$ ______________________

$9 \div 3 = ?$ ______________________

7 Heidi drove to visit her grandparents last weekend. She drove 215 miles each way. This weekend she drove to her friend's house. It was 174 miles each way. How many miles did she drive altogether on both weekends?

Show your work.

You can multiply by 2 to find the distance Heidi drove each weekend.

Solution: Heidi drove ______ miles.

Name: ____________________

Divide Three-Digit Numbers by One-Digit Numbers

Study the example problem showing how to divide a three-digit number by a one-digit number. Then solve problems 1–6.

Example

Muffins are packed and sold in boxes of 4.
How many boxes are needed to pack 260 muffins?

$260 \div 4 = ?$

Use an area model.
$260 \div 4 = 65$

	50	+ 10	+ 5	= 65
4	$(4 \times 50 = 200)$ 260 − 200 60	$(4 \times 10 = 40)$ 60 − 40 20	$(4 \times 5 = 20)$ 20 − 20 0	

65 boxes are needed.

Use multiplication to check:

$$4 \times 65 = (4 \times 60) + (4 \times 5)$$
$$= 240 + 20$$
$$= 260$$

1 Use the example above. Show how to subtract partial products to divide 260 by 4.

2 Identify the dividend, divisor, and quotient.

a. $900 \div 3 = 300$

dividend: _______ divisor: _______ quotient: _______

b. $120 = 600 \div 5$

dividend: _______ divisor: _______ quotient: _______

Vocabulary

dividend the number you divide in a division problem.

divisor the number you divide by in a division problem.

quotient the answer to a division problem.

dividend ÷ divisor = quotient
260 ÷ 4 = 65

$\text{divisor}\,\overline{)\,\text{dividend}}$ with quotient above; $4\overline{)260}$ with 65 above

Solve.

3 A health center raised $476. The money was divided equally among 7 programs. How much did each program get? Use an area model to solve the problem.

Show your work.

Solution: ____________________

4 Mike has 876 building pieces to share among himself and 2 friends. He wants each person to have an equal number of pieces. How many pieces does each person get?

Show your work.

Solution: ____________________

5 Look at how you solved problem 4. Explain how you could have used estimation before you divided so that you would know whether your answer was reasonable.

____

____

____

6 Explain how to use multiplication to check your answer in problem 4.

____

____

Name: ____________________

Divide Four-Digit Numbers by One-Digit Numbers

Study the example problem showing how to divide a four-digit number by a one-digit number. Then solve problems 1–5.

Example

A group of hikers plan to take 8 hours to hike a mountain trail 5,380 meters long. If they hike the same distance each hour, how many meters should they hike in an hour?

The sum of the partial quotients is 600 + 70 + 2 , or 672. The remainder is 4.

```
      2
     70
    600
8)5,380  ⟶ There are 600 groups of 8 in 5,000.
 −4,800  ⟶ Subtract 600 groups of 8; 8 × 600.
    580  ⟶ There are 70 groups of 8 in 580.
  − 560  ⟶ Subtract 70 groups of 8; 8 × 70.
     20  ⟶ There are 2 groups of 8 in 20.
   − 16  ⟶ Subtract 2 groups of 8; 8 × 2.
      4
```

$5{,}380 \div 8 = 672$ R4

The hikers should hike 672 meters each hour. Then they will need to hike 4 more meters to reach the end of the trail.

1 Complete the division problem.

$8{,}236 \div 5 =$ ____________

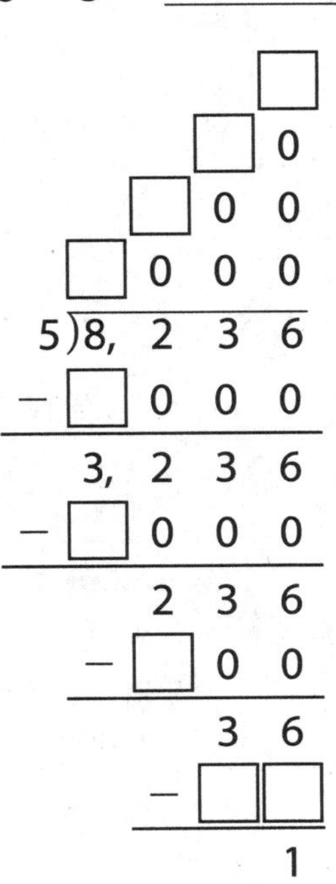

2 Complete the division problem.

$4{,}507 \div 4 =$ ____________

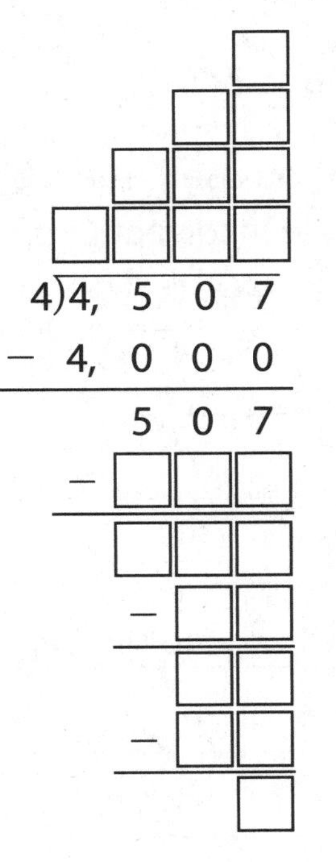

Solve.

3 One week has 7 days. How many weeks do 1,230 days make? What does the remainder mean?

Show your work.

Solution: ________________________________

4 Mugs are packed 6 to a box. How many boxes are needed to pack 1,524 mugs?

Show your work.

Solution: ________________________________

5 Tyson used a calculator to find the quotient for each of the problems below. Use estimation to tell whether each quotient is *Correct* or *Incorrect*.

a. 4,960 ÷ 2 = 9,920 ☐ Correct ☐ Incorrect

b. 7,095 ÷ 5 = 1,419 ☐ Correct ☐ Incorrect

c. 9,621 ÷ 3 = 230 R7 ☐ Correct ☐ Incorrect

d. 3,875 ÷ 6 = 645 R5 ☐ Correct ☐ Incorrect

6 Explain how you used estimation to tell which quotients were incorrect in problem 5.

____

____

____

____

____

____

____

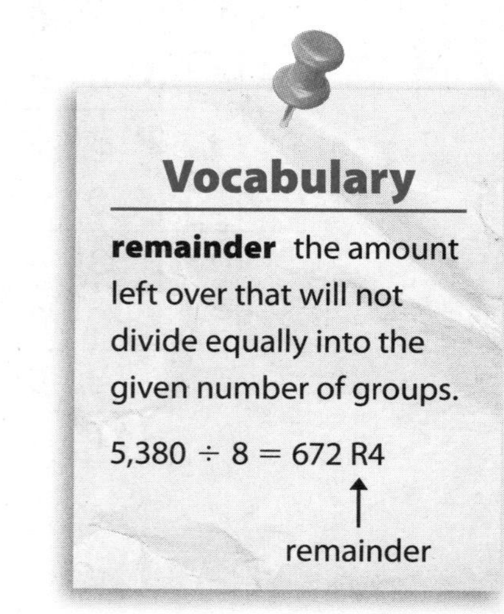

Name: ______________________

Divide Whole Numbers

Solve the problems.

1 Find the quotient.

3,752 ÷ 6

A 652 **C** 625

B 652 R2 **D** 625 R2

To check the quotient, multiply it by the divisor and add any remainder.

2 Carter has a pack of 800 rubber bands. Alicia has twice as many rubber bands as Carter. They combine their rubber bands so that they can make bracelets. Each bracelet needs 100 rubber bands. Which equation below can be used to find how many bracelets they can make?

A $(800 \times 2) \div 100$ **C** $(800 \div 100) \times 2$

B $(800 \times 3) \div 100$ **D** $(800 \times 100) \div 3$

Jon chose **A** as the correct answer. How did he get that answer?

____

____

Drawing a model or picture can help make sense of this problem.

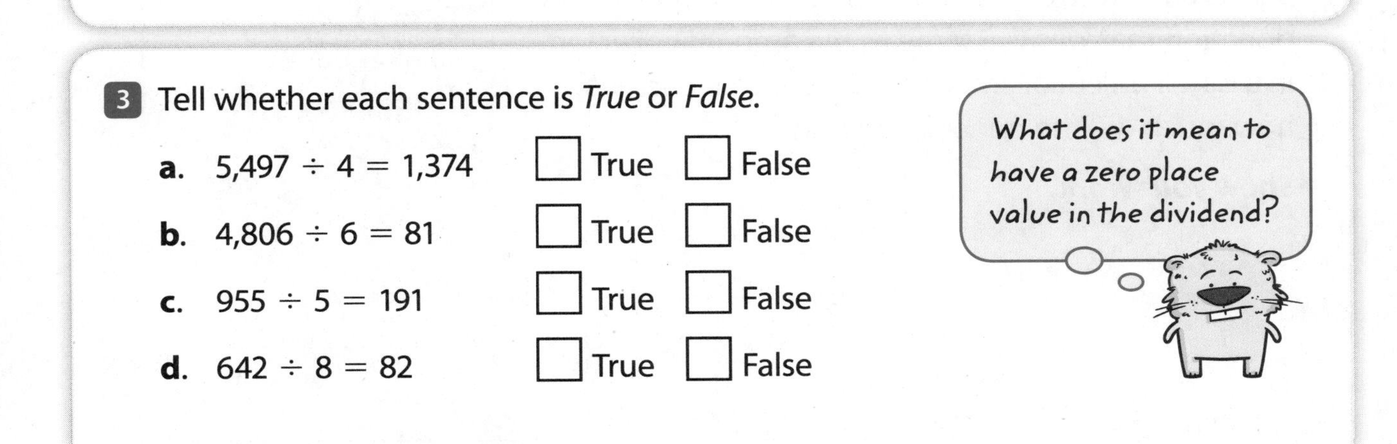

3 Tell whether each sentence is *True* or *False*.

a. 5,497 ÷ 4 = 1,374 ☐ True ☐ False

b. 4,806 ÷ 6 = 81 ☐ True ☐ False

c. 955 ÷ 5 = 191 ☐ True ☐ False

d. 642 ÷ 8 = 82 ☐ True ☐ False

Solve.

4 Chloe and Ingrid are packing boxes with books. They have 238 books. Each box will fit 8 books. Chloe says 29 boxes is enough to pack all the books. Ingrid thinks they need 30 boxes. Explain who is correct.

What does the remainder mean in this problem?

Show your work.

Solution: ______________________________

5 Carolyn has 1,090 photos that she wants to organize into an album. Each album page holds 6 photos. How many pages can she fill with 6 photos each?

Divide each place value in the dividend, 1,090, by the divisor, 6.

Show your work.

Solution: ______________________________

6 In 4 weeks, a school raised $2,560 for Health and Fitness awareness. Students collected donations 5 days each week. The principal agreed to make one donation that was the same as the amount collected in a day. If an equal amount was collected each day, how much did the principal donate?

Show your work.

Solution: ______________________________

Unit 3 Game

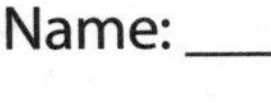

Name: ___________________

Multiplication Products

What you need: Recording Sheet, 2 sets of digit cards (0–9)

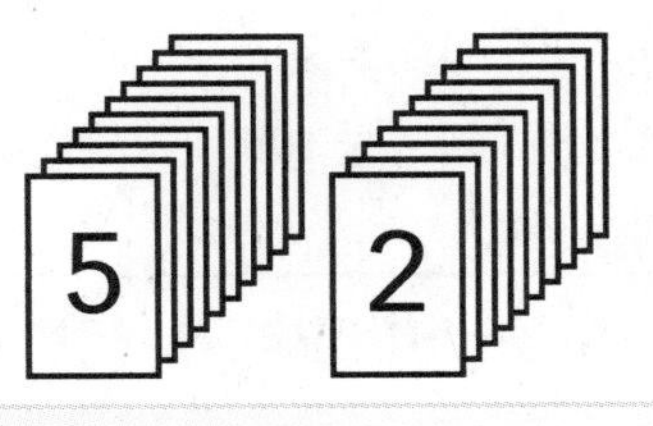

6 4 × 3 9

Directions

- Mix the cards and place them facedown in a stack. (Before each new round, you'll need to place the cards back in the stack and shuffle them again.)
- In Rounds 1 and 2, each player draws 4 cards. Players use the numbers on their cards to make 2 two-digit numbers. Players record their numbers on the Recording Sheet and multiply them. In Round 1, the player with the greater product wins the round. In Round 2, the player with the lesser product wins the round.
- In Rounds 3 and 4, each player draws 5 cards. Players use the numbers on their cards to make a four-digit and a one-digit-number. Players record their numbers on the Recording Sheet and multiply them. In Round 3, the player with the greater product wins. In Round 4, the player with the lesser product wins.
- In Round 5, players choose a round from Rounds 1–4 to repeat.
- The winner is the player with more wins after 5 rounds.

Name: ___________________

Multiplication Products Recording Sheet

Rosa — Player A Name

Henry — Player B Name

Round 1: Multiply a two-digit number by a two-digit number. Circle the greater product.

1. 64 × 39 = (2,496)   1. 71 × 28 = 1,988

Round 2: Multiply a two-digit number by a two-digit number. Circle the lesser product.

2. ____ × ____ = ______   2. ____ × ____ = ______

I multiplied 64 by 39 and got a product of 2,496. My product is greater than your product of 1,988, so I win the first round.

Name: ____________________

Multiplication Products Recording Sheet

____________________ ____________________

Player A Name **Player B Name**

Round 1: Multiply a two-digit number by a two-digit number. Circle the greater product.

Player A	Player B
1. _____ × _____ = __________	**1.** _____ × _____ = __________

Round 2: Multiply a two-digit number by a two-digit number. Circle the lesser product.

Player A	Player B
2. _____ × _____ = __________	**2.** _____ × _____ = __________

Round 3: Multiply a four-digit number by a one-digit number. Circle the greater product.

Player A	Player B
3. _____ × _____ = __________	**3.** _____ × _____ = __________

Round 4: Multiply a four-digit number by a one-digit number. Circle the lesser product.

Player A	Player B
4. _____ × _____ = __________	**4.** _____ × _____ = __________

Round 5: Choose Round 1, 2, 3, or 4 to repeat.

Player A	Player B
5. _____ × _____ = __________	**5.** _____ × _____ = __________

Final Score Player A ________ **Final Score Player B** ________

Digit Cards (0–9)

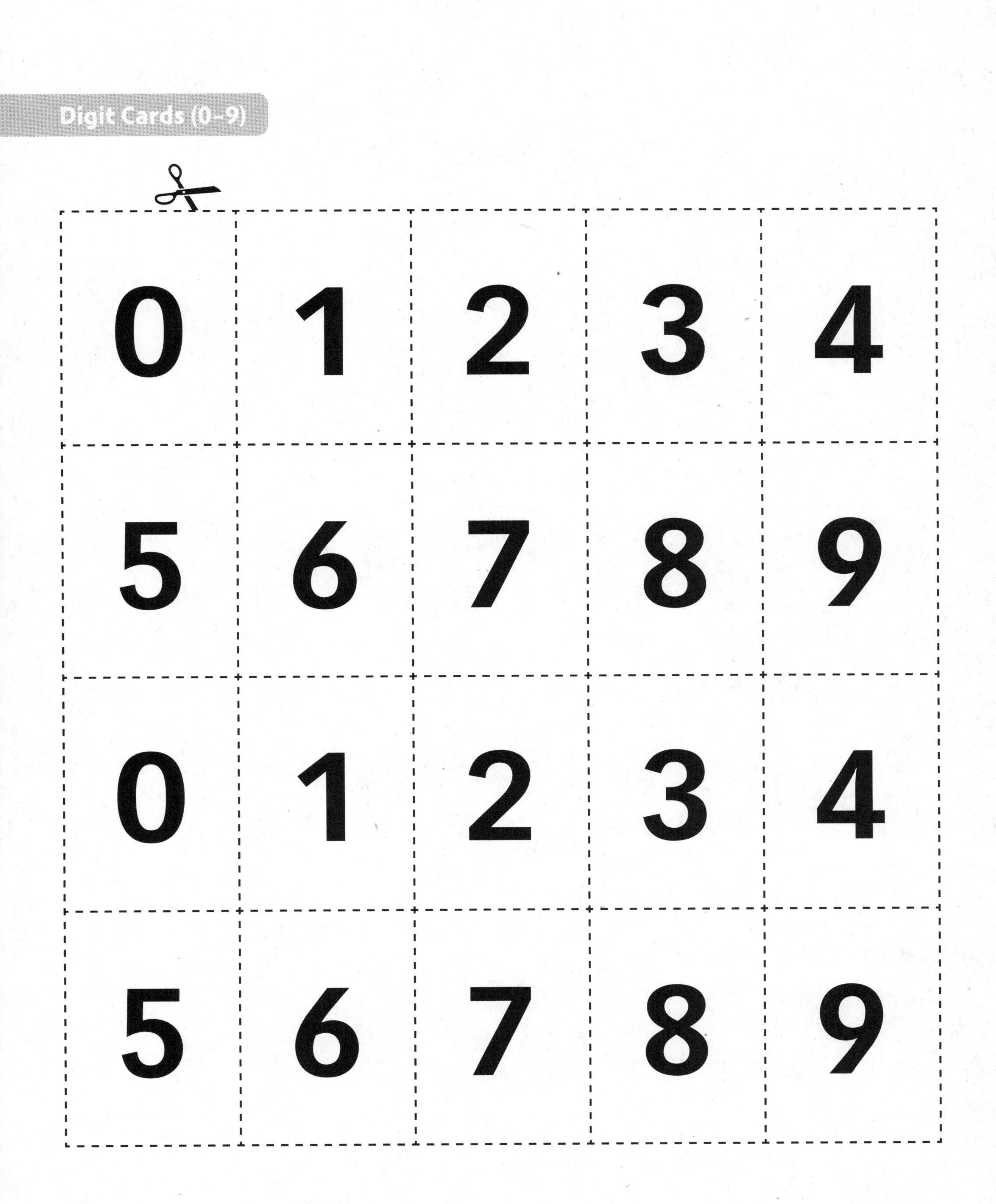

Unit 3 Practice

Name: ______________________

Computation

In this unit you learned to:	Lesson
multiply a 4-digit number by a 1-digit number, for example: $2{,}810 \times 3 = 8{,}430$.	11
multiply a 2-digit number by a 2-digit number, for example: $62 \times 33 = 2{,}046$.	11
divide a 4-digit number by a 1-digit number, for example: $6{,}328 \div 4 = 1{,}582$.	12
use area models and equations to explain calculations, for example: $7 \times 240 = (7 \times 200) + (7 \times 40)$.	11, 12

Use these skills to solve problems 1–5.

1 Write numbers in each section of the area model to complete the model. Then write the product to complete the equation. Use numbers from the gray number bank at the right to complete the model and the equation.

4	8	10
20	30	32
40	50	68
160	272	432

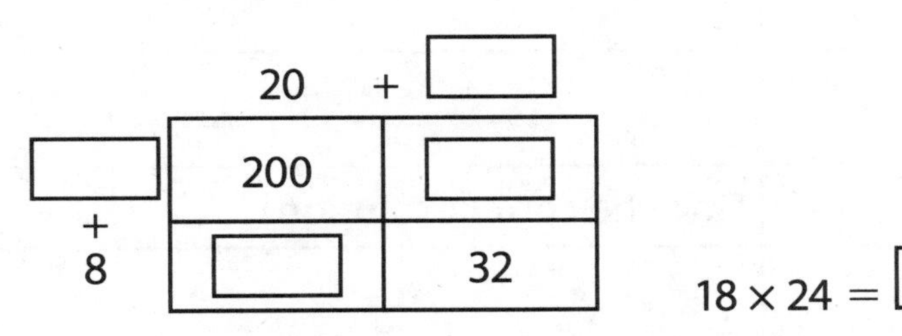

$18 \times 24 = \square$

2 Use numbers from the gray number bank in problem 1. Write numbers in each section of the area model to complete the model. Then write the quotient to complete the equation.

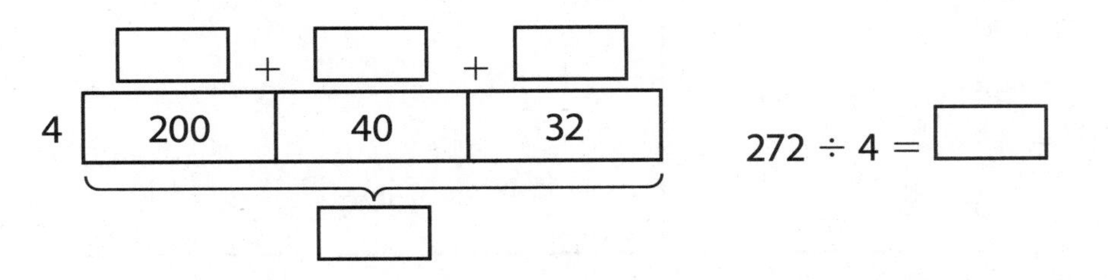

$272 \div 4 = \square$

For problems 3–5, circle the error in the student work. Then find the correct solution to the problem.

3 Circle the error.	Find the correct solution.
$3{,}490 \times 5$ $= (3{,}000 \times 5) + (400 \times 9) + (90 \times 5)$	$3{,}490 \times 5$

4 Circle the error.	Find the correct solution.
$\begin{array}{r} 61 \\ \times\ 23 \\ \hline 3 \\ 18 \\ 20 \\ +\ 1{,}200 \\ \hline 1{,}159 \end{array}$	$\begin{array}{r} 61 \\ \times\ 23 \\ \hline \end{array}$

5 Circle the error.	Find the correct solution.
$\begin{array}{r} 6 \\ 30 \\ 300 \\ 8\overline{)2{,}494} \\ -\ 2{,}200 \\ \hline 294 \\ -\ 2400 \\ \hline 54 \\ -\ 48 \\ \hline 6 \end{array}$	$8\overline{)2{,}494}$ $2{,}494 \div 8 =$ ______

Unit 3 Performance Task

Name: ______________________

Answer the questions and show all your work on separate paper.

Wooddale Summer Camp has 250 campers. Dan, the arts and crafts counselor, is planning two art projects.

For the paper project, each camper needs 8 sheets of paper and 3 bottles of paint. For the yarn project, each camper needs 2 balls of yarn and 9 wooden beads.

Dan has $4,000 to spend. The table below shows the cost of supplies. Use the information in the table to create a plan. In your plan, tell how many campers can do each art project and the total cost. Explain how you know that Dan can use your plan.

Supplies	Quantity in Package	Cost
Paper	5,000 sheets	$115
Paint	6 bottles	$8
Yarn	9 balls	$74
Beads	1,000 beads	$33

Checklist

Did you . . .

- ☐ create a plan?
- ☐ check your calculations?
- ☐ give a clear explanation?

Reflect on the Process Standards

After you complete the task, choose one of the following questions to answer.

1. **Model** How did you use equations to solve the problem?
2. **Make Sense of Problems** How did you find how many supplies were needed for the number of campers you chose?

Performance Task Tips

Word Bank Here are some words that you might use in your answer.

product	multiply	divide
remainder	quotient	need
each	total	compare

Model Here is a model that you might use to find the solution.

Supplies	Number for Each Camper	Number of Campers	Packages Needed	Cost
Paper				
Paint				
Yarn				
Beads				

Sentence Starters Here are some sentence starters that might help you write an explanation.

In my plan, ______________ campers do ________________

For each art project, I multiply _________________________

To find how many packages are needed, I divide _______

I compare the total cost to ________ in order to _________

Unit 3 Vocabulary

Name: ______________________

My Examples

multiplication

an operation used to find the total number of items in equal-sized groups

product

the result of multiplication

factors

numbers that are multiplied together to get a product

multiple

the product of a number and any other whole number; for example, 3, 6, 9, 12, and 15 are multiples of 3

My Examples

quotient

the answer to a division problem

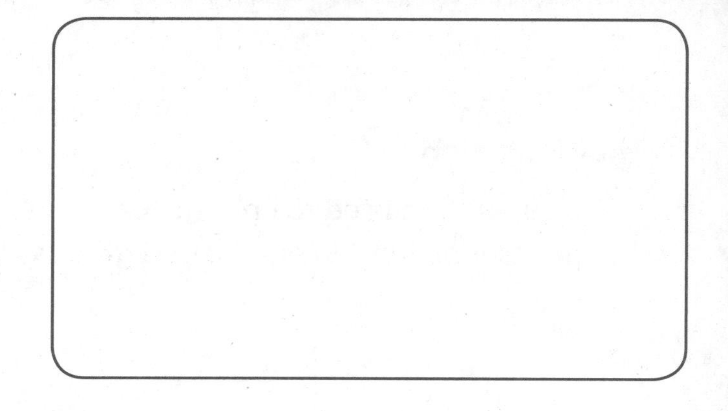

dividend

the number you divide in a division problem

divisor

the number you divide by in a division problem

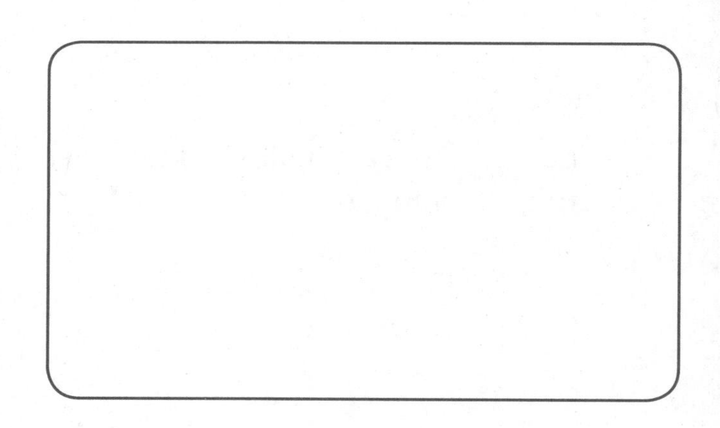

remainder

the amount left over that will not divide equally into the given number of groups

Dear Family,

This week your child is exploring equivalent fractions.

equivalent fractions: two or more fractions that name the same amount of a whole.
numerator: the top number in a fraction; it tells the number of parts in a whole that are being described.
denominator: the bottom number in a fraction; it tells the total number of equal parts in a whole.

You can show the equivalent fractions $\frac{1}{3}$, $\frac{2}{6}$, and $\frac{4}{12}$ with models.

The model at the right is divided into 3 equal parts. The shaded section shows the fraction $\frac{1}{3}$.

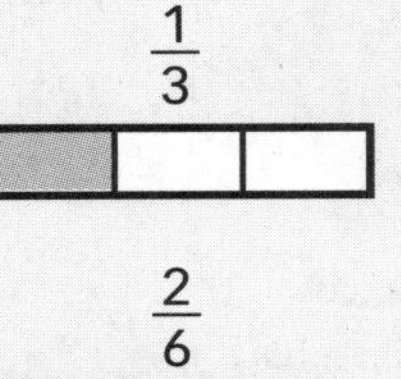

The same model can be divided into 6 equal parts. It has 2 times as many parts shaded and 2 times as many equal parts. The shaded section shows the fraction $\frac{2}{6}$.

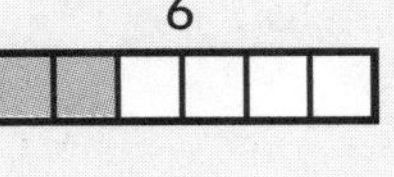

The same model can be divided again into 12 equal parts. Now it has 4 times as many parts shaded and 4 times as many equal parts. The shaded section shows the fraction $\frac{4}{12}$.

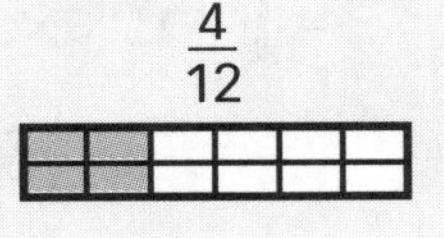

Another way to find equivalent fractions is to multiply both the numerator and denominator of a fraction by the same number. This is the same as multiplying by 1 because $\frac{2}{2} = 1$ and $\frac{4}{4} = 1$.

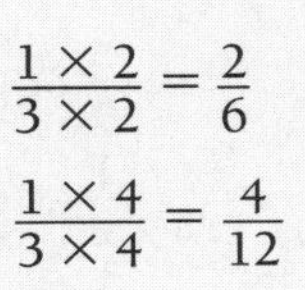

$$\frac{1 \times 2}{3 \times 2} = \frac{2}{6}$$

$$\frac{1 \times 4}{3 \times 4} = \frac{4}{12}$$

Invite your child to share what he or she knows about equivalent fractions by doing the following activity together.

Equivalent Fractions Activity

Do an activity with your child to explore equivalent fractions.

Materials: recipe ingredients, $\frac{1}{8}$-cup measuring cup, and soup pot (all optional)

Look at the recipe below for Mexican Bean Soup. Then follow the steps below to find equivalent fractions.

- Suppose the only measuring cup available is a $\frac{1}{8}$-cup measuring cup. Rewrite the recipe so all the ingredients can be measured using only the $\frac{1}{8}$-cup measuring cup. (This means that you will find equivalent fractions with 8 as the denominator.)
- Discuss how the numerator relates to using the $\frac{1}{8}$-cup to measure each ingredient. (The numerator is the number of times the measuring cup is filled.)
- Make the recipe for your family to enjoy.

Recipe for Mexican Bean Soup

Ingredients:

$\frac{4}{4}$ cup stewed tomatoes

$\frac{3}{4}$ cup canned black beans with liquid

$\frac{1}{2}$ cup cooked rice

$\frac{1}{4}$ cup salsa

Directions:

Mix all the ingredients together in a soup pot.

Stir. Heat and serve. Enjoy!

Understand Equivalent Fractions

Name: ____________________

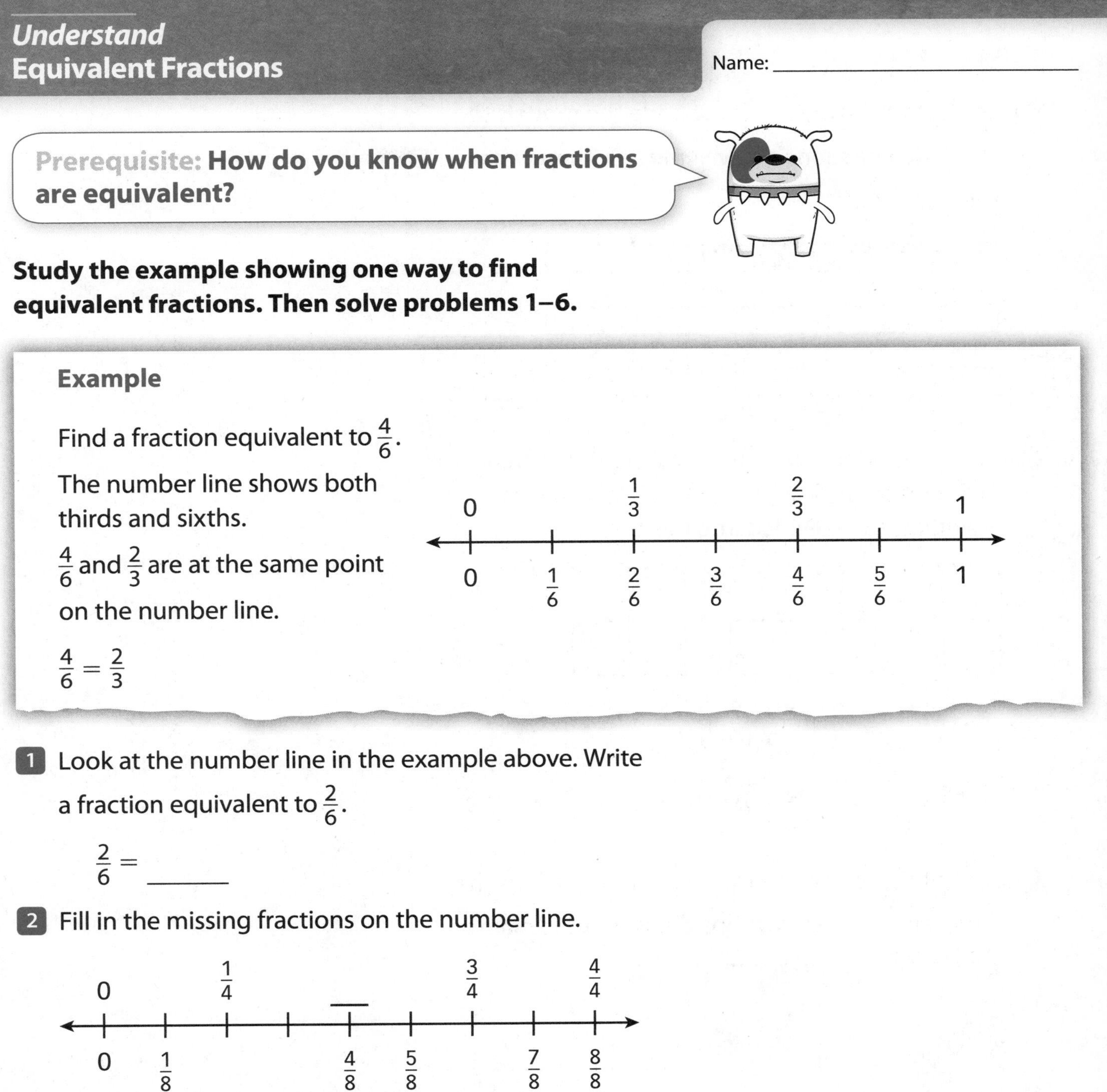

Prerequisite: How do you know when fractions are equivalent?

Study the example showing one way to find equivalent fractions. Then solve problems 1–6.

Example

Find a fraction equivalent to $\frac{4}{6}$.

The number line shows both thirds and sixths.

$\frac{4}{6}$ and $\frac{2}{3}$ are at the same point on the number line.

$\frac{4}{6} = \frac{2}{3}$

1 Look at the number line in the example above. Write a fraction equivalent to $\frac{2}{6}$.

$\frac{2}{6} =$ ______

2 Fill in the missing fractions on the number line.

3 Look at the number line in problem 2.

Write equivalent fractions.

$\frac{1}{4} =$ ______ ______ $= \frac{4}{8}$ $\frac{3}{4} =$ ______

Solve.

4 Look at the models below. Shade the models to show two fractions equivalent to $\frac{3}{4}$. Then write the fractions.

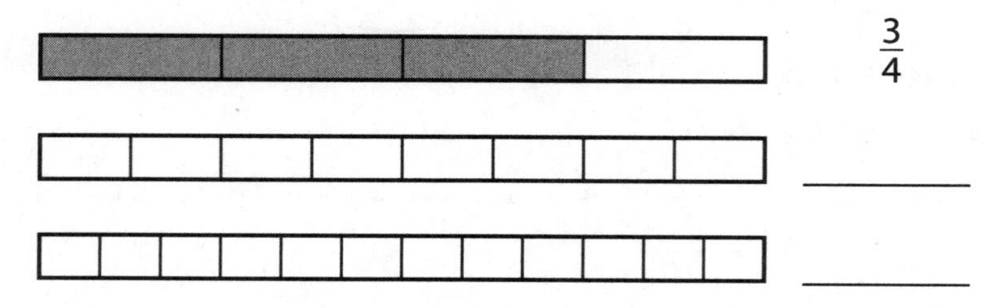

$\frac{3}{4}$

______

______

5 Use the models below to complete the sentences. The models show wholes and parts. There are 3 wholes, each divided into fourths.

Each part is ______ of a whole.

There are ______ fourths in all. $\frac{\square}{\square} = 3$

6 Look at the models below. Write the fractions they represent. Are the fractions equivalent? Explain.

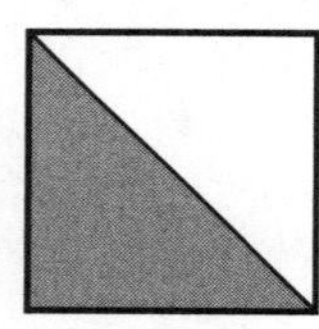

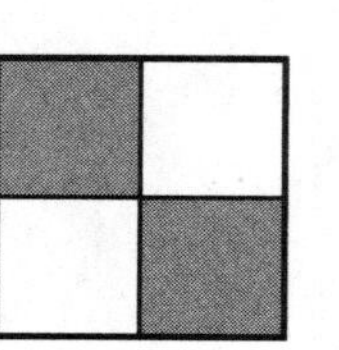

____

____

____

____

____

Name: ____________________

Show Equivalent Fractions

Study the example showing one way to model equivalent fractions. Then solve problems 1–8.

Example

A model can show equivalent fractions.

The model has 5 equal parts. It shows $\frac{3}{5}$.

Divide the model into 10 equal parts to show an equivalent fraction.

The model shows $\frac{6}{10}$.

$\frac{3}{5} = \frac{6}{10}$

1 Divide the model below to show $\frac{1}{2} = \frac{5}{10}$.

2 Draw a model to show $\frac{1}{6}$. Then divide the model into twice as many parts to find an equivalent fraction.

$\frac{1}{6} =$ ______

3 Multiply the numerator and denominator of $\frac{1}{6}$ by 2.

$\frac{1 \times 2}{6 \times 2} =$ ______

4 Why does it make sense that the fraction you wrote in problems 2 and 3 is the same?

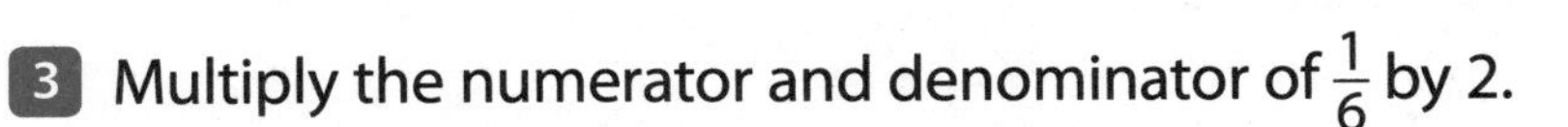

Solve.

5 Fill in the missing numbers to find two equivalent fractions to $\frac{4}{5}$.

$\frac{4 \times \square}{5 \times 2} = \frac{\square}{10}$ $\frac{4 \times 20}{5 \times 20} = \frac{\square}{100}$

6 Look at problem 5. Explain how $\frac{8}{10} = \frac{80}{100}$.

____

____

____

____

____

____

____

7 Shade the model below to show $\frac{1}{5}$. Then show 10 equal parts and write an equivalent fraction.

____

8 Shade the model below to show $\frac{2}{3}$. Then show 12 equal parts and write an equivalent fraction.

____

Name: ____________________

Reason and Write

Study the example. Underline two parts that you think make it a particularly good answer and a helpful example.

Example

Find a fraction equivalent to $\frac{1}{2}$ that has a denominator of 12.

Show your work. Use models, words, and numbers to explain your answer.

I draw a model that shows $\frac{1}{2}$.

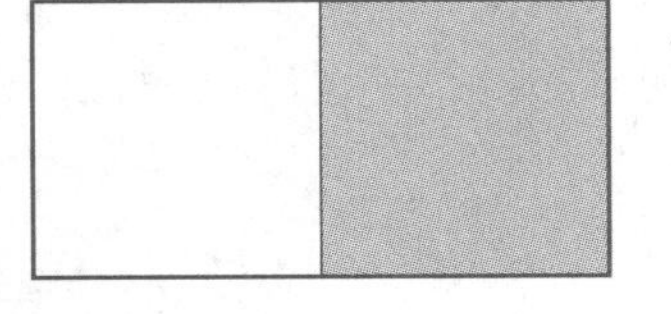

To find an equivalent fraction with a denominator of 12, I divide the model into 12 equal parts. The model shows $\frac{6}{12}$. So $\frac{1}{2} = \frac{6}{12}$.

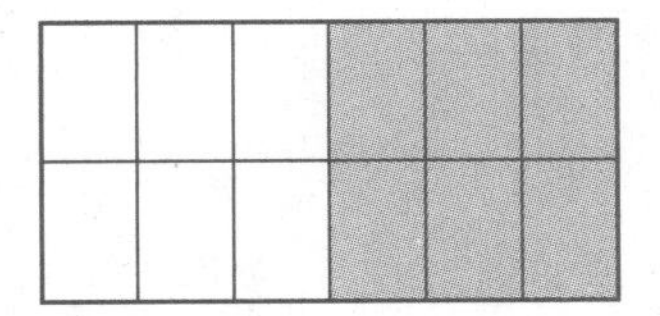

I can also multiply both the numerator and denominator of $\frac{1}{2}$ by 6 to find an equivalent fraction with a denominator of 12.

$$\frac{1 \times 6}{2 \times 6} = \frac{6}{12}$$

Where does the example . . .

- use models to show equivalent fractions?
- use numbers to write equivalent fractions?
- use words to explain?

Solve the problem. Use what you learned from the example.

Find a fraction equivalent to $\frac{2}{5}$ that has a denominator of 20.

Show your work. Use models, words, and numbers to explain your answer.

Did you . . .

- use models to show equivalent fractions?
- use numbers to write equivalent fractions?
- use words to explain?

Dear Family,

This week your child is exploring whole numbers, mixed numbers, and improper fractions.

Your child can use a model to help write an **improper fraction** that represents a whole number, such as 3. An **improper fraction** is a fraction with a numerator that is greater than or equal to the denominator, such as $\frac{3}{2}$.

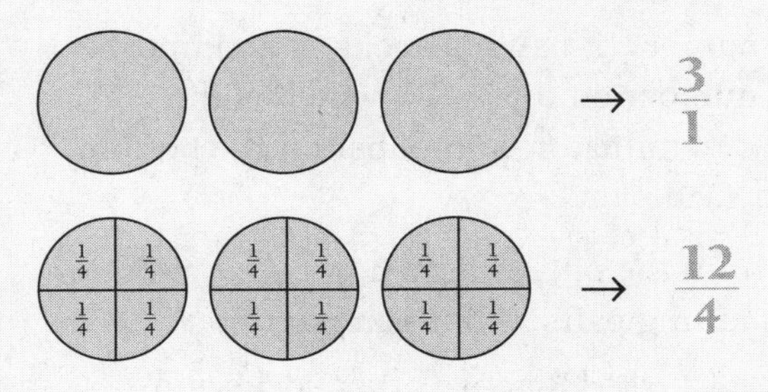

Your child can use a model or a number line to help find the improper fraction that is equivalent to mixed number. A **mixed number** is whole number with a fraction, such as $1\frac{1}{3}$.

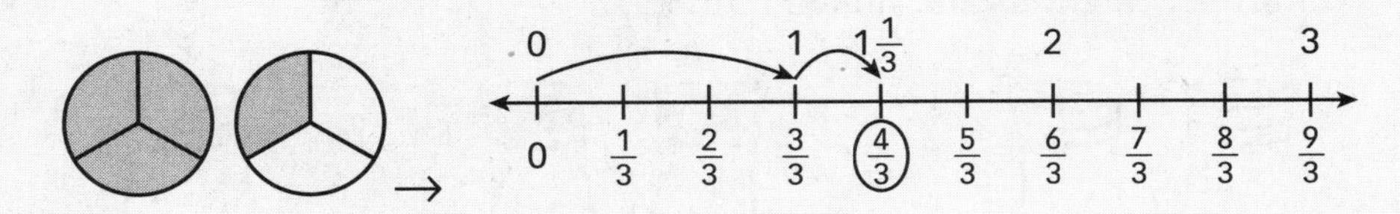

Total number of all the parts ⟶ $\frac{4}{3} = 1\frac{1}{3}$
Number of parts in each whole ⟶

Invite your child to share what he or she knows about finding and comparing whole numbers, improper fractions, and mixed numbers by doing the following activity together.

Equivalent Improper Fractions and Mixed Numbers Activity

Materials: 5 pairs of socks (or shoes, gloves, or other paired items), pencil, paper

- Line up the socks in pairs across the floor. Ask your child the following questions: How many pairs of socks are there? How many socks, or parts, are in each pair? How many socks are there in all? Have your child record his or her answers on a sheet of paper.
- Help your child understand that each pair of socks is a whole, and that each whole pair is made up of two parts.
- Ask your child to write the number of pairs of socks as an improper fraction. The numerator, or number on top, is 10, which is the number of socks in all. The denominator, or number on the bottom, is 2, which is the number in each pair.
- Next, remove a single sock from the pile, and then ask your child to write the number of the remaining pairs as both an improper fraction and a mixed number. $\left(\frac{9}{2}, 4\frac{1}{2}\right)$ Remove other socks and repeat the activity.
- You can reverse the game so that your child removes socks and then checks your work to see if you have written down the correct improper fractions and mixed numbers.

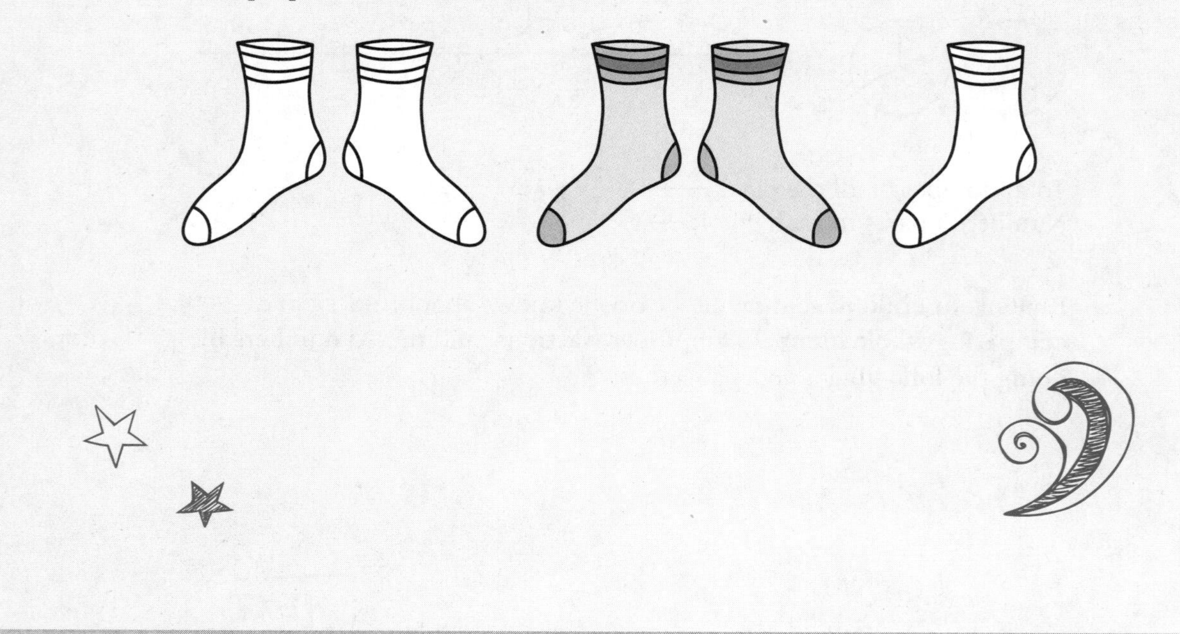

Whole Numbers, Mixed Numbers, and Improper Fractions

Name: ______________________

Prerequisite: Identify Equivalent Fractions, Improper Fractions, and Mixed Numbers

Study the example showing how to identify equivalent fractions. Then solve problems 1–7.

Example

Sherry uses 3 sections of a dark chocolate bar to make a cake. She needs the same amount of white chocolate for the icing. How many pieces of white chocolate will she use?

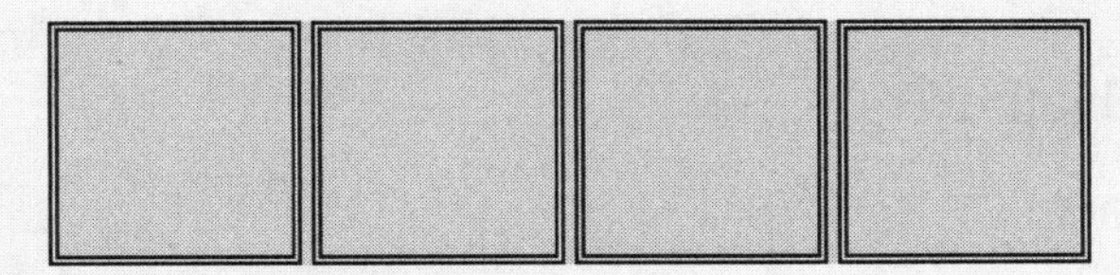

3 pieces of dark chocolate equals 6 pieces of white chocolate.

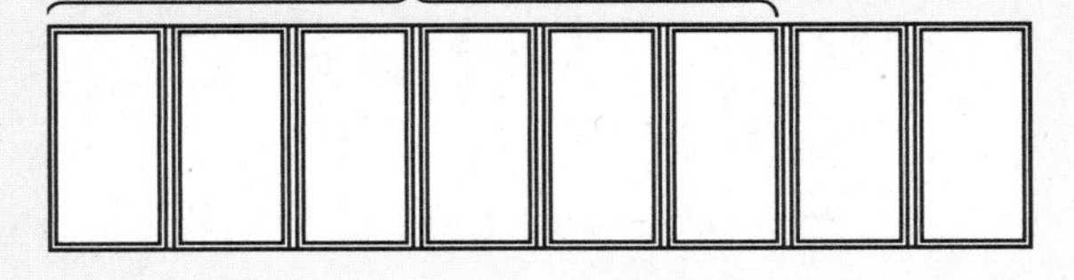

Sherry will use 6 pieces of white chocolate.

1 What fraction of the white chocolate is 6 pieces?

______

2 What fraction of the dark chocolate bar is 3 pieces?

______

3 Are the fractions you found in problems 1 and 2 equal? Explain.

____

____

____

Vocabulary

improper fraction a fraction with a numerator greater than or equal to the denominator.

mixed number a number that has a whole-number part and a fraction part, such as $1\frac{1}{2}$.

Solve.

Use the model for problems 4 and 5.

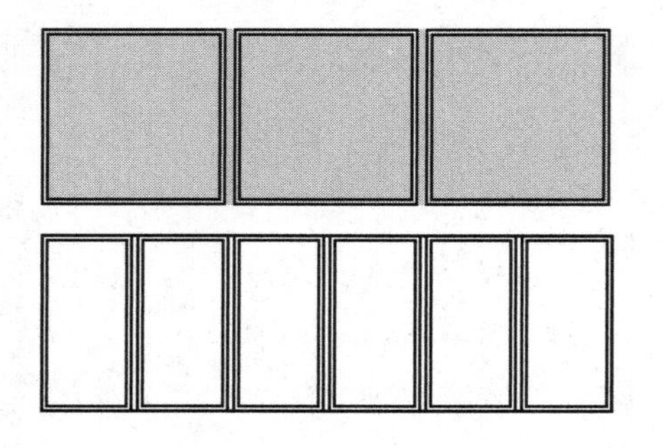

4 You use $\frac{2}{3}$ of the dark chocolate bar. What fraction names an equal amount of the white chocolate bar?

____

5 One whole dark chocolate bar is $\frac{3}{3}$. What equivalent fraction names one whole white chocolate bar?

____

6 Draw a model that shows $\frac{5}{5}$.

7 Look at the number line. What improper fraction is equivalent to $1\frac{2}{3}$? _______

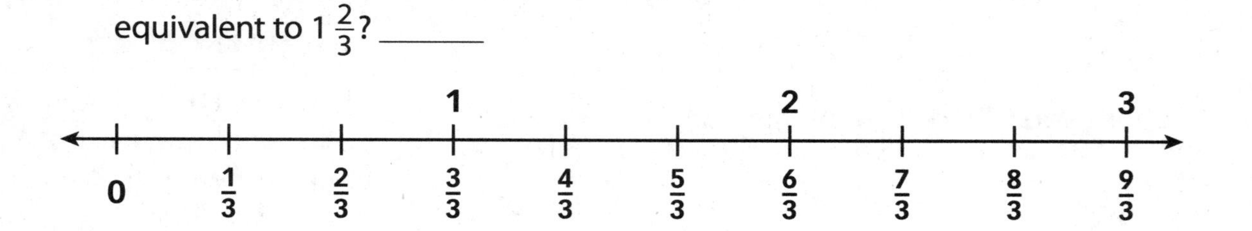

Name: ______________________

Write a Whole Number as a Fraction

Study the example showing how to write a whole number as a fraction. Then solve problems 1–7.

Example

Kaya bought 3 wheels of cheese. She cut each wheel into thirds. How many thirds of cheese does she have?

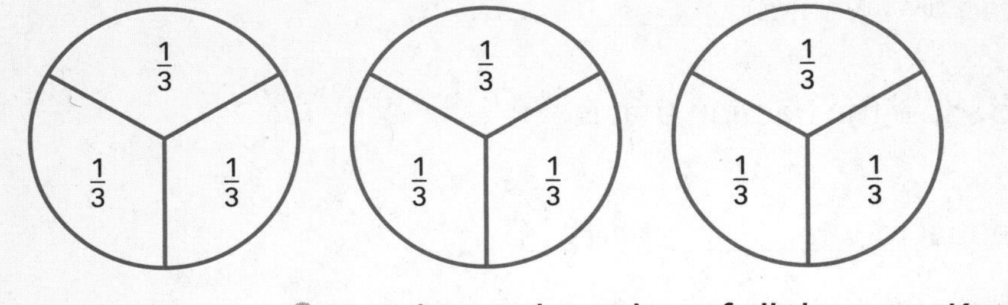

In all, Kaya has $\frac{9}{3}$ ← the total number of all the parts Kaya has; ← the number of parts in 1 whole wheel of cheese

1 Look at the example above. Count the number of equal parts in 1 whole wheel of cheese. What fraction names the whole? ______

2 How many equal parts are there in 2 whole wheels of cheese? Explain how you know.

____

____

3 Write a fraction to show the number of parts in 2 whole wheels. ______

Solve.

Use the number line to answer questions 4 and 5.

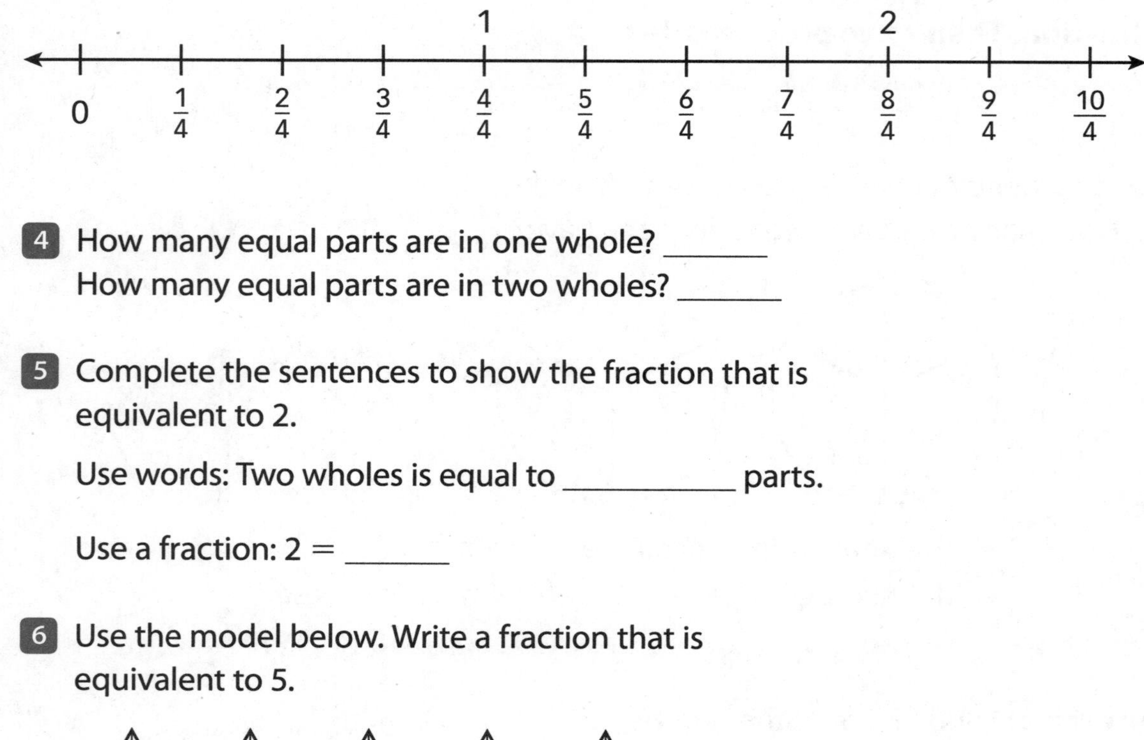

4 How many equal parts are in one whole? _______
How many equal parts are in two wholes? _______

5 Complete the sentences to show the fraction that is equivalent to 2.

Use words: Two wholes is equal to ___________ parts.

Use a fraction: $2 =$ _______

6 Use the model below. Write a fraction that is equivalent to 5.

____

7 Draw a model to show $5 = \frac{15}{3}$.

Name: ______________________

Write a Whole Number as a Fraction

Study the example showing how to write a whole number as a fraction. Then solve problems 1–6.

Example

Jeff buys 4 whole pizzas. The pizza shop does not cut them into slices. How can you write this whole number as a fraction?

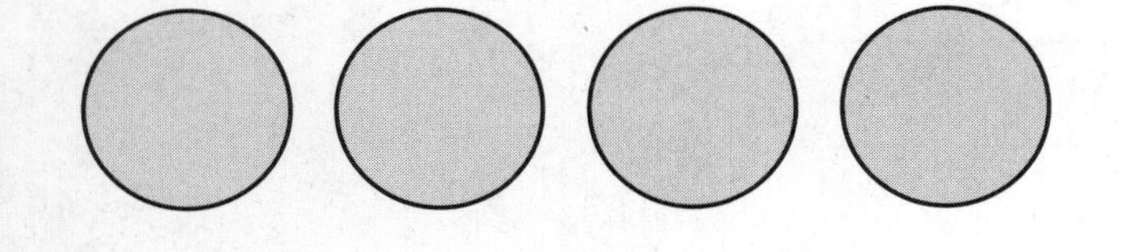

Each circle stands for 1 pizza: $1 + 1 + 1 + 1 = 4$. $\rightarrow$ 4

Each pizza has 1 part, so the denominator is 1. $\longrightarrow$ 1

$$\frac{4}{1}$$

1 Use the number line below. Circle the fraction that is the equivalent of 2.

0	1	2	3	4	5
0	$\frac{1}{1}$	$\frac{2}{1}$	$\frac{3}{1}$	$\frac{4}{1}$	$\frac{5}{1}$

2 Use the number line above. What fraction is equivalent to 5? ______

3 Explain why you write 5 as $\frac{5}{1}$.

____

____

____

Solve.

4 Look at the number line. What fraction is equivalent to 2? Explain how you know.

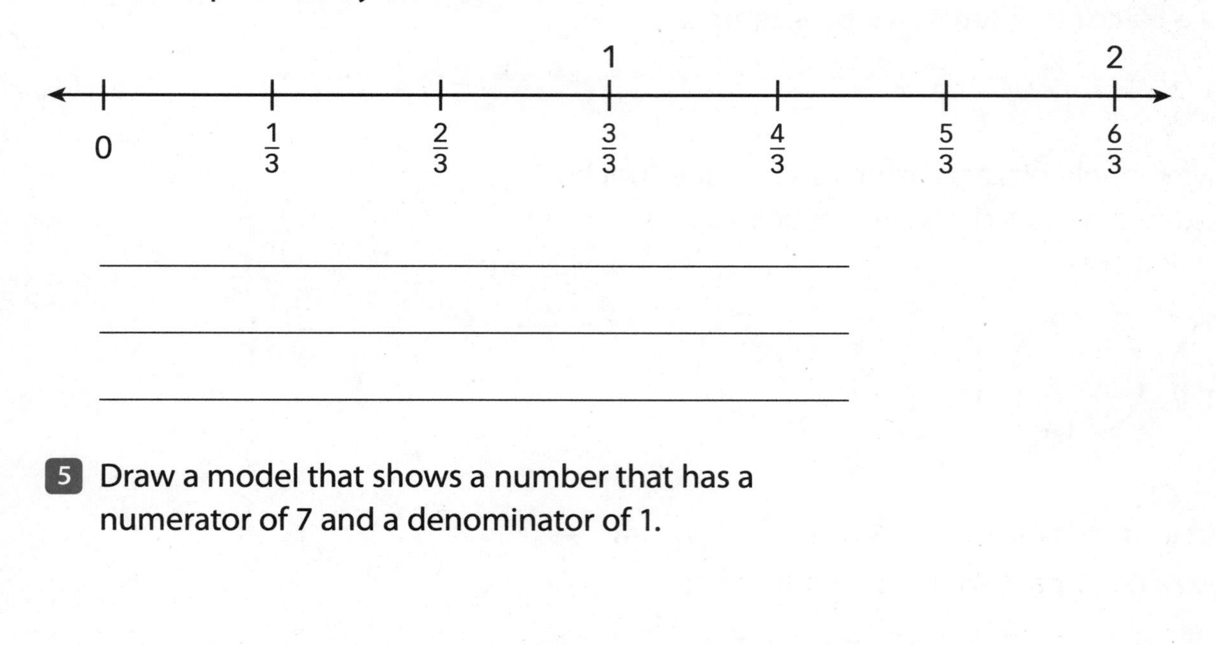

____

____

____

5 Draw a model that shows a number that has a numerator of 7 and a denominator of 1.

6 Look at the model. Count the number of diamonds. What is the equivalent fraction for all the diamonds? Explain how you know.

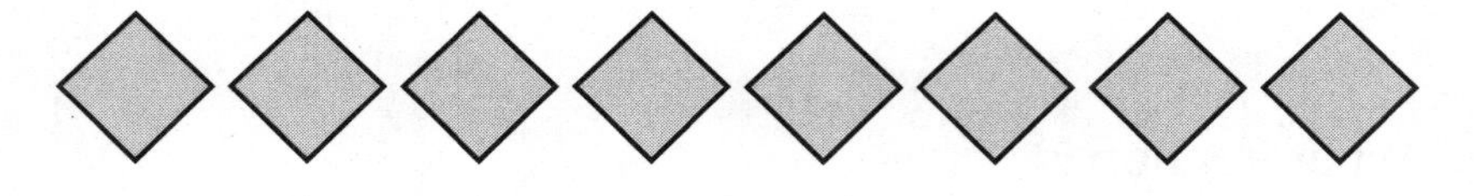

____

____

____

____

Name: ____________________

Write a Mixed Number as an Improper Fraction.

Study the example showing how to write a mixed number as an improper fraction. Then solve problems 1–7.

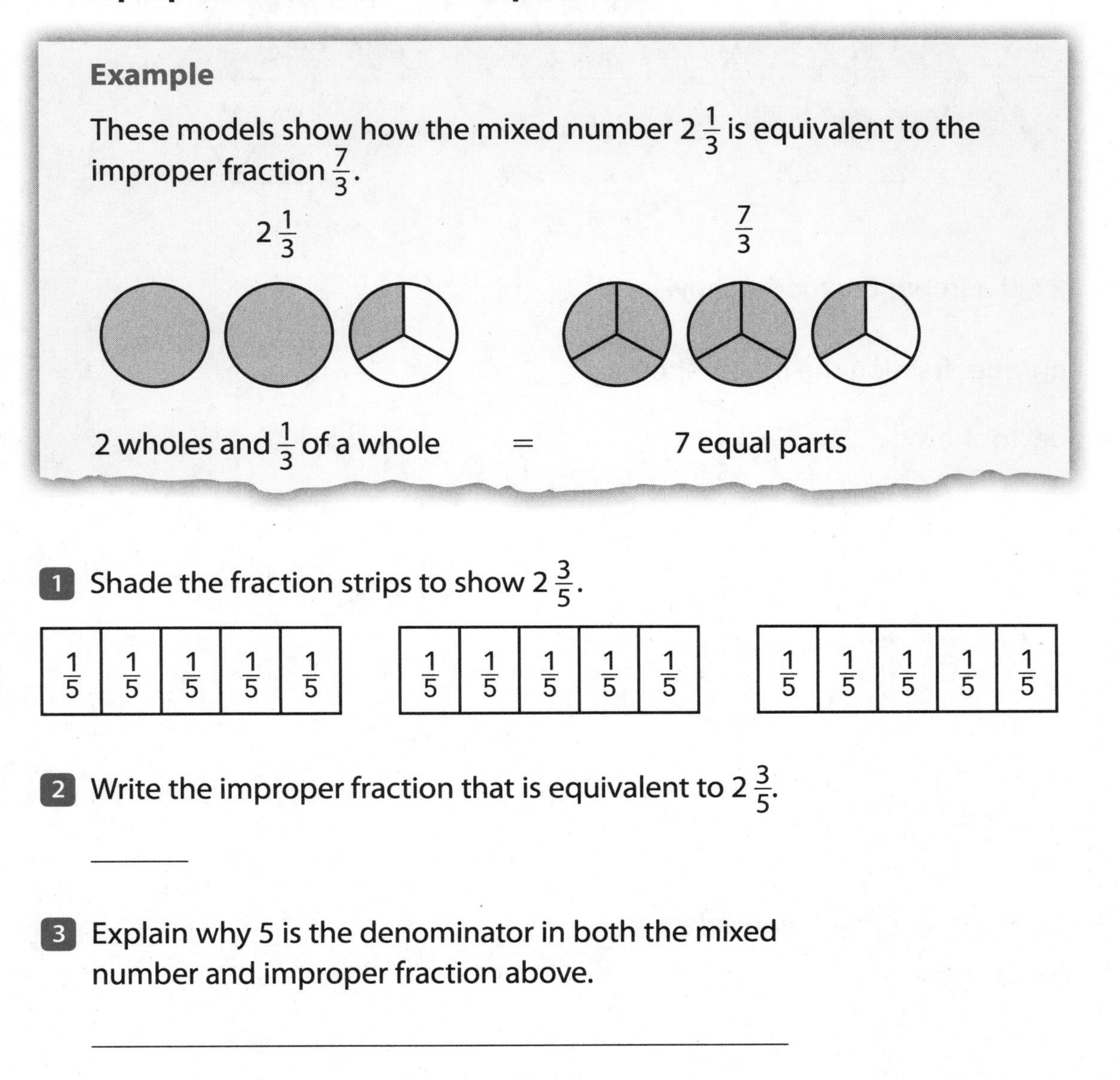

Example

These models show how the mixed number $2\frac{1}{3}$ is equivalent to the improper fraction $\frac{7}{3}$.

1 Shade the fraction strips to show $2\frac{3}{5}$.

2 Write the improper fraction that is equivalent to $2\frac{3}{5}$.

______

3 Explain why 5 is the denominator in both the mixed number and improper fraction above.

____

____

____

Solve.

Use the model to answer problems 4–5.

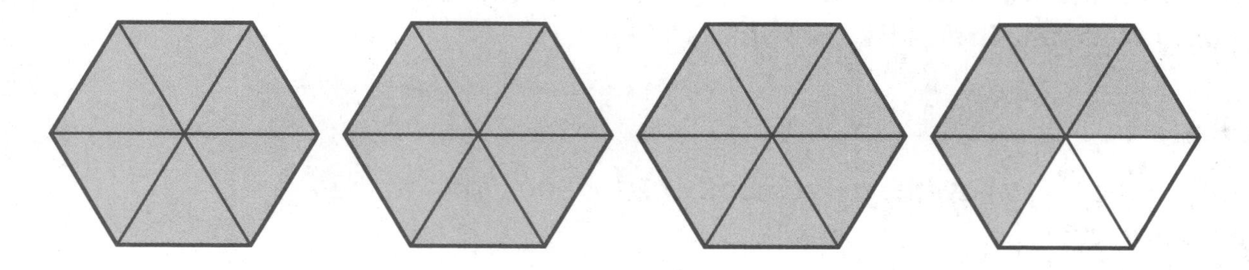

4 Write the mixed number the model shows. ______

5 Write the improper fraction the model shows. ______

6 Draw a model to show $\frac{5}{2}$.

7 Write the mixed number that is equivalent to $\frac{8}{3}$.
Explain how you know.

Name: ____________________

Write Mixed Numbers and Improper Fractions

Solve the problems.

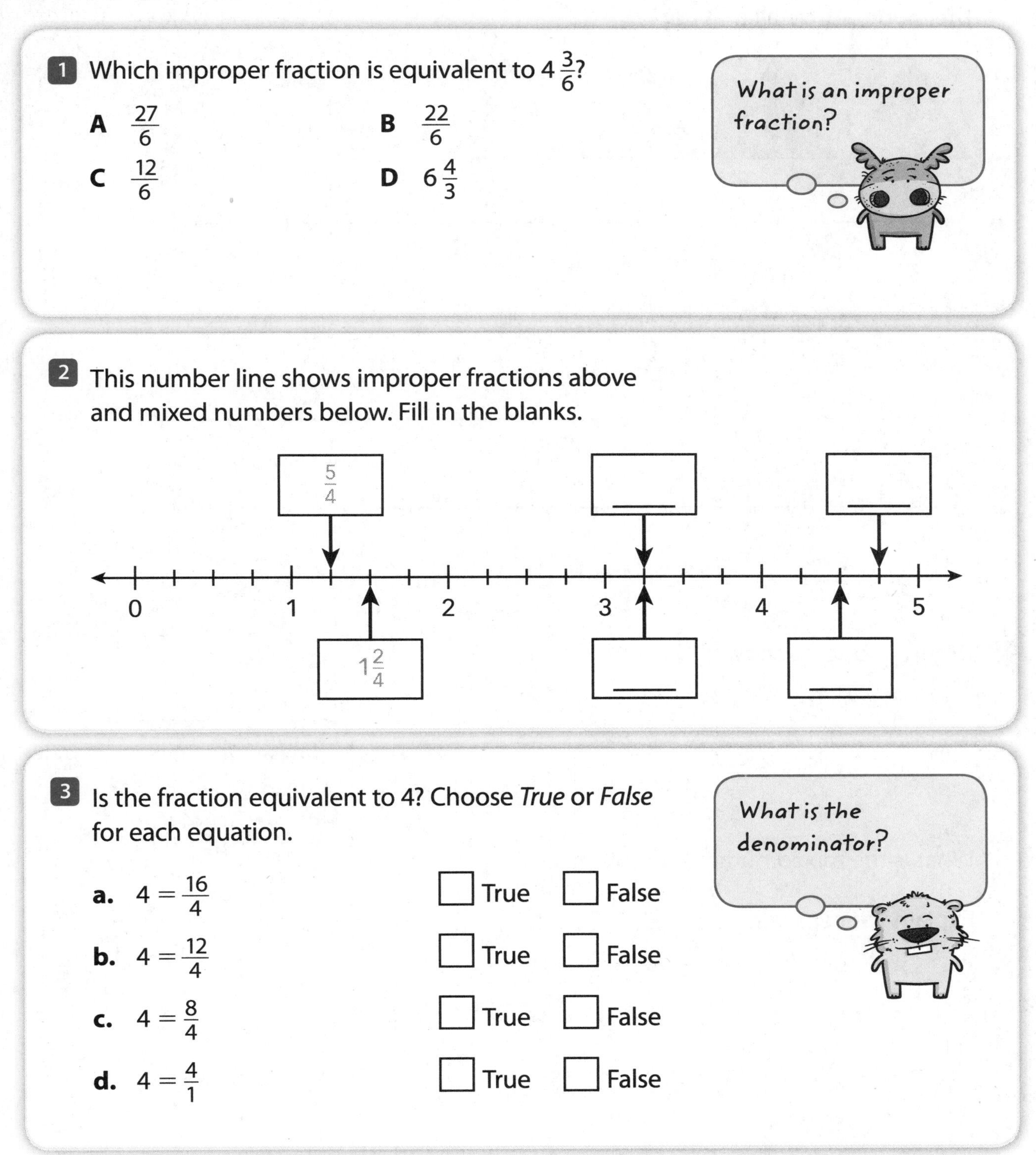

1 Which improper fraction is equivalent to $4\frac{3}{6}$?

A $\frac{27}{6}$

B $\frac{22}{6}$

C $\frac{12}{6}$

D $6\frac{4}{3}$

2 This number line shows improper fractions above and mixed numbers below. Fill in the blanks.

3 Is the fraction equivalent to 4? Choose *True* or *False* for each equation.

a. $4 = \frac{16}{4}$ ☐ True ☐ False

b. $4 = \frac{12}{4}$ ☐ True ☐ False

c. $4 = \frac{8}{4}$ ☐ True ☐ False

d. $4 = \frac{4}{1}$ ☐ True ☐ False

Solve.

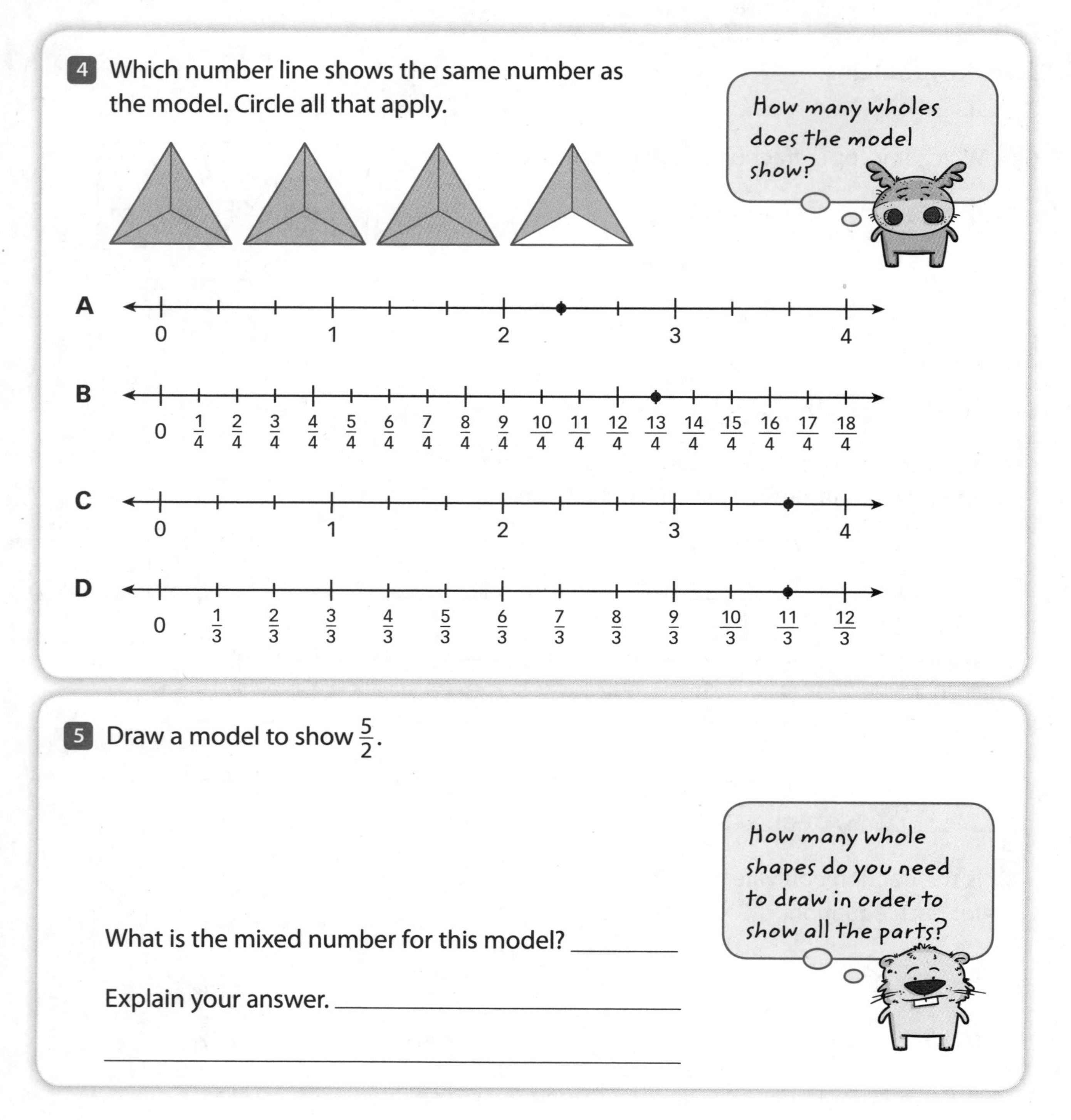

4 Which number line shows the same number as the model. Circle all that apply.

5 Draw a model to show $\frac{5}{2}$.

What is the mixed number for this model? ________

Explain your answer. ______________________________

____

Dear Family,

This week your child is learning to compare fractions.

There are different ways to compare fractions.

One way to compare fractions like $\frac{2}{4}$ and $\frac{2}{5}$ is to use models. You must use the same-size whole for both. If the wholes are different sizes, it doesn't make sense to compare the parts. Each whole model below is the same size.

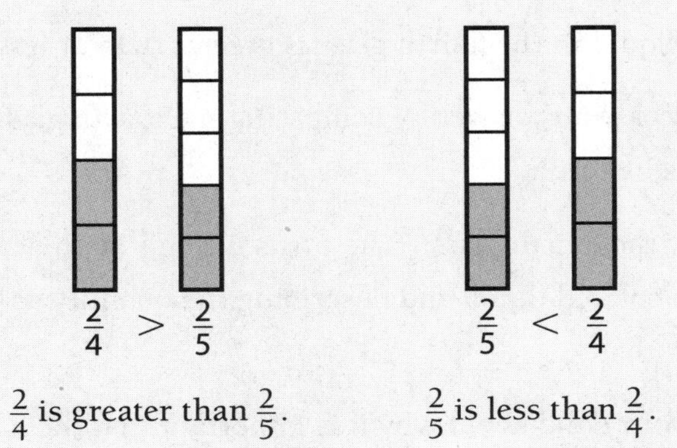

$\frac{2}{4}$ is greater than $\frac{2}{5}$. $\frac{2}{5}$ is less than $\frac{2}{4}$.

Another way to compare fractions is to write equivalent fractions with the same denominators. Using the same denominators means that there are the same number of parts in each whole. Then you can compare the numerators to find which fraction has a greater number of parts.

$$\frac{2 \times 4}{5 \times 4} = \frac{8}{20} \qquad \frac{2 \times 5}{4 \times 5} = \frac{10}{20}$$

$$\frac{8}{20} < \frac{10}{20}, \text{ so } \frac{2}{5} < \frac{2}{4}$$

Your child might also use a number line to compare fractions by comparing each fraction to a benchmark fraction, such as $\frac{1}{2}$.

Invite your child to share what he or she knows about comparing fractions by doing the following activity together.

Comparing Fractions Activity

Do an activity with your child to compare fractions.

Materials: 4 same-size clear glasses, colored liquid

- Fill one glass to the top with colored liquid. This glass represents 1 whole. Fill another glass half full to represent $\frac{1}{2}$. Leave a third glass empty to represent 0.
- Pour any amount of liquid into the fourth glass. Compare the fourth glass to the full glass and the empty glass to determine if the amount of liquid is closer to 0 or to 1. Then determine if the amount of liquid in the fourth glass is greater than or less than $\frac{1}{2}$.
- You can check your answer by comparing the fourth glass to the glass that is half full.
- Now empty the fourth glass. Take turns filling it with various amounts of colored liquid and describing the quantity as greater than or less than $\frac{1}{2}$.
- Talk with your child about why it is important that the four glasses are the same size and shape. (Half of a tall glass is a different amount of liquid than half of a short glass.)

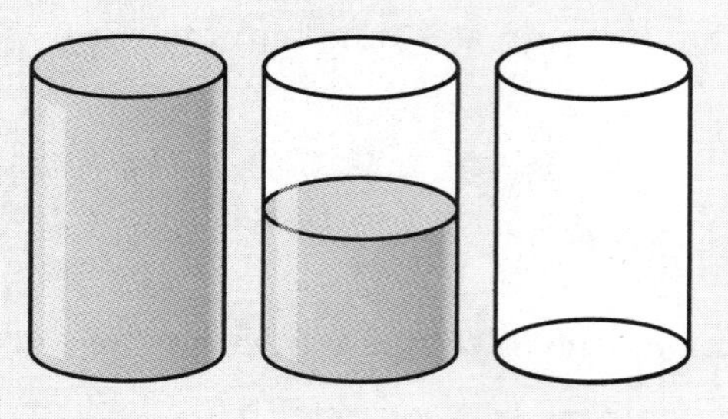

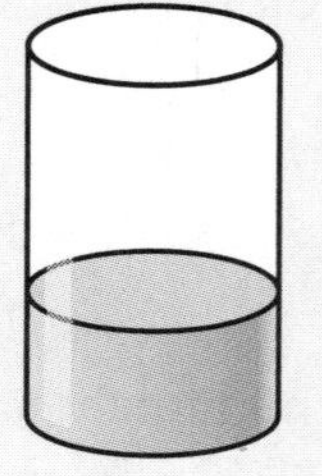

Compare Fractions

Name: ______________________

Prerequisite: Model Comparing Fractions

Study the example problem showing ways to compare fractions. Then solve problems 1–9.

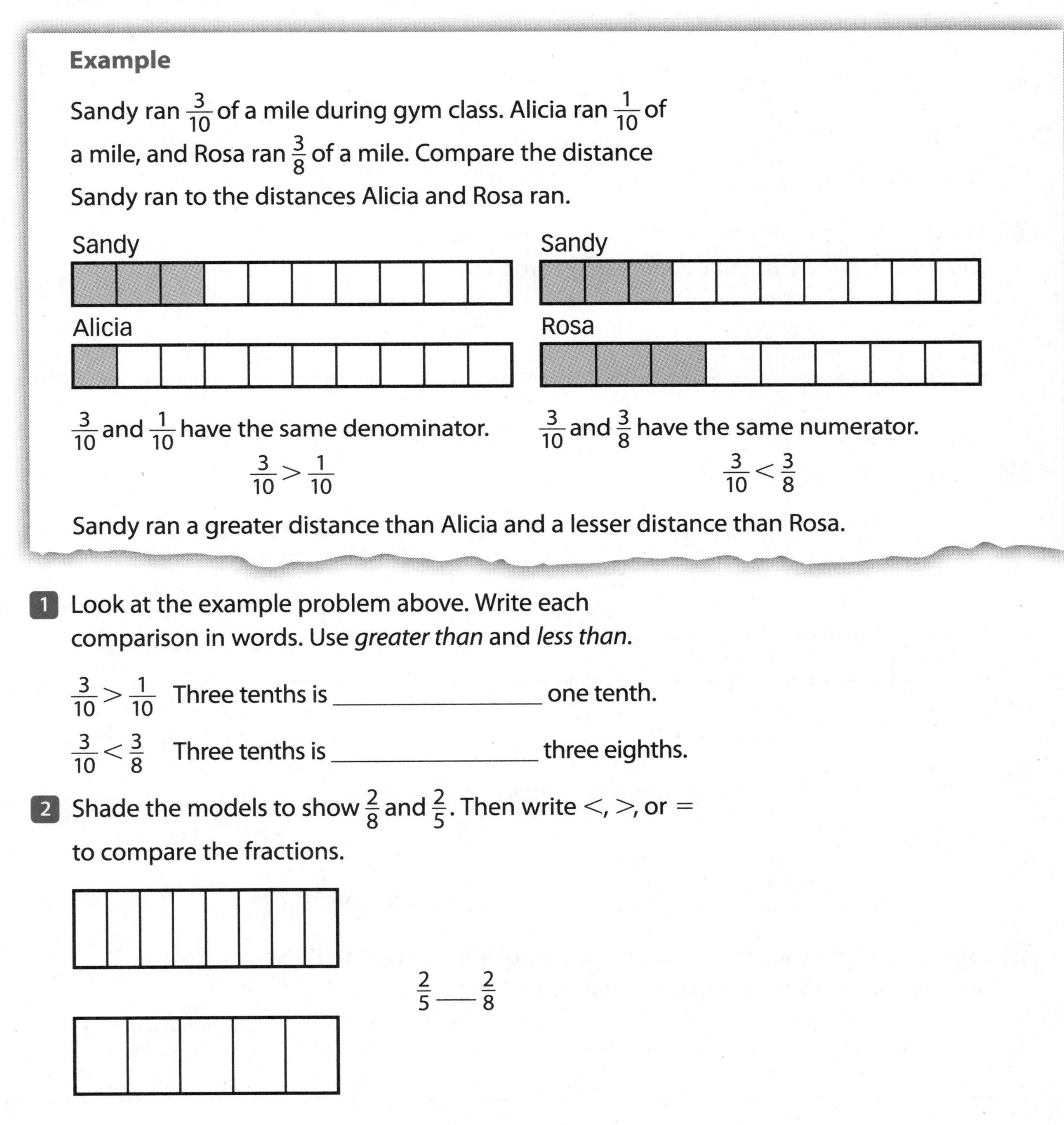

Example

Sandy ran $\frac{3}{10}$ of a mile during gym class. Alicia ran $\frac{1}{10}$ of a mile, and Rosa ran $\frac{3}{8}$ of a mile. Compare the distance Sandy ran to the distances Alicia and Rosa ran.

$\frac{3}{10}$ and $\frac{1}{10}$ have the same denominator.

$$\frac{3}{10} > \frac{1}{10}$$

$\frac{3}{10}$ and $\frac{3}{8}$ have the same numerator.

$$\frac{3}{10} < \frac{3}{8}$$

Sandy ran a greater distance than Alicia and a lesser distance than Rosa.

1 Look at the example problem above. Write each comparison in words. Use *greater than* and *less than*.

$\frac{3}{10} > \frac{1}{10}$ Three tenths is ____________________ one tenth.

$\frac{3}{10} < \frac{3}{8}$ Three tenths is ____________________ three eighths.

2 Shade the models to show $\frac{2}{8}$ and $\frac{2}{5}$. Then write $<$, $>$, or $=$ to compare the fractions.

$\frac{2}{5}$ ___ $\frac{2}{8}$

Solve.

3 Shade the models to show $\frac{5}{12}$ and $\frac{7}{12}$.

4 Compare $\frac{5}{12}$ and $\frac{7}{12}$ using symbols and words.

$\frac{5}{12}$ ___ $\frac{7}{12}$

Five twelfths is ________________ seven twelfths.

5 Explain how you used the models in problem 3 to show how the two fractions compare in problem 4.

____

____

____

6 Label $\frac{7}{8}$ on the number line below.

0 ——|——|——|——|——|——|——|——|—— 1

7 Label $\frac{7}{12}$ on the number line below.

0 ——|——|——|——|——|——|——|——|——|——|——|——|—— 1

8 Compare $\frac{7}{8}$ and $\frac{7}{12}$ using symbols and words.

$\frac{7}{8}$ ___ $\frac{7}{12}$

Seven ________________ is ________________ seven twelfths.

9 Explain how you used the number lines in problems 6 and 7 to show how the two fractions compare in problem 8.

____

____

Name: ______________________

Find a Common Numerator or Denominator

Study the example problem showing how to compare fractions by finding a common denominator. Then solve problems 1–7.

Example

A length of ribbon is $\frac{3}{4}$ foot. Another length of ribbon is $\frac{5}{6}$ foot. Compare the lengths using a symbol.

Find a common denominator. $\frac{3 \times 3}{4 \times 3} = \frac{9}{\mathbf{12}}$ $\frac{5 \times 2}{6 \times 2} = \frac{10}{\mathbf{12}}$

Write the equivalent fractions. $\frac{3}{4} = \frac{9}{12}$ $\frac{5}{6} = \frac{10}{12}$

Compare the numerators. $\frac{\mathbf{9}}{12} < \frac{\mathbf{10}}{12}$

$9 < 10$ so $\frac{9}{12} < \frac{10}{12}$

$\frac{3}{4} < \frac{5}{6}$

1 Shade the models below to show $\frac{3}{4}$ and $\frac{5}{6}$.

Fill in the blank to show the comparison. $\frac{3}{4}$ ___ $\frac{5}{6}$

2 Divide each model in problem 1 into 12 equal parts to show an equivalent fraction. Write the equivalent fractions and symbol to show the comparison.

$\frac{\square}{12}$ ___ $\frac{\square}{12}$

3 Compare $\frac{2}{3}$ and $\frac{9}{12}$ by finding a common denominator.

a. Write a fraction equivalent to $\frac{2}{3}$ with a denominator of 12. $\frac{2 \times \square}{3 \times \square} = \frac{\square}{12}$

b. Compare the fractions. $\frac{\square}{12}$ ___ $\frac{9}{12}$. So, $\frac{2}{3}$ ___ $\frac{9}{12}$.

Vocabulary

denominator the number below the line in a fraction. It tells how many equal parts are in the whole.

$\rightarrow \frac{3}{4}$

4 equal parts

numerator the number above the line in a fraction. It tells how many equal parts are described.

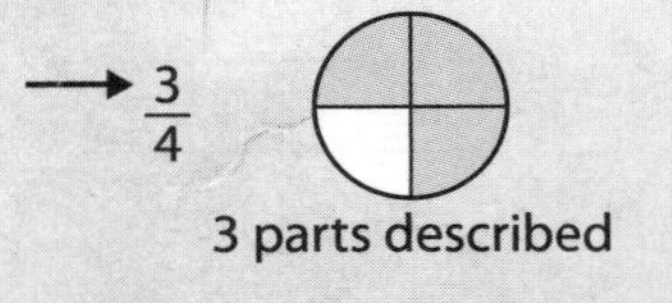

3 parts described

Solve.

4 Compare $\frac{1}{5}$ and $\frac{2}{12}$ by finding a common numerator.

a. Write a fraction equivalent to $\frac{1}{5}$ with a numerator of 2.

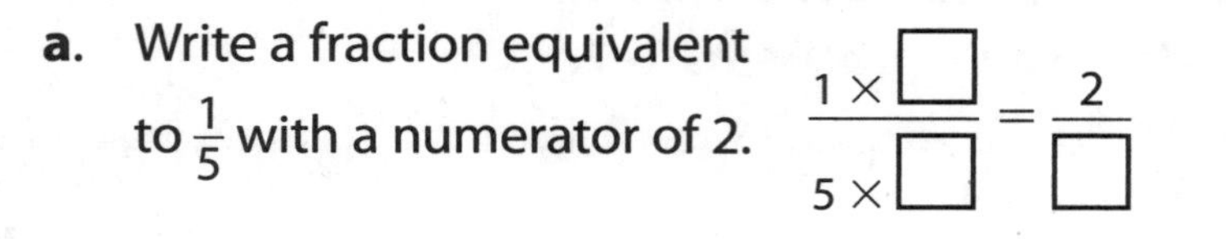

$\frac{1 \times \square}{5 \times \square} = \frac{2}{\square}$

b. Compare the fractions. $\frac{2}{\square}$ ___ $\frac{2}{12}$. So, $\frac{1}{5}$ ___ $\frac{2}{12}$.

5 Compare the fractions. Use the symbols $<$, $>$, and $=$.

a. $\frac{2}{5}$ ___ $\frac{8}{10}$

b. $\frac{5}{12}$ ___ $\frac{1}{3}$

c. $\frac{3}{5}$ ___ $\frac{60}{100}$

d. $\frac{9}{100}$ ___ $\frac{9}{10}$

6 Tell whether each sentence is *True* or *False*.

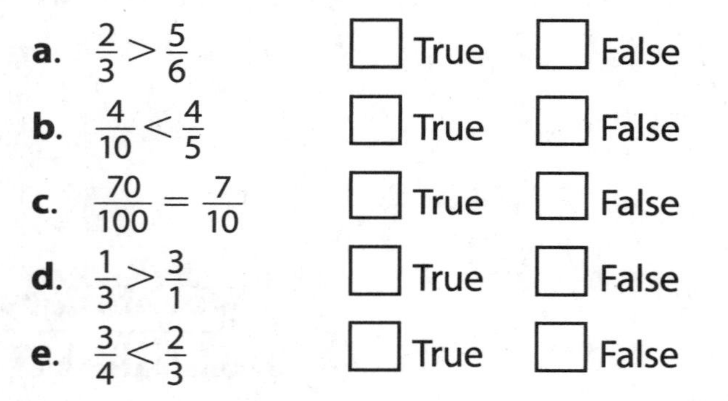

a. $\frac{2}{3} > \frac{5}{6}$ ☐ True ☐ False

b. $\frac{4}{10} < \frac{4}{5}$ ☐ True ☐ False

c. $\frac{70}{100} = \frac{7}{10}$ ☐ True ☐ False

d. $\frac{1}{3} > \frac{3}{1}$ ☐ True ☐ False

e. $\frac{3}{4} < \frac{2}{3}$ ☐ True ☐ False

7 Can two fractions with the same numerator and different denominators be equal? Use words and numbers to explain.

___

___

___

___

___

Name: ______________________

Use a Benchmark to Compare Fractions

Study the example problem using 1 as a benchmark to compare fractions. Then solve problems 1–4.

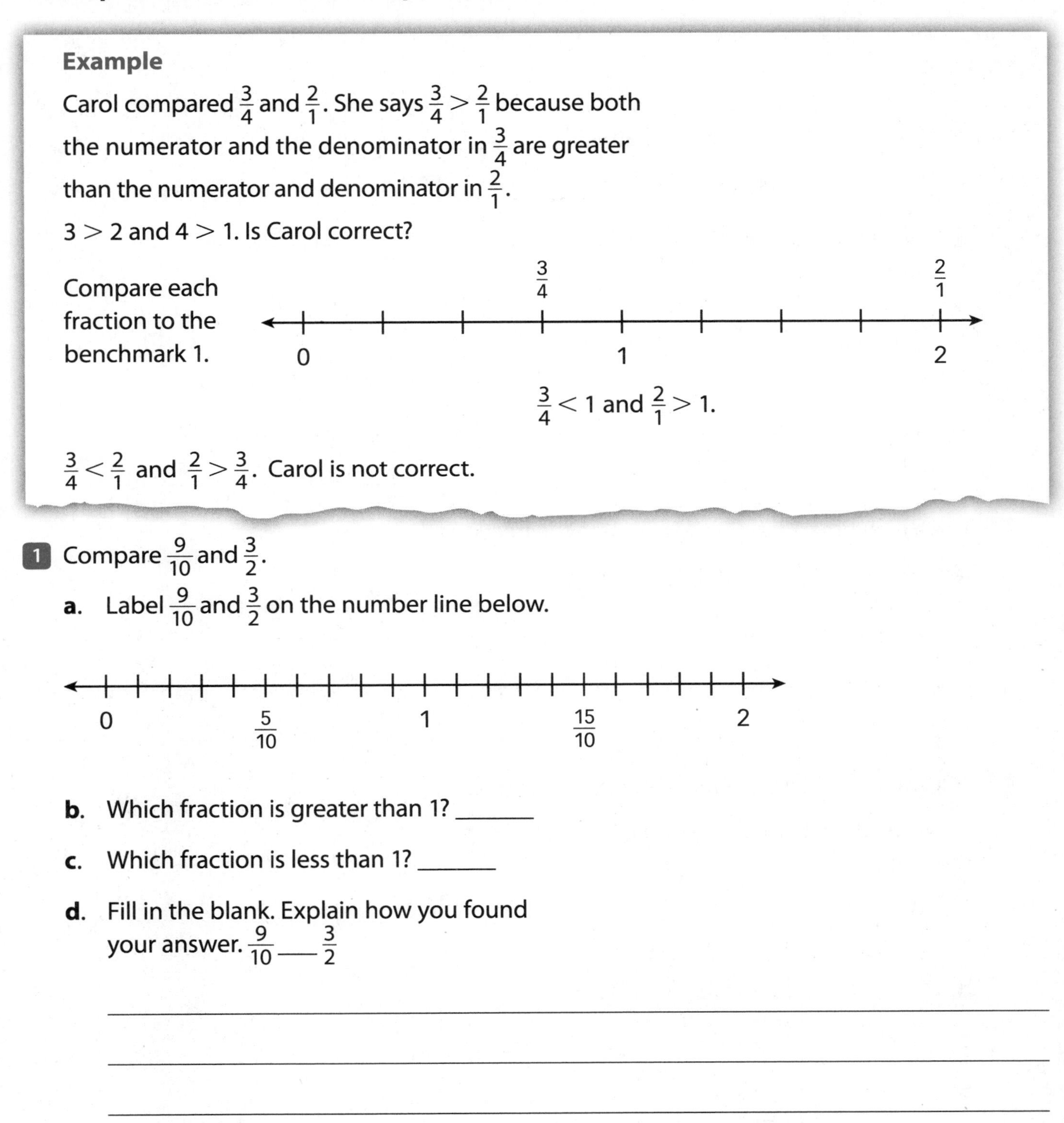

Example

Carol compared $\frac{3}{4}$ and $\frac{2}{1}$. She says $\frac{3}{4} > \frac{2}{1}$ because both the numerator and the denominator in $\frac{3}{4}$ are greater than the numerator and denominator in $\frac{2}{1}$.

$3 > 2$ and $4 > 1$. Is Carol correct?

Compare each fraction to the benchmark 1.

$\frac{3}{4} < 1$ and $\frac{2}{1} > 1$.

$\frac{3}{4} < \frac{2}{1}$ and $\frac{2}{1} > \frac{3}{4}$. Carol is not correct.

1 Compare $\frac{9}{10}$ and $\frac{3}{2}$.

a. Label $\frac{9}{10}$ and $\frac{3}{2}$ on the number line below.

b. Which fraction is greater than 1? _______

c. Which fraction is less than 1? _______

d. Fill in the blank. Explain how you found your answer. $\frac{9}{10}$ ___ $\frac{3}{2}$

____

____

____

Solve.

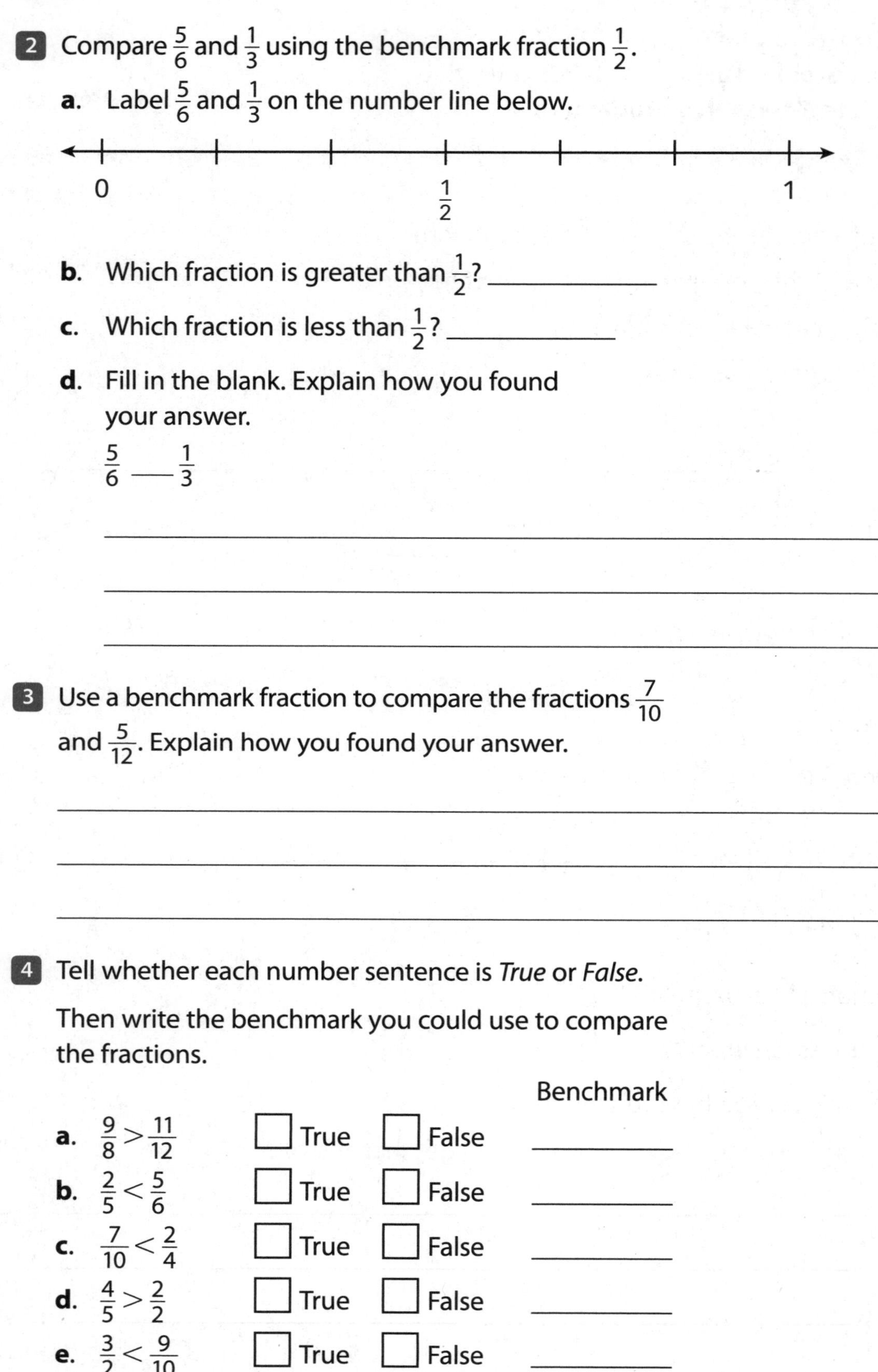

2 Compare $\frac{5}{6}$ and $\frac{1}{3}$ using the benchmark fraction $\frac{1}{2}$.

a. Label $\frac{5}{6}$ and $\frac{1}{3}$ on the number line below.

b. Which fraction is greater than $\frac{1}{2}$? ____________

c. Which fraction is less than $\frac{1}{2}$? ____________

d. Fill in the blank. Explain how you found your answer.

$\frac{5}{6}$ ___ $\frac{1}{3}$

____

____

____

3 Use a benchmark fraction to compare the fractions $\frac{7}{10}$ and $\frac{5}{12}$. Explain how you found your answer.

____

____

____

4 Tell whether each number sentence is *True* or *False*.

Then write the benchmark you could use to compare the fractions.

				Benchmark
a.	$\frac{9}{8} > \frac{11}{12}$	☐ True	☐ False	________
b.	$\frac{2}{5} < \frac{5}{6}$	☐ True	☐ False	________
c.	$\frac{7}{10} < \frac{2}{4}$	☐ True	☐ False	________
d.	$\frac{4}{5} > \frac{2}{2}$	☐ True	☐ False	________
e.	$\frac{3}{2} < \frac{9}{10}$	☐ True	☐ False	________

Name: ______________________________

Compare Fractions

Solve the problems.

1 Which of the following is greater than $\frac{2}{3}$?

Circle all that apply.

A $\frac{3}{4}$

B $\frac{5}{6}$

C $\frac{8}{12}$

D $\frac{3}{2}$

Find a common denominator for each pair of fractions.

2 Harry ate $\frac{5}{8}$ of a sandwich. Sven ate $\frac{2}{5}$ of a sandwich. Micah ate $\frac{3}{4}$ of a sandwich. Gabe ate $\frac{6}{12}$ of a sandwich. Who ate the most of his sandwich?

A Harry

B Sven

C Micah

D Gabe

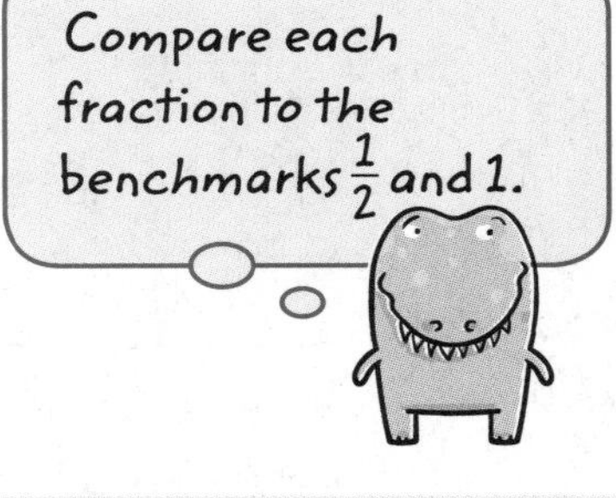

3 Erica and Matt earn the same amount of money each month. Erica saves $\frac{3}{10}$ of her earnings. Matt saves $\frac{3}{6}$ of his earnings. Which explanation correctly tells who saves more?

A Erica saves more because tenths are greater than sixths.

B Matt saves less because sixths are less than tenths.

C Erica saves more because $\frac{3}{10} < \frac{3}{6}$.

D Matt saves more because $\frac{3}{6} > \frac{3}{10}$.

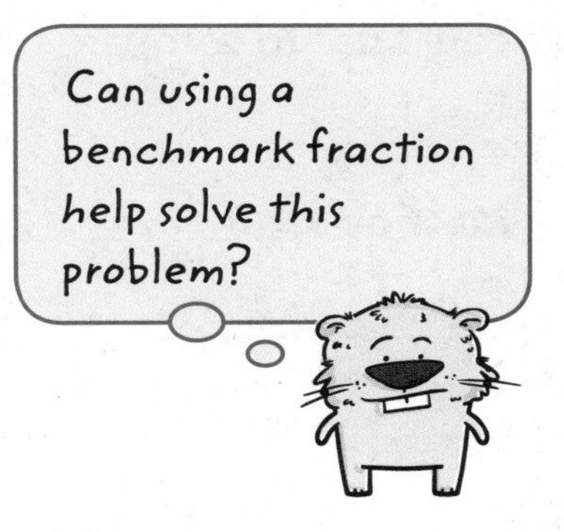

Fran chose **C** as the correct answer. How did she get that answer?

____

____

____

Solve.

4 Melanie read 45 pages of a 100-page book. Her younger sister read $\frac{1}{2}$ of a 10-page book. Who read a greater fraction of her book, Melanie or her sister?

Show your work.

One fraction has a denominator of 100; the other fraction has a denominator of 10.

Solution: ______________________________

5 Compare $\frac{5}{4}$ and $\frac{9}{10}$. Describe two methods you could use to compare the fractions.

$\frac{5}{4}$ ___ $\frac{9}{10}$

Method A ______________________________

____

____

____

____

Method B ______________________________

____

____

____

____

Some ways to compare fractions are finding a common denominator, finding a common numerator, and using a benchmark.

Dear Family,

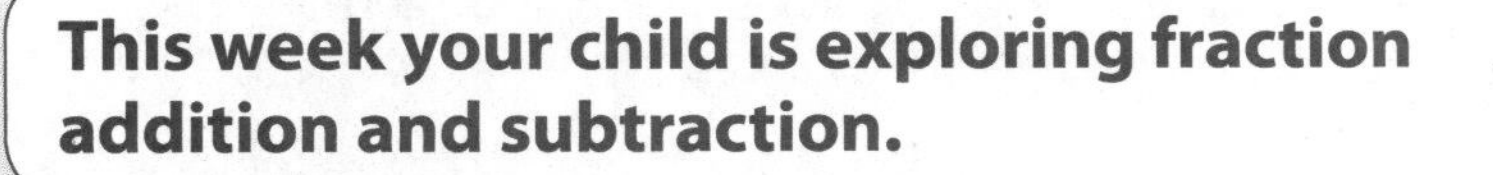

Adding fractions means joining or putting together parts of the same whole. When you add $\frac{2}{4} + \frac{3}{4}$, you are putting one-fourths together.

You can use a number line to show $\frac{2}{4} + \frac{3}{4}$.

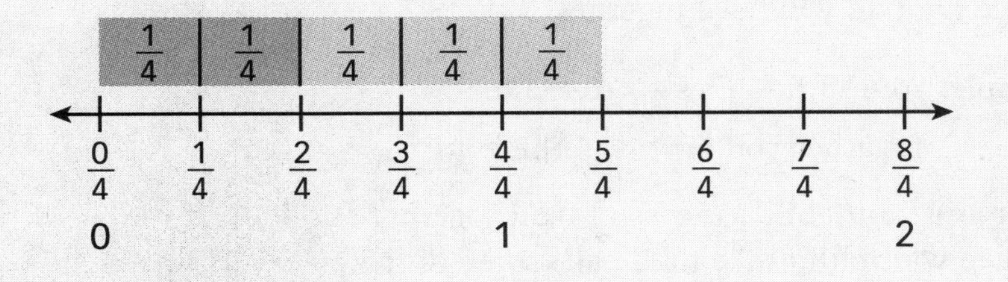

Subtracting fractions means separating or taking away. You can use a number line to show fraction subtraction, too.

The number line below shows a segment of length $\frac{5}{4}$. Take away a segment of length $\frac{2}{4}$ to show $\frac{5}{4} - \frac{2}{4}$.

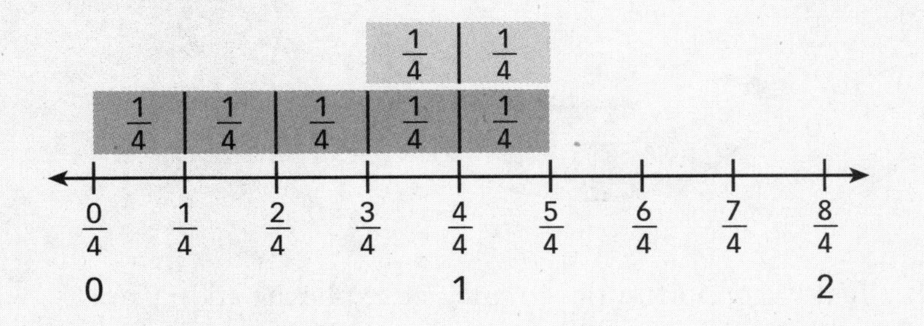

Adding and subtracting fractions is just like adding and subtracting whole numbers. When the denominators of the fractions are the same, you can just add or subtract the numerators.

Invite your child to share what he or she knows about fraction addition and subtraction by doing the following activity together.

Fraction Addition and Subtraction Activity

Do an activity with your child to explore adding and subtracting fractions.

Materials: one piece of fruit (or a picture of one piece of fruit)

- Cut the fruit (or the picture of the fruit) into sixths.
- Have your child take some of the pieces. You take some of the pieces.
- Now talk about putting your pieces of fruit together. How much of the whole fruit do you have together?

  Example: Your child takes $\frac{2}{6}$. You take $\frac{3}{6}$.
  Together you have $\frac{5}{6}$ of the fruit.

- Put your and your child's pieces of fruit together and look at the total. Have your child take (and eat!) some of the pieces. How much of the whole fruit is left?

  Example: Your child takes 3 pieces.
  Start with $\frac{5}{6}$. Take away $\frac{3}{6}$.
  That means $\frac{2}{6}$ of the fruit is left.

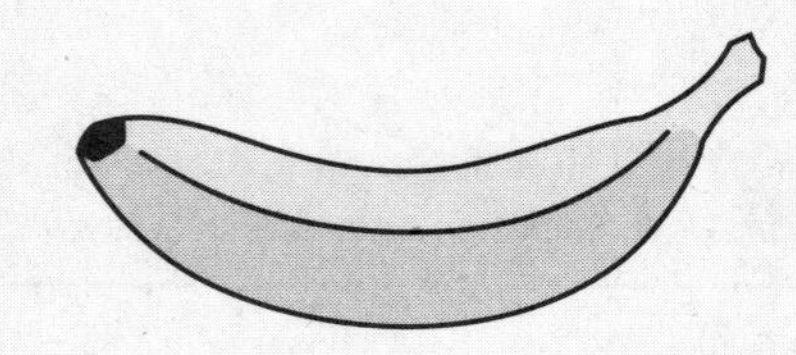

Look for other real-life opportunities to practice exploring adding and subtracting fractions with your child.

Lesson 15

Understand Fraction Addition and Subtraction

Name: ____________________

Prerequisite: How do you show fractions with number lines and area models?

Study the example problem showing fractions with number lines and area models. Then solve problems 1–7.

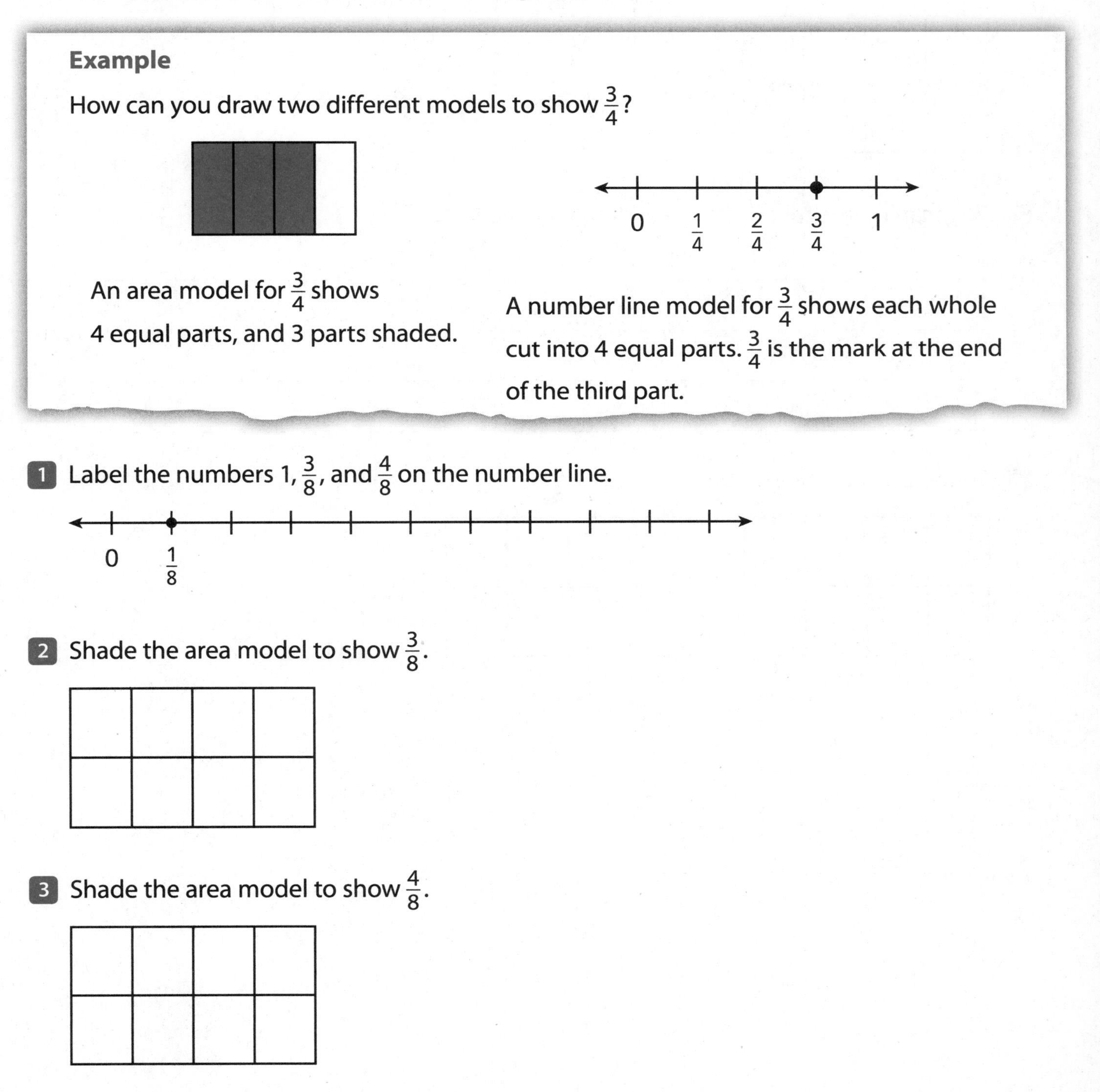

Example

How can you draw two different models to show $\frac{3}{4}$?

An area model for $\frac{3}{4}$ shows 4 equal parts, and 3 parts shaded.

A number line model for $\frac{3}{4}$ shows each whole cut into 4 equal parts. $\frac{3}{4}$ is the mark at the end of the third part.

1 Label the numbers 1, $\frac{3}{8}$, and $\frac{4}{8}$ on the number line.

2 Shade the area model to show $\frac{3}{8}$.

3 Shade the area model to show $\frac{4}{8}$.

Solve.

4 Show the numbers $\frac{8}{8}$ and $\frac{10}{8}$ on the number line.

0 $\frac{1}{8}$

5 Shade the area model to show $\frac{8}{8}$.

6 Why can't you show $\frac{10}{8}$ on the area model above?

____

____

____

____

7 Shade the area models below to show $\frac{10}{8}$.

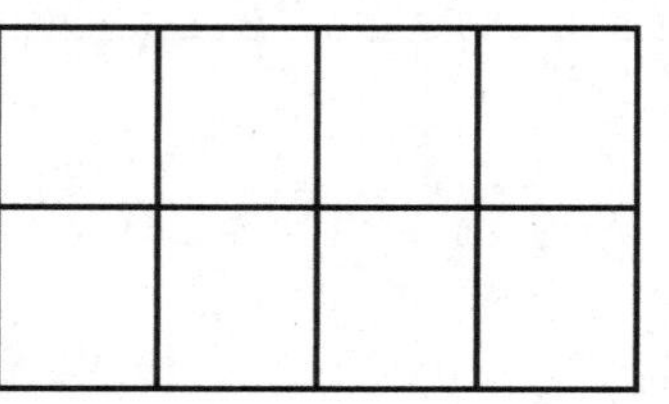

Name: ____________________

Show Adding and Subtracting Fractions

Study how the example shows adding fractions. Then solve problems 1–12.

Example

You can count on or count back to add or subtract whole numbers. You can do the same to add or subtract fractions.

To add fourths, use a number line that shows fourths.

Add $\frac{3}{4} + \frac{2}{4}$.

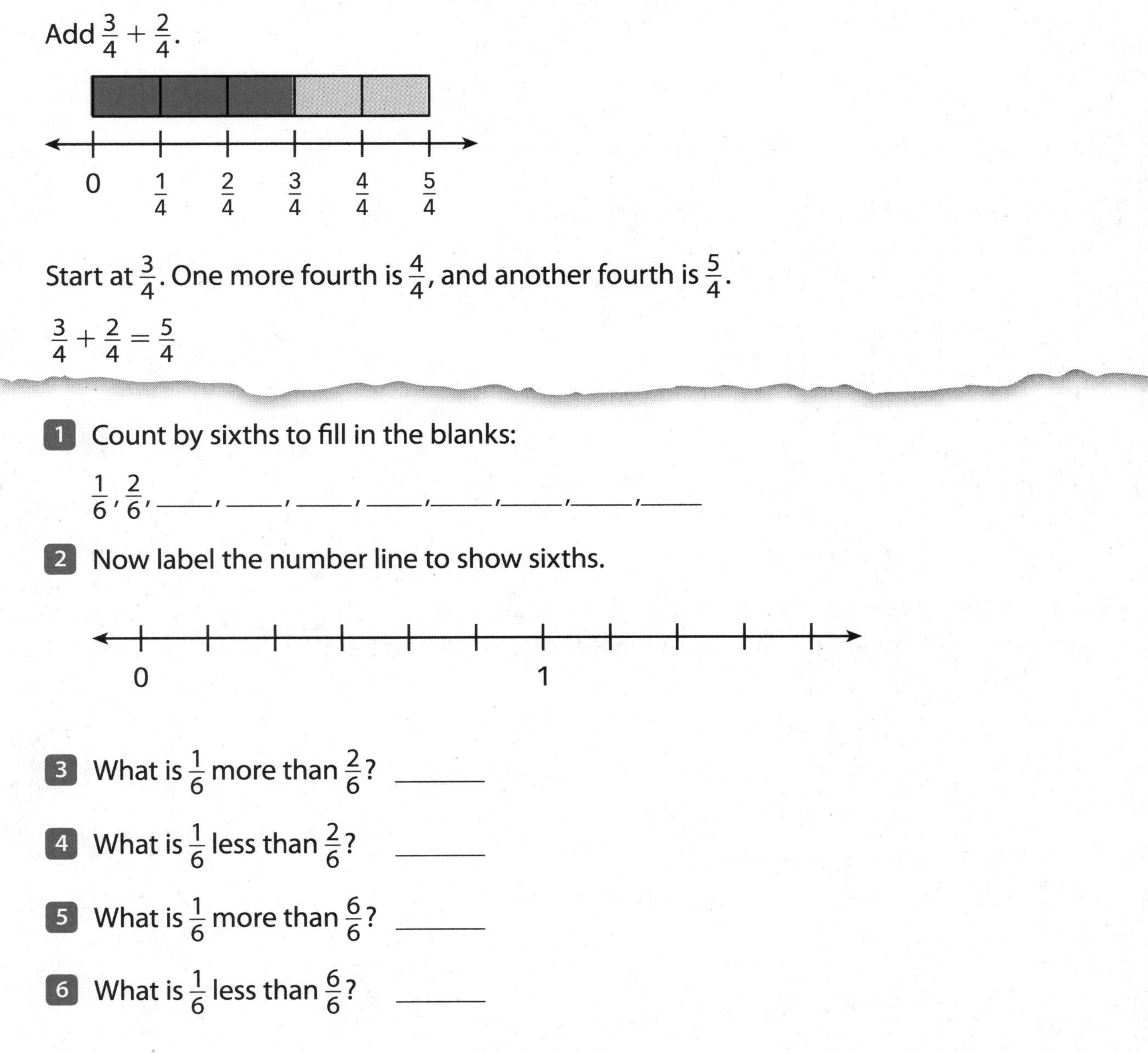

Start at $\frac{3}{4}$. One more fourth is $\frac{4}{4}$, and another fourth is $\frac{5}{4}$.

$\frac{3}{4} + \frac{2}{4} = \frac{5}{4}$

1 Count by sixths to fill in the blanks:

$\frac{1}{6}$, $\frac{2}{6}$, ____, ____, ____, ____, ____, ____, ____, ____

2 Now label the number line to show sixths.

0 1

3 What is $\frac{1}{6}$ more than $\frac{2}{6}$? ______

4 What is $\frac{1}{6}$ less than $\frac{2}{6}$? ______

5 What is $\frac{1}{6}$ more than $\frac{6}{6}$? ______

6 What is $\frac{1}{6}$ less than $\frac{6}{6}$? ______

Solve.

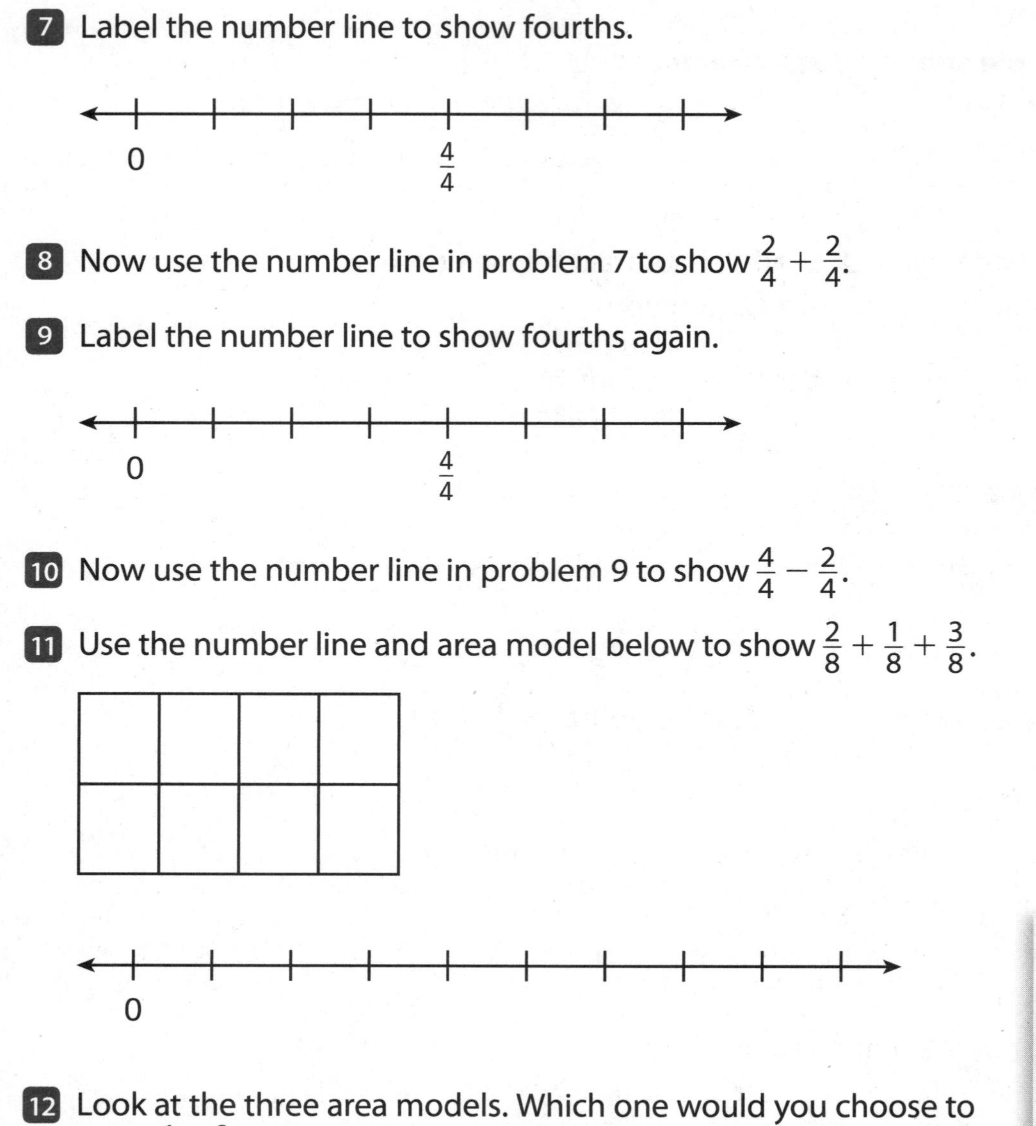

7 Label the number line to show fourths.

8 Now use the number line in problem 7 to show $\frac{2}{4} + \frac{2}{4}$.

9 Label the number line to show fourths again.

10 Now use the number line in problem 9 to show $\frac{4}{4} - \frac{2}{4}$.

11 Use the number line and area model below to show $\frac{2}{8} + \frac{1}{8} + \frac{3}{8}$.

12 Look at the three area models. Which one would you choose to show $\frac{1}{8} + \frac{2}{8}$? Explain how the denominator of the fraction helps you choose the model.

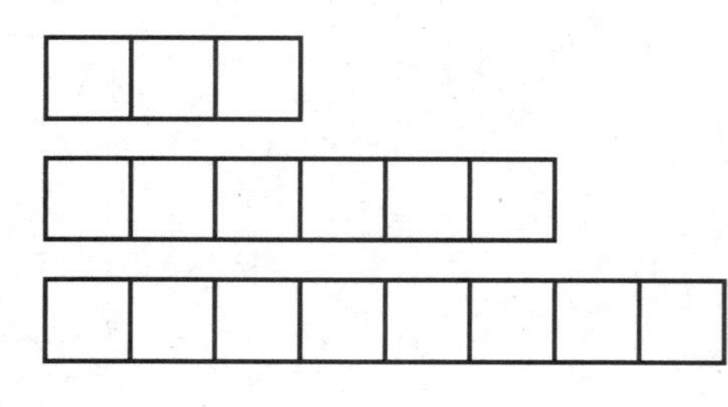

____

____

____

Vocabulary

denominator the number below the line in a fraction. It tells how many equal parts are in the whole.

$\longrightarrow \frac{3}{4}$

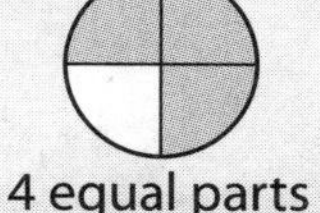

4 equal parts

numerator the number above the line in a fraction. It tells how many equal parts are described.

$\longrightarrow \frac{3}{4}$

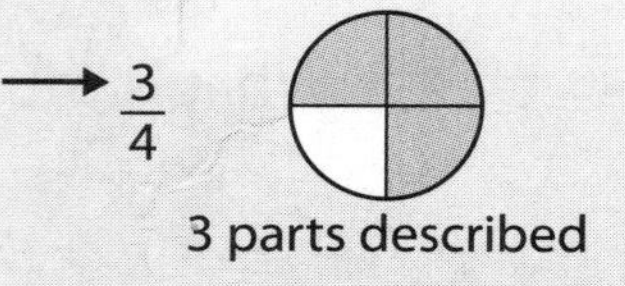

3 parts described

Name: ______________________________

Reason and Write

Study the example. Underline two parts that you think make it a particularly good answer and a helpful example.

Example

Rob drew this diagram to show $\frac{1}{10} + \frac{3}{10} + \frac{4}{10}$

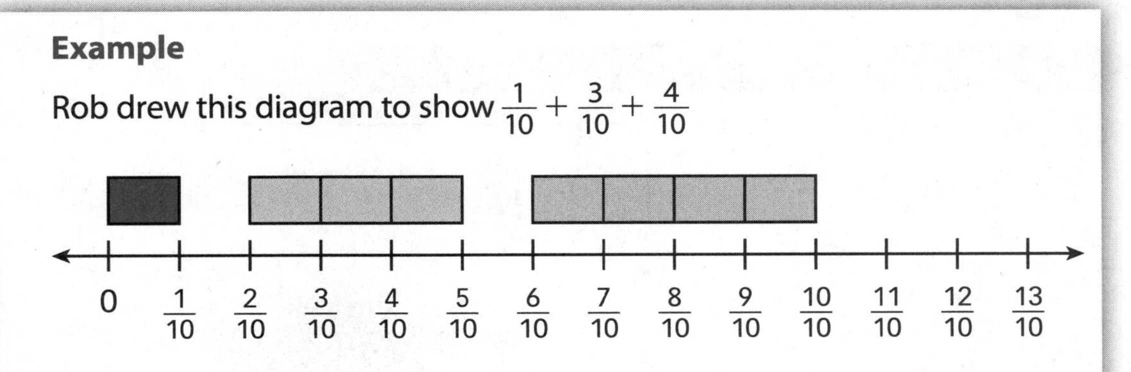

Rob says that his picture shows that

$\frac{1}{10} + \frac{3}{10} + \frac{4}{10} = \frac{10}{10}$ or 1 whole.

What did Rob do right? What did he do wrong?

Show your work. Use pictures, words, or numbers to explain your answer.

Rob drew the number line the right way. He marked it to show tenths because the fractions in the problem are in tenths. He also showed that $\frac{10}{10}$ is one whole.

He shaded 1 tenth and 3 tenths and 4 tenths because the numbers in the problem are $\frac{1}{10}$ and $\frac{3}{10}$ and $\frac{4}{10}$.

His mistake was leaving spaces between the shaded parts. When you count up on a number line, you can't skip numbers. He should have drawn this.

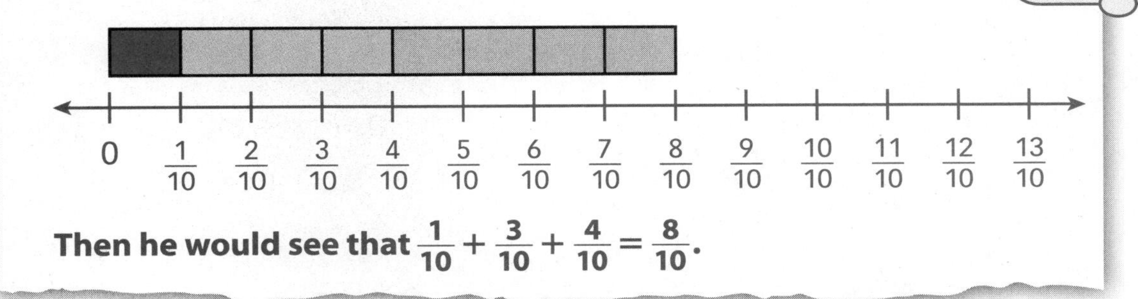

Then he would see that $\frac{1}{10} + \frac{3}{10} + \frac{4}{10} = \frac{8}{10}$.

Where does the example . . .

- answer both parts of the question?
- use a picture to explain?
- use numbers to explain?
- use words to explain?
- give details?

Solve the problem. Use what you learned from the example.

Paul drew this diagram to show $\frac{12}{10} - \frac{3}{10}$.

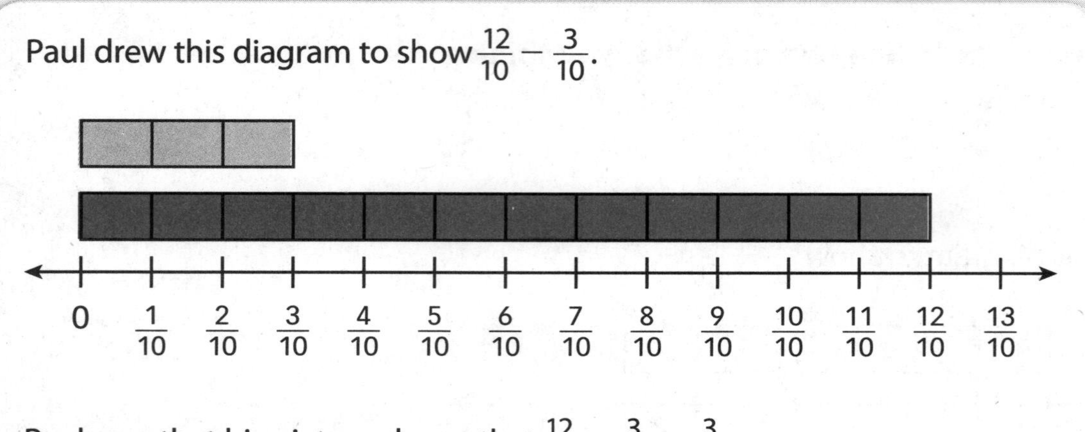

Paul says that his picture shows that $\frac{12}{10} - \frac{3}{10} = \frac{3}{10}$.

What did Paul do right? What did he do wrong?

Show your work. Use pictures, words, or numbers to explain your answer.

Did you . . .

- answer both parts of the question?
- use a picture to explain?
- use numbers to explain?
- use words to explain?
- give details?

Dear Family,

This week your child is learning how to add and subtract like fractions.

Like fractions have denominators that are the same.

like fractions: $\frac{1}{4}$ and $\frac{3}{4}$ **unlike fractions:** $\frac{1}{2}$ and $\frac{3}{4}$

To find the sum of like fractions, understand that you are just adding like units. Just as 3 apples plus 2 apples is 5 apples, 3 eighths plus 2 eighths is 5 eighths. Similarly, when you take away, or subtract, 2 eighths from 5 eighths, you have 3 eighths left.

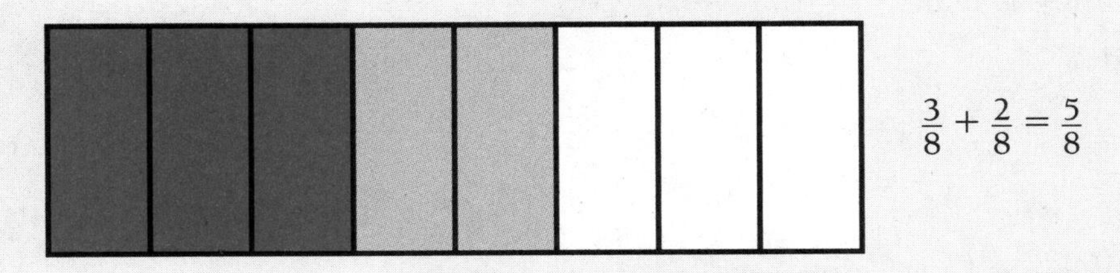

$\frac{3}{8} + \frac{2}{8} = \frac{5}{8}$

You can also use a number line to understand adding and subtracting like fractions.

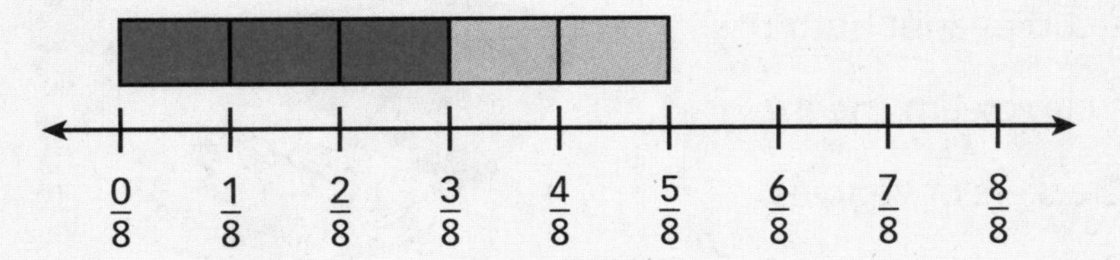

Remember that the denominator just names the units in the same way as "apples" names units. So,

- to add two fractions with the same denominator, the sum of the numerators tells how many of those units you have.
- to subtract two fractions with like denominators, the difference of the numerators tells how many of those units you have.

Invite your child to share what he or she knows about adding and subtracting fractions by doing the following activity together.

Add and Subtract Fractions Activity

Do an activity with your child to add and subtract fractions.

Materials: a bowl, a measuring cup, and the ingredients shown in the recipe

Follow the recipe below to make a creamy cracker spread or veggie dip. Then add and subtract fractions with these next steps.

- What fraction of a cup is the total amount of spread? $\left(\frac{7}{8}\right)$
- Spread $\frac{1}{8}$ cup on crackers or veggies. How much spread is left? $\left(\frac{6}{8}\right)$
- Make up a simple recipe using fractions for someone else in the family to make.

Recipe for Creamy Spread

Ingredients:

$\frac{5}{8}$ cup peanut butter

$\frac{2}{8}$ cup cream cheese

Crackers or veggies

Directions:

Mix the peanut butter and cream cheese together in a medium size bowl. Serve immediately with crackers or sliced fresh veggies. Enjoy!

Add and Subtract Fractions

Name: ______________________

Prerequisite: Model Fraction Addition and Subtraction

Study the example problem showing fraction addition with number line and area models. Then solve problems 1–8.

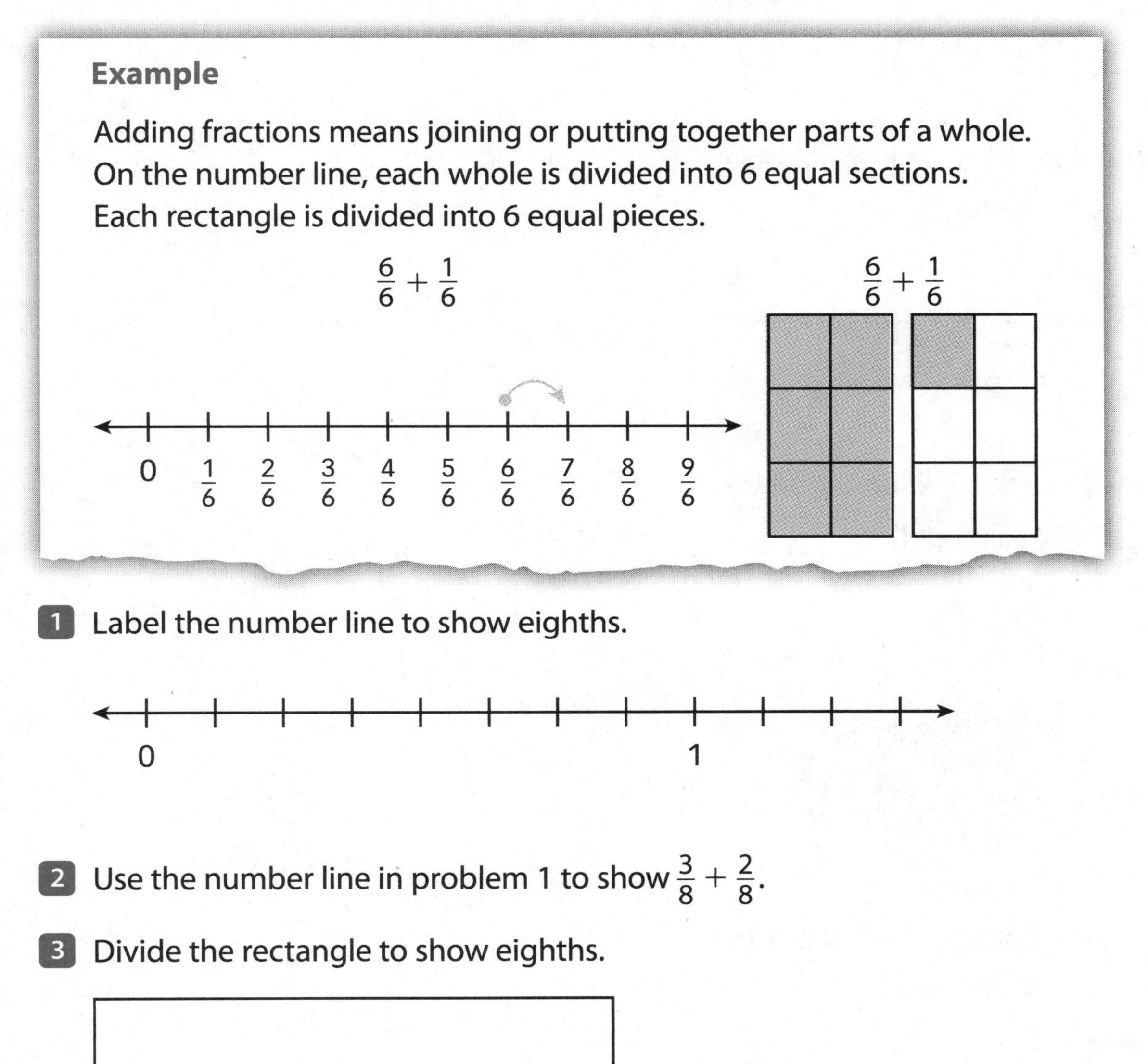

Example

Adding fractions means joining or putting together parts of a whole. On the number line, each whole is divided into 6 equal sections. Each rectangle is divided into 6 equal pieces.

1 Label the number line to show eighths.

2 Use the number line in problem 1 to show $\frac{3}{8} + \frac{2}{8}$.

3 Divide the rectangle to show eighths.

4 Use the rectangle in problem 3 to show $\frac{3}{8} + \frac{2}{8}$.

Solve.

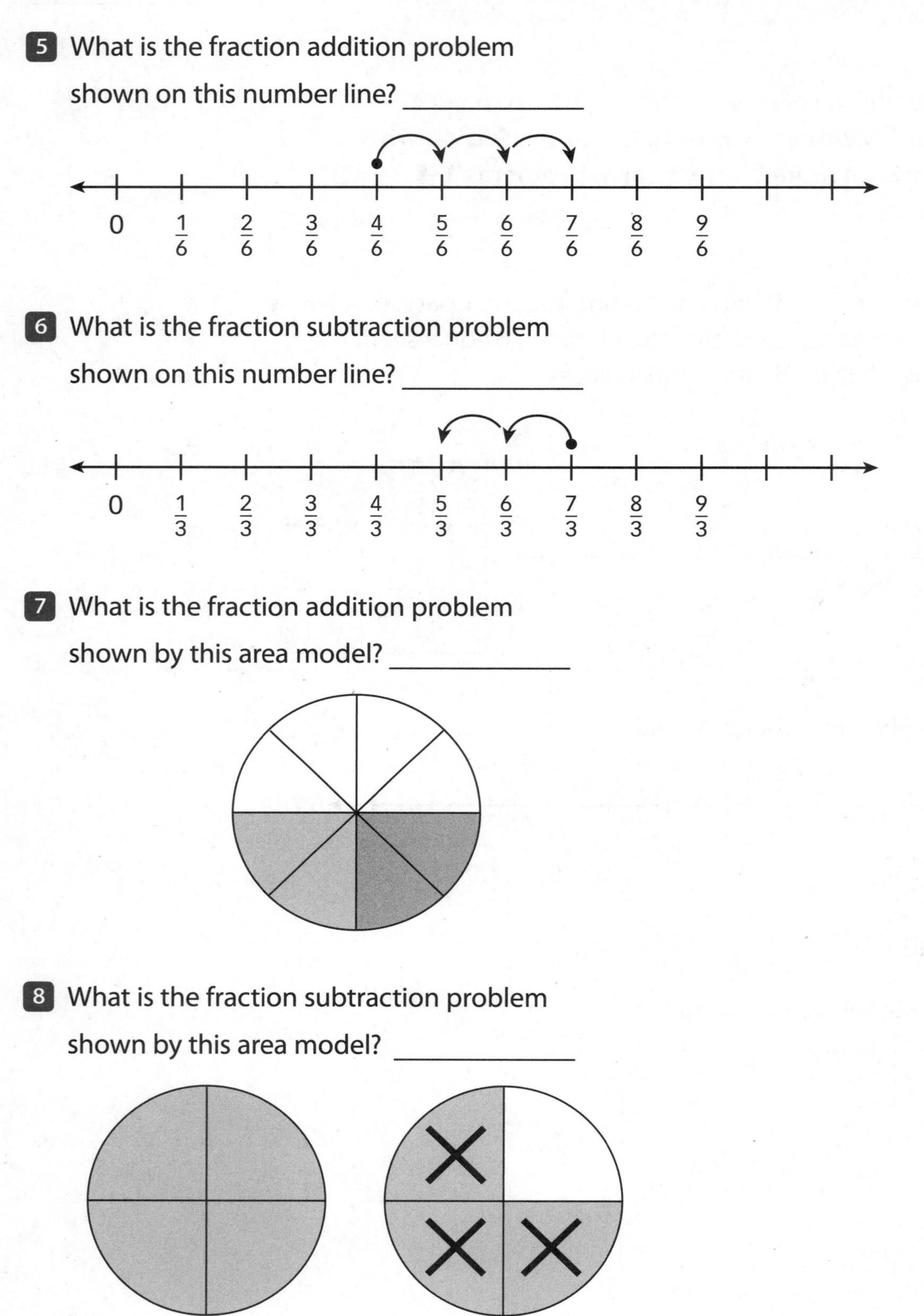

5 What is the fraction addition problem shown on this number line? ______________

6 What is the fraction subtraction problem shown on this number line? ______________

7 What is the fraction addition problem shown by this area model? ______________

8 What is the fraction subtraction problem shown by this area model? ______________

Name: ____________________

Add Fractions

Study the example problem showing one way to add fractions. Then solve problems 1–13.

Example

Shrina has a muffin tray that holds 12 muffins. She fills $\frac{3}{12}$ of the tray with apple muffin batter. Then she fills $\frac{6}{12}$ with pumpkin muffin batter. What fraction of the tray is filled?

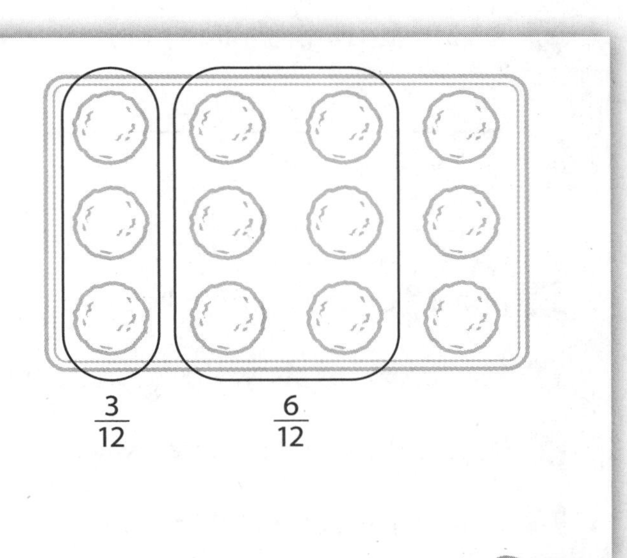

$\frac{3}{12} + \frac{6}{12} = \frac{9}{12}$

So, $\frac{9}{12}$ of the muffin tray is filled.

1 Shade $\frac{2}{12}$ of the muffin tray.

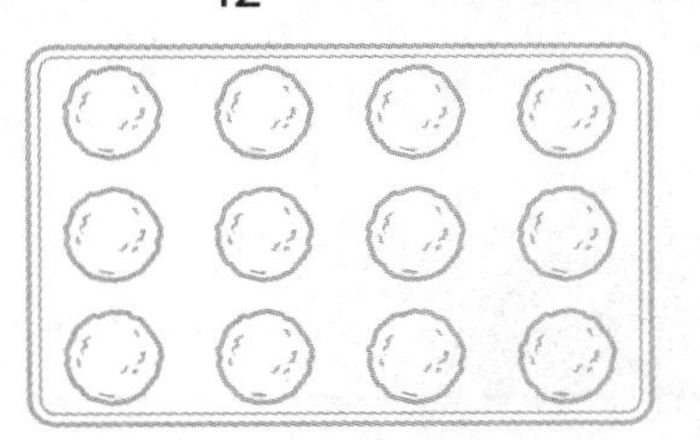

2 Sam fills $\frac{2}{12}$ of the tray with banana muffin batter. Then she fills $\frac{6}{12}$ with lemon muffin batter. Shade the diagram to show this.

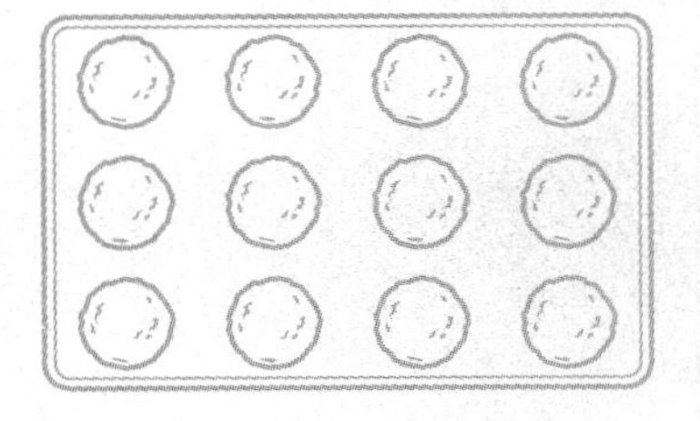

3 In problem 2, what fraction of the tray is filled? ______

Write an equation for this problem that includes your answer. ______________________________

Solve.

Kay ran $\frac{6}{8}$ mile and rested. Then she ran another $\frac{6}{8}$ mile.

4 Divide the number line below to show eighths.

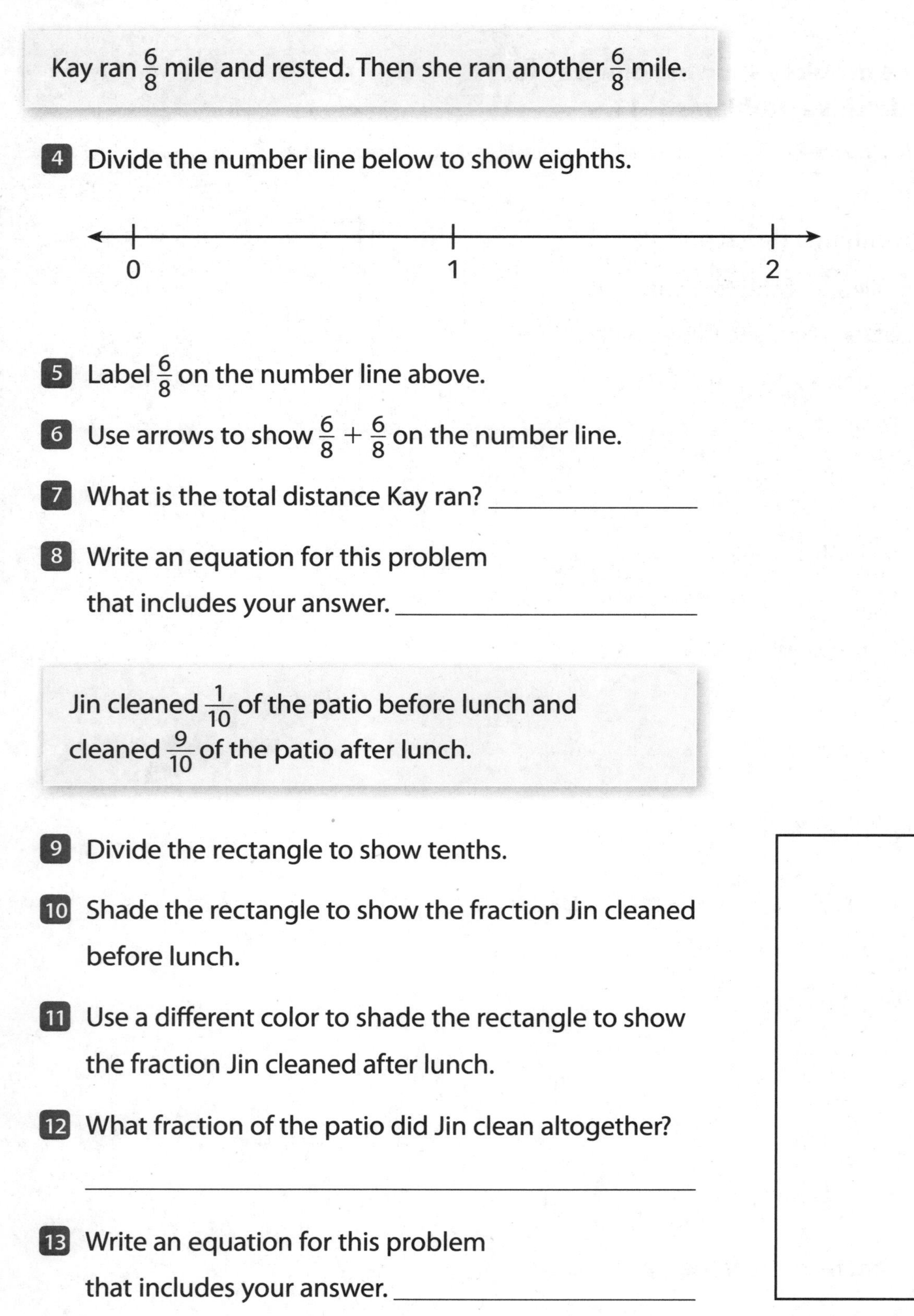

5 Label $\frac{6}{8}$ on the number line above.

6 Use arrows to show $\frac{6}{8} + \frac{6}{8}$ on the number line.

7 What is the total distance Kay ran? ______________

8 Write an equation for this problem that includes your answer. ____________________

Jin cleaned $\frac{1}{10}$ of the patio before lunch and cleaned $\frac{9}{10}$ of the patio after lunch.

9 Divide the rectangle to show tenths.

10 Shade the rectangle to show the fraction Jin cleaned before lunch.

11 Use a different color to shade the rectangle to show the fraction Jin cleaned after lunch.

12 What fraction of the patio did Jin clean altogether?

____

13 Write an equation for this problem that includes your answer. ____________________

Name: ______________________

Subtract Fractions

Study the example showing one way to subtract fractions. Then solve problems 1–7.

Example

Ali bought a carton of eggs. He used $\frac{3}{12}$ of the eggs to cook breakfast. He used another $\frac{2}{12}$ to make a dessert for dinner. What fraction of the carton is left?

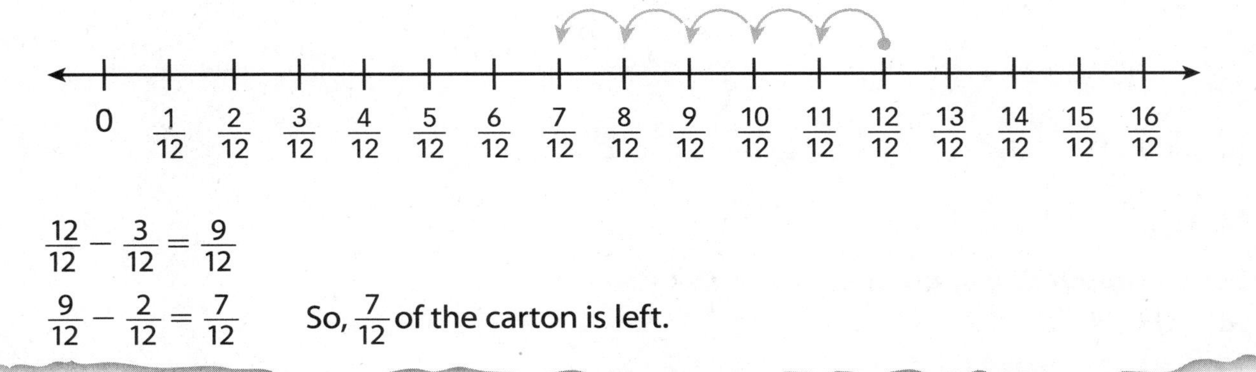

$\frac{12}{12} - \frac{3}{12} = \frac{9}{12}$

$\frac{9}{12} - \frac{2}{12} = \frac{7}{12}$ So, $\frac{7}{12}$ of the carton is left.

Keisha is going to her friend's house $\frac{8}{10}$ mile from home. Her mother drives her partway, then she walks the last $\frac{3}{10}$ mile.

1 Divide the number line below to show tenths. Then label each tick mark.

0 ——————————————— 1

2 Use arrows to show the problem on the number line you drew in problem 1.

3 How far did Keisha's mother drive her? ____________

4 Write an equation for this problem that includes your answer. ______________________________

Solve.

5 Anna made a quilt by sewing together green, white, and yellow fabric. When she was done, $\frac{2}{6}$ of the quilt was green and $\frac{3}{6}$ was yellow. The rest was white. What fraction of the quilt was white?

Show your work.

Solution: ___________________________

6 What is $\frac{9}{8} - \frac{8}{8}$?

Use a number line or an area model to show your thinking.

Solution: ___________________________

7 Shanice had 1 whole pizza. After eating some of it, she had $\frac{4}{6}$ of the pizza left. What fraction of the pizza did she eat?

Show your work.

Solution: ___________________________

Name: ______________________________

Add and Subtract Fractions

Solve the problems.

1 Lin bought $\frac{3}{4}$ pound of cheddar cheese and some Swiss cheese. Altogether she bought $\frac{7}{4}$ pounds of cheese. How much Swiss cheese did Lin buy?

A $\frac{4}{8}$ of a pound

B $\frac{4}{4}$ of a pound

C $\frac{10}{8}$ pounds

D $\frac{10}{4}$ pounds

2 Carrie has 2 meters of ribbon. She cuts off pieces of ribbon that are $\frac{5}{10}$ meter, $\frac{1}{10}$ meter, and $\frac{7}{10}$ meter. How long is the remaining piece of ribbon?

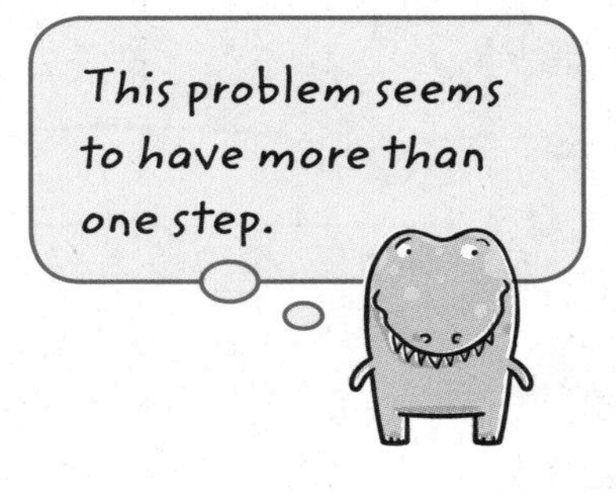

A $\frac{1}{10}$ meter

B $\frac{3}{10}$ meter

C $\frac{7}{10}$ meter

D $\frac{13}{10}$ meters

Lee chose **D** as the correct answer. How did she get that answer?

____

____

____

3 Ms. Atkins had a basket of tomatoes. She used $\frac{5}{12}$ of the tomatoes to make soup. She used $\frac{2}{12}$ in a salad. What fraction of the tomatoes are left?

What fraction can you use to represent all of the tomatoes?

Show your work.

Solution: ____

Solve.

4 Jo and Kira are raking leaves in the yard. They divide the yard into 8 equal sections. Jo rakes 4 sections. Kira rakes 2 sections. Which model can be used to find the total fraction of the yard they rake? Circle the letter of all that apply.

Two different models could show the same problem.

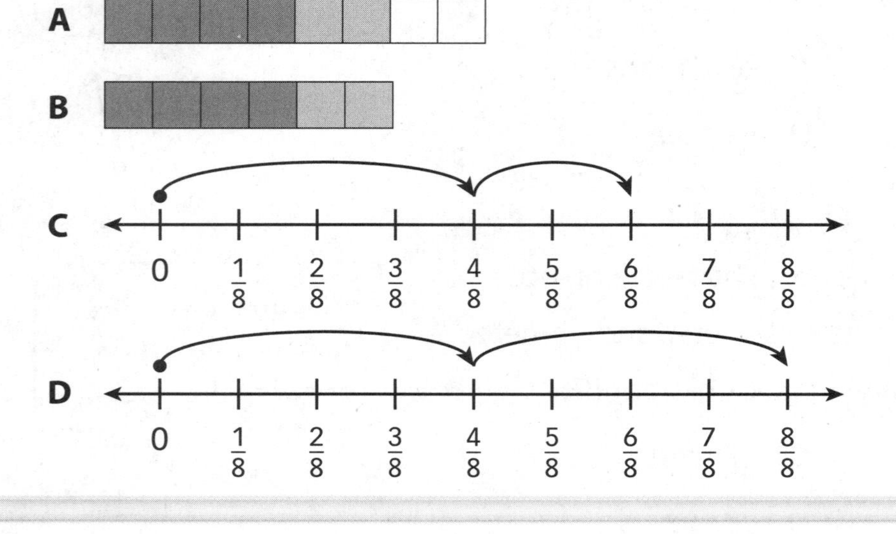

5 A pizza is cut into 6 equal pieces. After Eli and Dan eat some, $\frac{1}{6}$ of the pizza is left. What fraction could each boy eat? Give one possible answer.

Show your work.

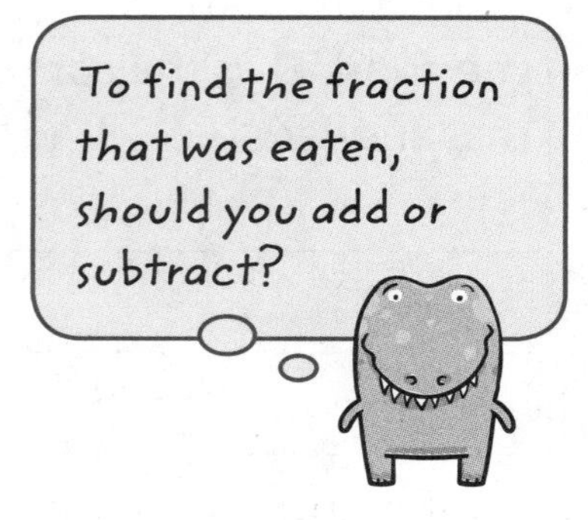

Solution: ______________________________

6 Milo has 2 hours of free time. He spends $\frac{2}{4}$ of an hour with his dog. He spends $\frac{3}{4}$ of an hour drawing. What fraction of an hour does he have left?

Show your work.

Solution: ______________________________

Dear Family,

This week your child is learning to add and subtract mixed numbers.

mixed number: a number with a whole number part and a fractional part.

Using models can help your child add mixed numbers, such as $1\frac{5}{8} + 1\frac{6}{8}$.

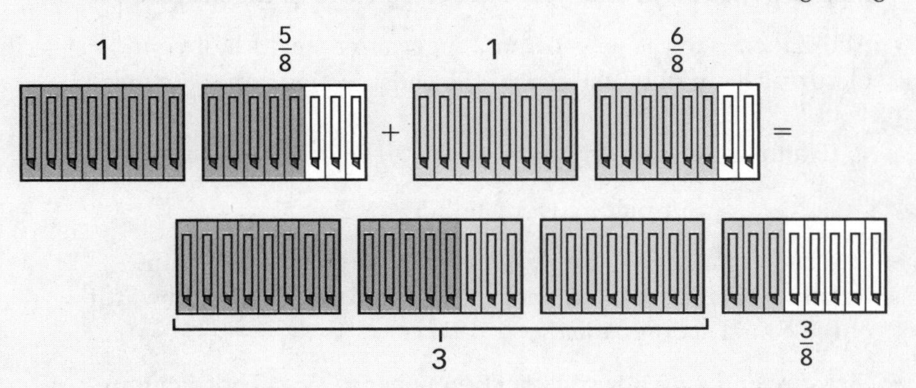

The model shows that you can add the wholes, $1 + 1 = 2$.

Then you can add the parts, $\frac{5}{8} + \frac{6}{8} = \frac{11}{8}$.

$\frac{11}{8}$ is another whole, $\frac{8}{8}$ or 1, and $\frac{3}{8}$.

The model shows the sum is 3 wholes and $\frac{3}{8}$ of a whole.

$1\frac{5}{8} + 1\frac{6}{8} = 3\frac{3}{8}$

Invite your child to share what he or she knows about adding and subtracting mixed numbers by doing the following activity together.

Add and Subtract Mixed Numbers Activity

Do an activity with your child to add and subtract mixed numbers.

Materials: construction paper ($8\frac{1}{2} \times 11$ inches, or 9×12 inches), magazine or newspaper with pictures (or a picture of your own), scissors, ruler, glue or tape

- Use a sheet of construction paper to make a paper frame for a fun photo. Choose a picture from a newspaper or a magazine, or use a photo of your own. Choose a picture that is less than 5 by 8 inches.
- Measure the length and width of your picture to the nearest $\frac{1}{8}$ inch.
- Add 2 inches to the length and 2 inches to the width of your picture. That will be the size of the construction paper you need.

  Example: Your picture is $5\frac{7}{8}$ wide. $5\frac{7}{8} + 2 = 7\frac{7}{8}$

  Your picture is $3\frac{3}{8}$ tall. $3\frac{3}{8} + 2 = 5\frac{3}{8}$
- Subtract your totals from the construction paper's width and length. That is how many inches to cut off the length and width of the construction paper.
- Measure and cut your construction paper to size. Then center the photo and attach it so that there is a 2-inch frame all around the photo.

Look for other real-life opportunities to practice adding and subtracting mixed numbers with your child.

Add and Subtract Mixed Numbers

Name: ______________________

Prerequisite: Add and Subtract Fractions

Study the example problem showing a way to add fractions. Then solve problems 1–5.

Example

Darcy used $\frac{5}{8}$ of a carton of strawberries to make a cake. She used another $\frac{2}{8}$ of a carton of strawberries to decorate the cake. What fraction of a carton of strawberries did Darcy use in all?

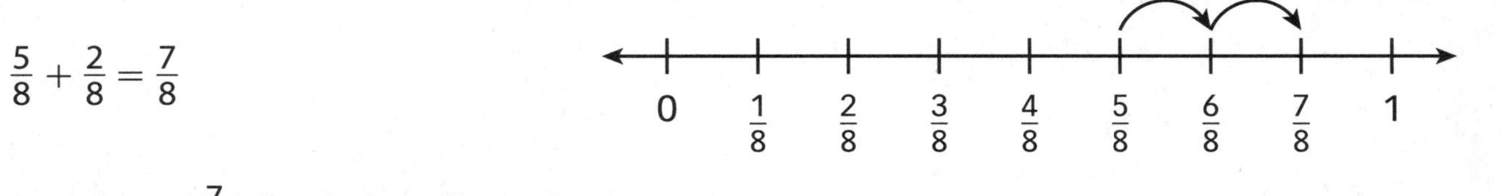

Darcy used $\frac{7}{8}$ of a carton of strawberries.

Jeremy biked $\frac{3}{10}$ of a mile to a friend's house. Then he biked $\frac{5}{10}$ of a mile to school.

0 $\frac{1}{10}$ $\frac{2}{10}$ $\frac{3}{10}$ $\frac{4}{10}$ $\frac{5}{10}$ $\frac{6}{10}$ $\frac{7}{10}$ $\frac{8}{10}$ $\frac{9}{10}$ 1

1 Draw jumps on the number line to show $\frac{3}{10} + \frac{5}{10}$.

2 Fill in the boxes to write an equation that shows how far Jeremy biked.

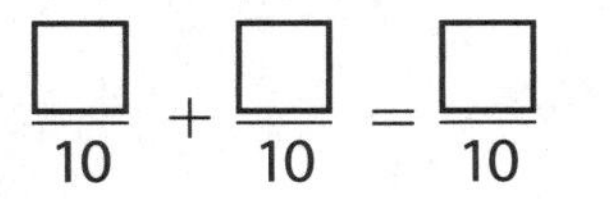

Solve.

3 George used $\frac{4}{6}$ of a box of raisins to make granola. His sister used $\frac{1}{6}$ of the box of raisins for her cereal. How much more of the box of raisins did George use than his sister?

Show your work.

Solution: George used _______ more of the box of raisins.

4 Sam and his friends shared a pizza. They ate $\frac{5}{8}$ of the pizza. What fraction of the pizza is left?

Show your work.

Solution: _______

5 Sophie read $\frac{1}{5}$ of a book each day from Monday to Friday. What fraction of her book had she read after she finished reading on Tuesday?

Show your work.

Solution: _______

6 Use the numbers below to write true equations. There is more than one correct answer and each number can be used more than once.

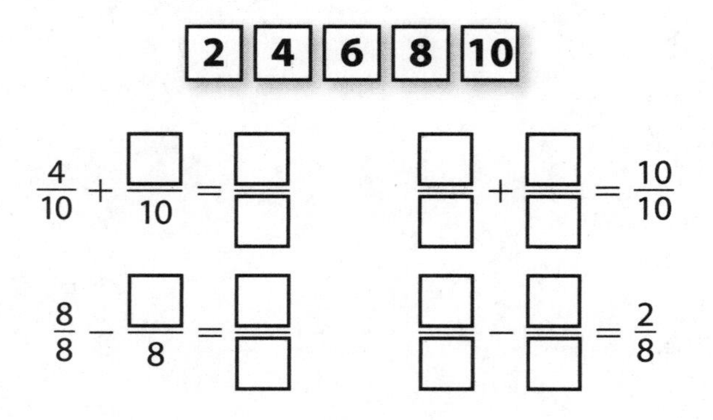

Name: ____________________

Add Mixed Numbers

Study the example problem showing a way to add mixed numbers. Then solve problems 1–6.

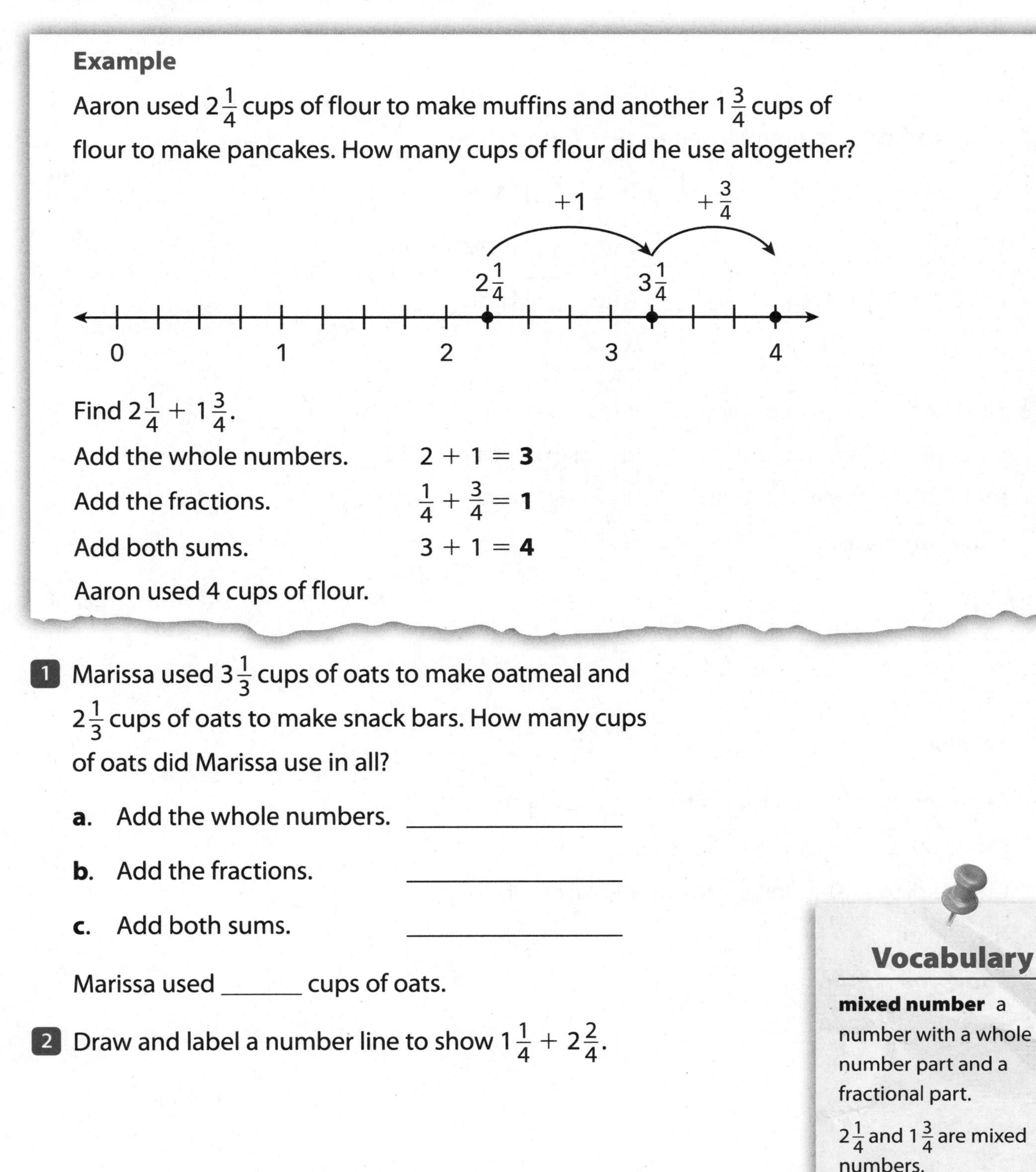

Example

Aaron used $2\frac{1}{4}$ cups of flour to make muffins and another $1\frac{3}{4}$ cups of flour to make pancakes. How many cups of flour did he use altogether?

Find $2\frac{1}{4} + 1\frac{3}{4}$.

Add the whole numbers. $2 + 1 = \mathbf{3}$

Add the fractions. $\frac{1}{4} + \frac{3}{4} = \mathbf{1}$

Add both sums. $3 + 1 = \mathbf{4}$

Aaron used 4 cups of flour.

1 Marissa used $3\frac{1}{3}$ cups of oats to make oatmeal and $2\frac{1}{3}$ cups of oats to make snack bars. How many cups of oats did Marissa use in all?

a. Add the whole numbers. ____________

b. Add the fractions. ____________

c. Add both sums. ____________

Marissa used ______ cups of oats.

2 Draw and label a number line to show $1\frac{1}{4} + 2\frac{2}{4}$.

Vocabulary

mixed number a number with a whole number part and a fractional part.

$2\frac{1}{4}$ and $1\frac{3}{4}$ are mixed numbers.

Solve.

3 Which of the following is equal to $7\frac{5}{6} + 2\frac{3}{6}$?

Circle all that apply.

A $9\frac{8}{12}$

B $9 + 1\frac{2}{6}$

C $7 + 2 + \frac{5}{6} + \frac{3}{6}$

D $5\frac{2}{6}$

4 Tell whether each number sentence is *True* or *False*.

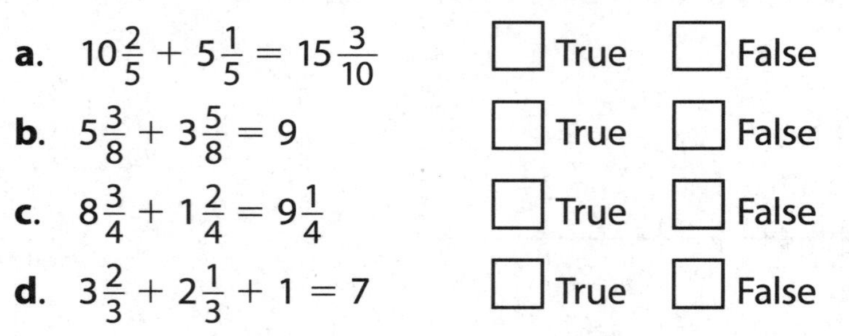

a. $10\frac{2}{5} + 5\frac{1}{5} = 15\frac{3}{10}$ ☐ True ☐ False

b. $5\frac{3}{8} + 3\frac{5}{8} = 9$ ☐ True ☐ False

c. $8\frac{3}{4} + 1\frac{2}{4} = 9\frac{1}{4}$ ☐ True ☐ False

d. $3\frac{2}{3} + 2\frac{1}{3} + 1 = 7$ ☐ True ☐ False

5 Tim used $4\frac{1}{2}$ cups of oranges, $3\frac{1}{2}$ cups of apples, and $5\frac{1}{2}$ cups of pears in a fruit salad. How many cups of fruit did Tim use altogether?

Show your work.

Solution: ______________________________

6 Jerry and two friends took a trip together. Jerry drove $80\frac{7}{10}$ miles. Arthur drove $60\frac{5}{10}$ miles. Charlie drove $40\frac{8}{10}$ miles. How many miles did they drive in all?

Show your work.

Solution: ______________________________

Name: ______________________

Subtract Mixed Numbers

Study the example problem showing a way to subtract mixed numbers. Then solve problems 1–5.

Example

On a holiday, Sara's family drove $3\frac{1}{4}$ hours to her cousin's house. The drive usually takes $2\frac{2}{4}$ hours. How much longer did the drive take on the holiday?

Find $3\frac{1}{4} - 2\frac{2}{4}$.

$3\frac{1}{4} - 2\frac{2}{4} = \frac{3}{4}$

$-\frac{2}{4}$ -2

$\frac{3}{4}$ $1\frac{1}{4}$ $3\frac{1}{4}$

0   1   2   3   4

The drive took $\frac{3}{4}$ hour longer on the holiday.

Steve made $9\frac{3}{6}$ cups of pancake batter on a weekend camping trip. He used $3\frac{4}{6}$ cups of batter for breakfast on Saturday.

1 Write each mixed number as a fraction greater than one.

$9\frac{3}{6} = \frac{\square}{6} + \frac{3}{6} = \frac{\square}{6}$ $3\frac{4}{6} = \frac{\square}{6} + \frac{4}{6} = \frac{\square}{6}$

2 Subtract the fractions to find how many cups of batter were left for breakfast on Sunday.

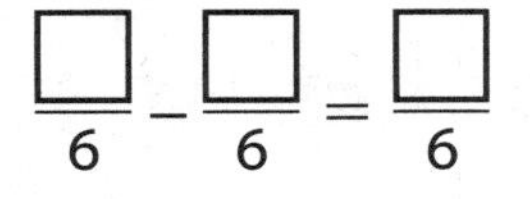

3 Write the difference as a mixed number.

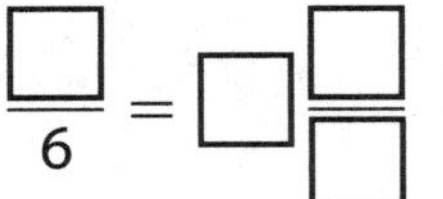

4 Use addition to check the answer.

$3\frac{4}{6} + \square\frac{\square}{\square} =$ ______________________

Solve.

5 Which of the following has the same value as $7\frac{5}{6} - 2\frac{3}{6}$?

Circle all that apply.

A $10\frac{2}{6}$

B $\frac{47}{6} - \frac{15}{6}$

C $(7 - 2) + \left(\frac{5}{6} - \frac{3}{6}\right)$

D $5\frac{2}{6}$

6 Helen bought 5 pounds of oranges. She sliced $2\frac{3}{10}$ pounds of oranges to bring to a party. How many pounds of oranges does Helen have left?

Show your work.

Solution: ______________________

7 Kira reasoned that $6\frac{1}{4} - 2\frac{3}{4} = 4\frac{2}{4}$ because the difference between 6 and 2 is 4 and the difference between $\frac{1}{4}$ and $\frac{3}{4}$ is $\frac{2}{4}$. Is Kira's reasoning correct? Explain why or why not.

Name: ______________________

Add and Subtract Mixed Numbers

Solve the problems.

1 Alexandra ran $2\frac{4}{5}$ miles last weekend. This weekend she ran $3\frac{1}{5}$ miles. How many miles did she run in all?

A $1\frac{3}{5}$ miles

B $5\frac{5}{10}$ miles

C $5\frac{3}{5}$ miles

D 6 miles

Do you move left or right on a number line to solve this problem?

2 Madelyn bought $12\frac{5}{8}$ yards of fabric. She used $6\frac{7}{8}$ yards of the fabric for a costume. How much fabric did Madelyn have left?

A $5\frac{2}{8}$ yards

B $5\frac{6}{8}$ yards

C $6\frac{2}{8}$ yards

D $19\frac{4}{8}$ yards

Cory chose **C** as the correct answer. How did he get that answer?

____

____

3 Look at Mina's work below.

$$10\frac{7}{12} - \frac{9}{12} = \left(\frac{10}{12} + \frac{7}{12}\right) - \frac{9}{12}$$
$$= \frac{17}{12} - \frac{9}{12}$$
$$= \frac{8}{12}$$

Is Mina's solution reasonable? Explain.

You can estimate to find out whether a solution is reasonable.

____

____

____

Solve.

4 Which statement(s) below have the same value as $4\frac{3}{5} - 2\frac{1}{5}$? Circle all that apply.

A $(4 - 2) + \left(\frac{3}{5} - \frac{1}{5}\right)$

B $(4 - 2) - \left(\frac{3}{5} - \frac{1}{5}\right)$

C $\left(\frac{20}{5} + \frac{3}{5}\right) - \left(\frac{10}{5} + \frac{1}{5}\right)$

D $\frac{7}{5} - \frac{3}{5}$

5 Jackson ordered 4 submarine sandwiches for a lunch party. Each sandwich was cut into thirds. At the party, 8 people each ate $\frac{1}{3}$ of a sandwich. How much of the sandwiches were left?

Show your work.

Solution: ______________________________

6 Julie, Ellen, and Jenny shared a pizza. Julie ate $\frac{1}{8}$ of the pizza. Ellen and Jenny each ate $\frac{3}{8}$ of the pizza. Did the girls eat the whole pizza? Explain.

Show your work.

Solution: ______________________________

Dear Family,

This week your child is exploring fraction multiplication.

Multiplying fractions is finding the total number of equal-size parts in equal groups.

Your child can use a model to understand fraction multiplication.

This model shows $5 \times \frac{3}{8}$.

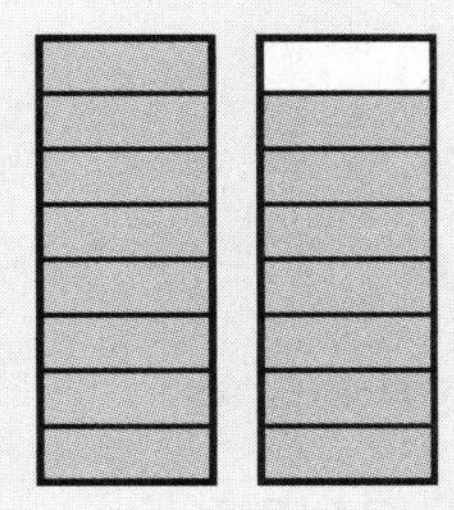

You can see that there are 5 groups of $\frac{3}{8}$.

There are $\frac{15}{8}$ in all.

The denominator tells the number of equal-size parts in the whole.

There are 8 equal-size parts in each whole.

Your child can also think about repeated addition to understand fraction multiplication.

Adding $\frac{3}{8}$ five times is the same as multiplying $5 \times \frac{3}{8}$.

$\frac{3}{8} + \frac{3}{8} + \frac{3}{8} + \frac{3}{8} + \frac{3}{8} = \frac{15}{8}$

Invite your child to share what he or she knows about fraction multiplication by doing the following activity together.

Fraction Multiplication

Do an activity with your child to explore fraction multiplication.

Materials: a bowl and the ingredients shown in the recipe

- Look at the recipe below for snack mix.
- Rewrite the recipe so that you can make four times as much snack mix. Multiply the amount of each ingredient by 4.
- Make the recipe and enjoy!

Recipe for Snack Mix

Ingredients:

$\frac{1}{4}$ cup pretzels

$\frac{3}{4}$ cup nuts of your choice

$\frac{1}{2}$ cup raisins

$\frac{2}{3}$ cup dried fruit

$\frac{1}{3}$ cup chocolate chips (optional)

Directions:

Mix all the ingredients together. Store in a container.

Name: ______________

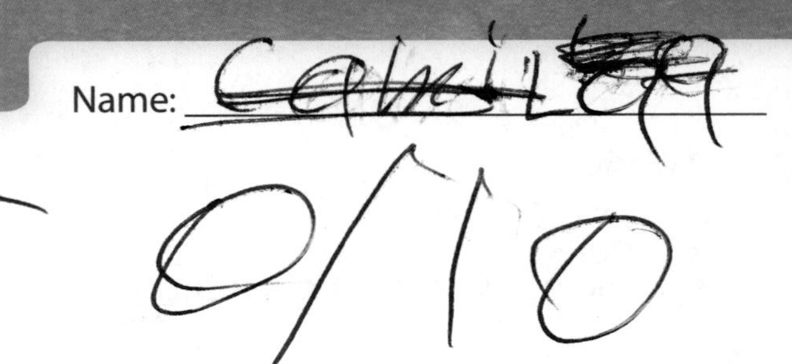

Show Multiplying Fractions

Study how the example shows how to multiply fractions. Then solve problems 1–9.

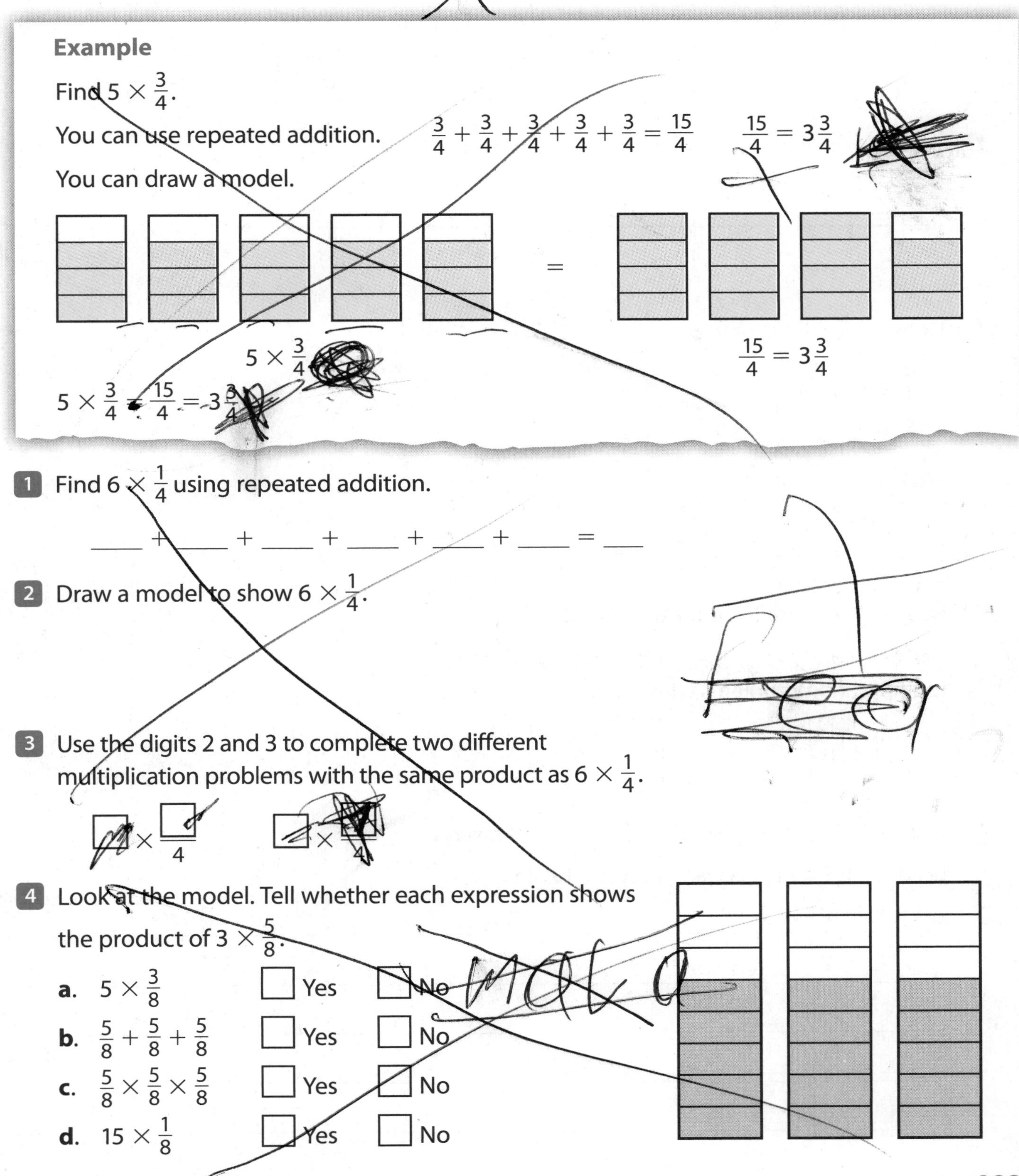

Example

Find $5 \times \frac{3}{4}$.

You can use repeated addition. $\frac{3}{4} + \frac{3}{4} + \frac{3}{4} + \frac{3}{4} + \frac{3}{4} = \frac{15}{4}$ $\quad \frac{15}{4} = 3\frac{3}{4}$

You can draw a model.

$5 \times \frac{3}{4}$ = $\frac{15}{4} = 3\frac{3}{4}$

$5 \times \frac{3}{4} = \frac{15}{4} = 3\frac{3}{4}$

1 Find $6 \times \frac{1}{4}$ using repeated addition.

____ + ____ + ____ + ____ + ____ + ____ = ____

2 Draw a model to show $6 \times \frac{1}{4}$.

3 Use the digits 2 and 3 to complete two different multiplication problems with the same product as $6 \times \frac{1}{4}$.

$\square \times \frac{\square}{4}$ $\quad \square \times \frac{\square}{4}$

4 Look at the model. Tell whether each expression shows the product of $3 \times \frac{5}{8}$.

a. $5 \times \frac{3}{8}$ ☐ Yes ☐ No

b. $\frac{5}{8} + \frac{5}{8} + \frac{5}{8}$ ☐ Yes ☐ No

c. $\frac{5}{8} \times \frac{5}{8} \times \frac{5}{8}$ ☐ Yes ☐ No

d. $15 \times \frac{1}{8}$ ☐ Yes ☐ No

Solve.

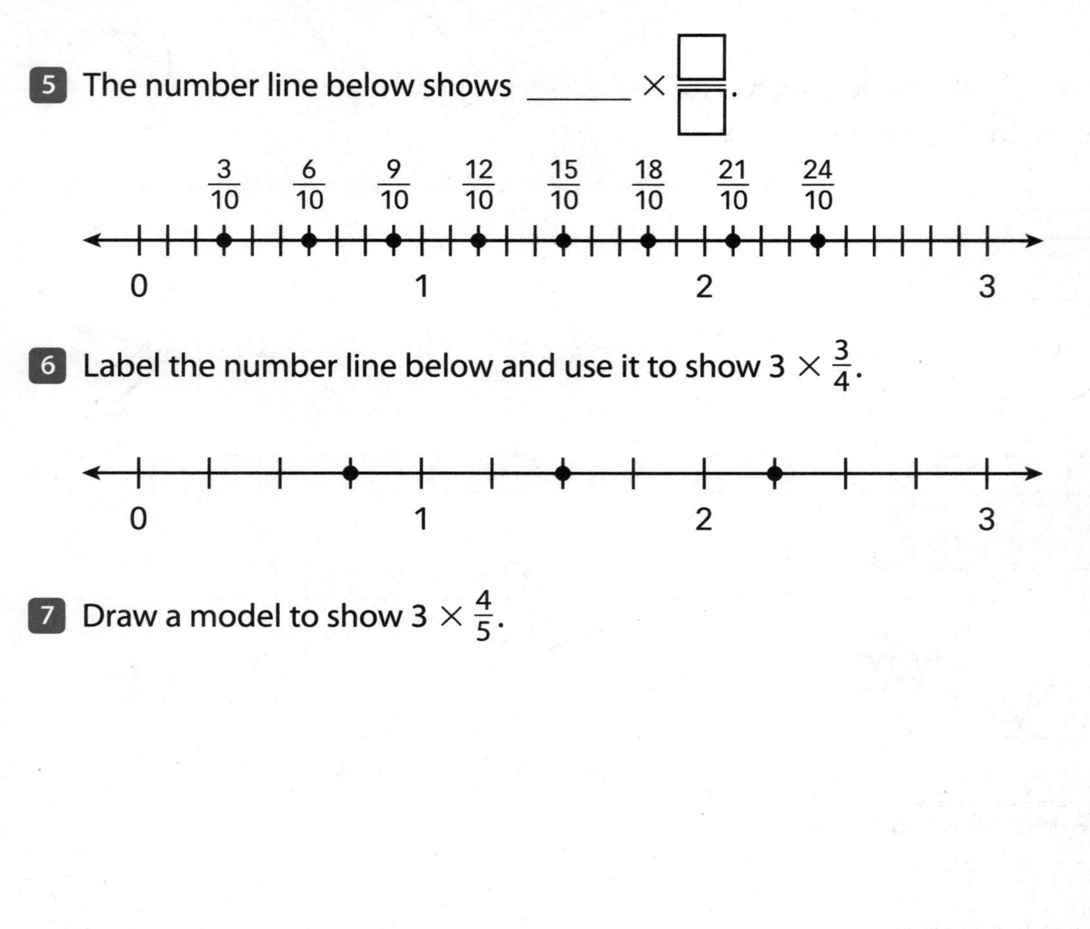

5 The number line below shows ______ $\times \frac{\square}{\square}$.

6 Label the number line below and use it to show $3 \times \frac{3}{4}$.

7 Draw a model to show $3 \times \frac{4}{5}$.

8 Look at the model you drew in problem 7.

Use the digits 2, 3, 4, 5, and 6 to write two different multiplication problems with the same product as $3 \times \frac{4}{5}$.

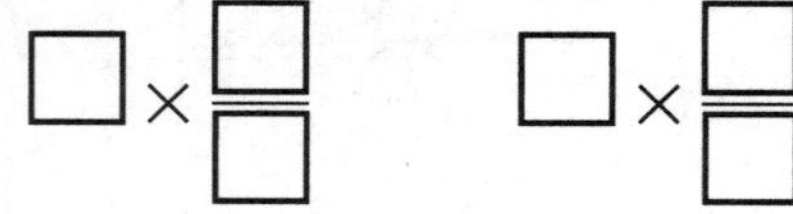

9 Lisa says that $3 \times \frac{1}{6}$ and $\frac{1}{6} \times \frac{1}{6} \times \frac{1}{6}$ have the same product. Is Lisa's reasoning correct? Explain.

____

____

____

____

____

Name: ______________________

Reason and Write

Study the example. Underline two parts that you think make it a particularly good answer and a helpful example.

Example

Describe how you can use the same methods to find the product 4×2 and the product $4 \times \frac{2}{3}$.

Show your work. Use models, words, and numbers to explain your answer.

I can think of 4×2 as 4 groups of 2.
$4 \times 2 = 8$. 8 is 4 times as many as 2.

I can think of $4 \times \frac{2}{3}$ as 4 groups of 2 thirds. $4 \times \frac{2}{3} = \frac{8}{3}$.
$\frac{8}{3}$ is 4 times as many as $\frac{2}{3}$.

I can find both products using repeated addition.

$2 + 2 + 2 + 2 = 8$

$\frac{2}{3} + \frac{2}{3} + \frac{2}{3} + \frac{2}{3} = \frac{8}{3}$

I can use a model to show $4 \times 2 = 8$.

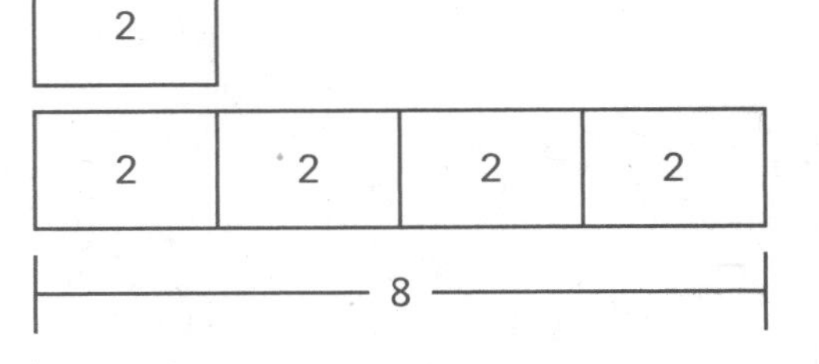

I can use a model to show $4 \times \frac{2}{3} = \frac{8}{3}$.

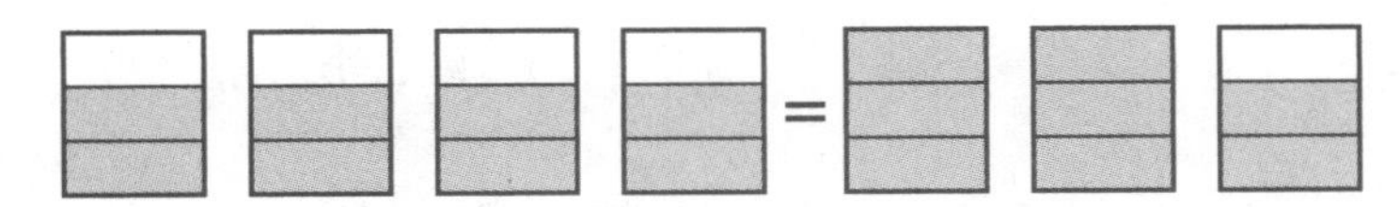

Where does the example . . .

- use words to explain?
- use numbers to explain?
- use models to show how the products are alike?

Solve the problem. Use what you learned from the example.

Describe how you can use the same methods to find the product 2×3 and the product $2 \times \frac{3}{4}$.

Show your work. Use words, models, and numbers to explain your answer.

Did you . . .

- use words to explain?
- use numbers to explain?
- use models to show how the products are alike?

Dear Family,

This week your child is learning to multiply fractions to solve word problems.

Your child might see a problem like this:

> Randy practiced guitar for $\frac{2}{3}$ of an hour on 4 days this week. How long did Randy practice this week?

Using fraction strips can help your child solve this word problem.

Each fraction strip below is divided into thirds and shows $\frac{2}{3}$, the length of time that Randy practiced each day.

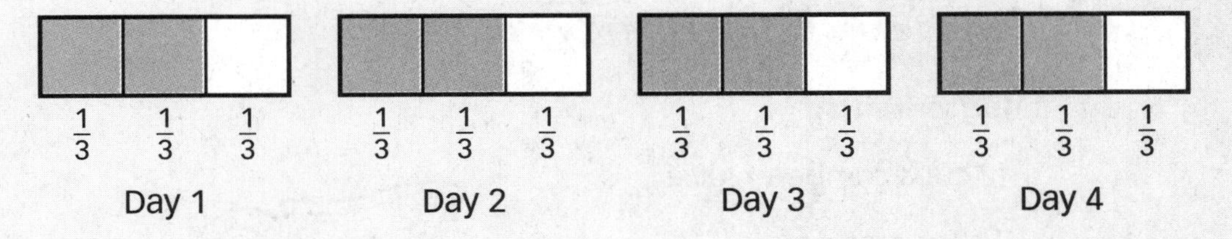

The fraction strips show $4 \times \frac{2}{3}$. The fraction strips show $\frac{8}{3}$.

Your child can also write an equation to find how long Randy practiced.

$$4 \times \frac{2}{3} = \frac{8}{3}$$

Then your child can check his or her answer by using repeated addition.

$$\frac{2}{3} + \frac{2}{3} + \frac{2}{3} + \frac{2}{3} = \frac{8}{3} \text{ hours}$$

The answer is that Randy practiced $\frac{8}{3}$, or $2\frac{2}{3}$, hours this week.

Invite your child to share what he or she knows about multiplying fractions by doing the following activity together.

Multiplying Fractions Activity

Do an activity with your child to multiply fractions.

Materials: a large pitcher, a measuring cup, and the ingredients shown in the recipe

- Look at the recipe below for party punch. It makes a large amount of punch.
- Rewrite the recipe so that it will be more suitable for your family. Just multiply the amount of each ingredient by $\frac{1}{4}$.
- Make the recipe and enjoy!

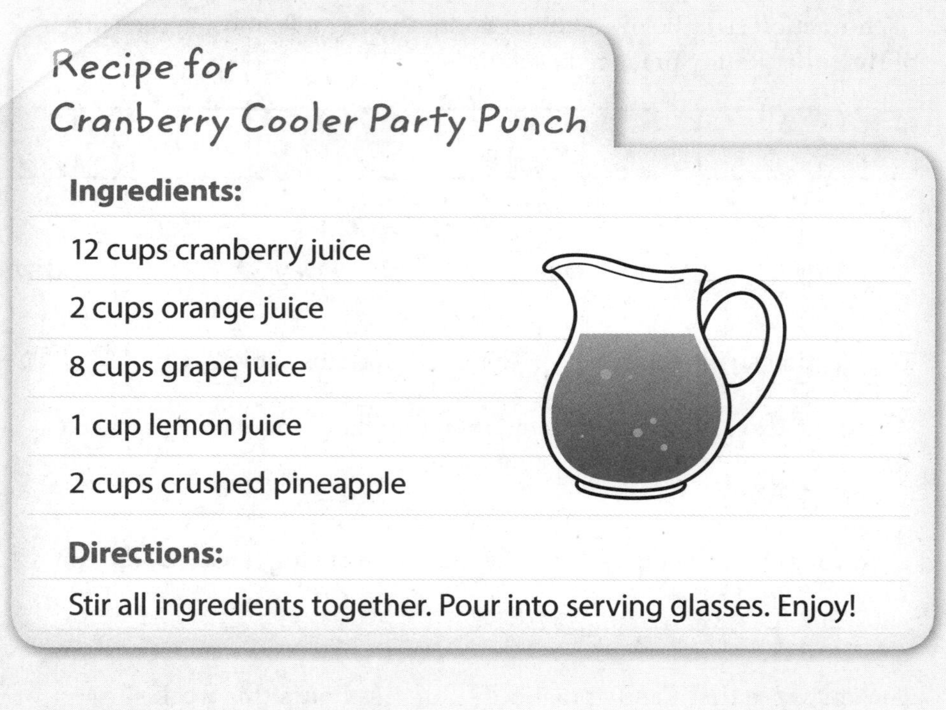

Multiply Fractions

Name: ______________________

Prerequisite: Model Fraction Multiplication

Study the example showing fraction multiplication with models. Then solve problems 1–10.

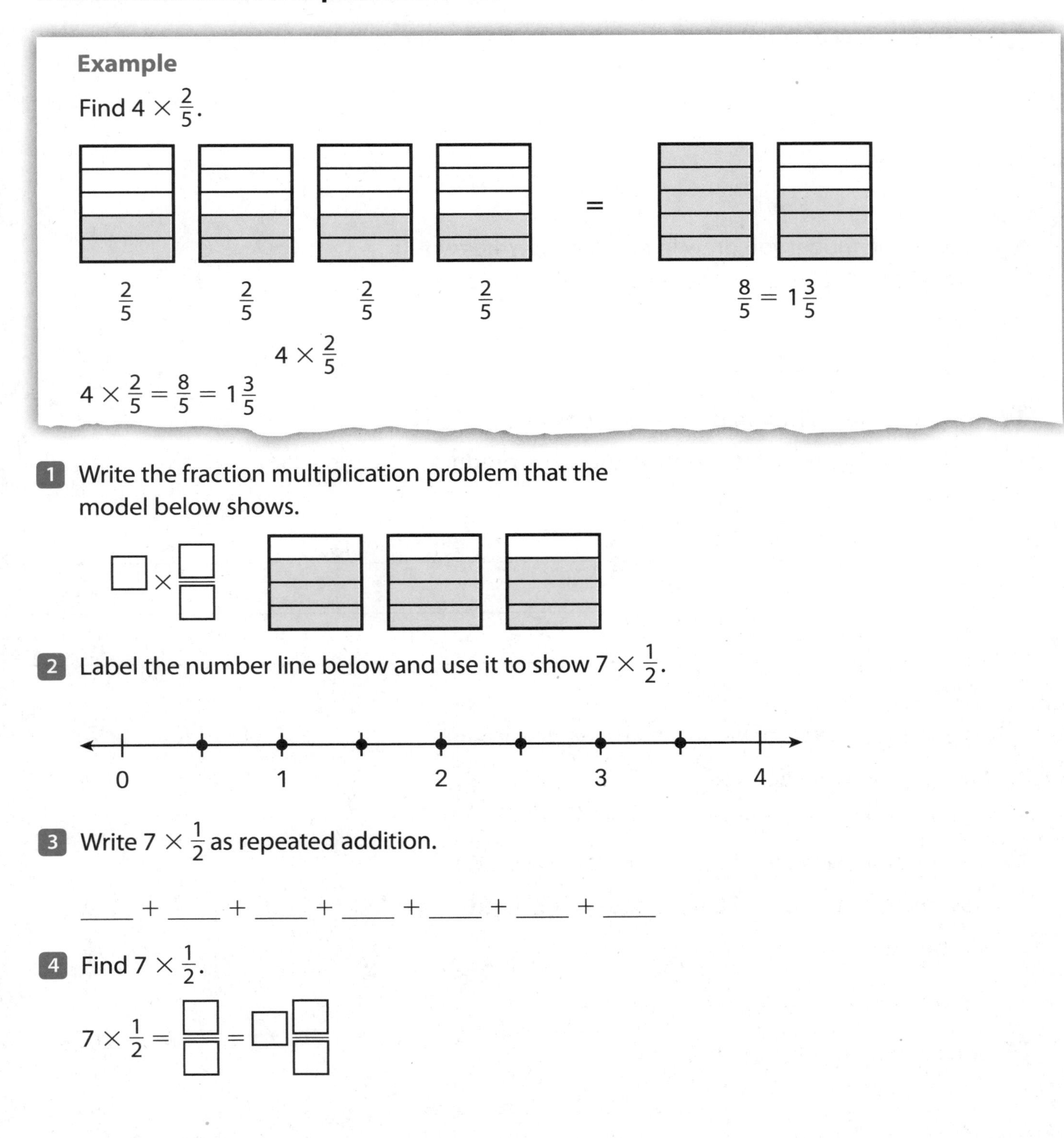

Example

Find $4 \times \frac{2}{5}$.

$\frac{2}{5}$ $\frac{2}{5}$ $\frac{2}{5}$ $\frac{2}{5}$ = $\frac{8}{5} = 1\frac{3}{5}$

$4 \times \frac{2}{5}$

$4 \times \frac{2}{5} = \frac{8}{5} = 1\frac{3}{5}$

1 Write the fraction multiplication problem that the model below shows.

$\square \times \frac{\square}{\square}$

2 Label the number line below and use it to show $7 \times \frac{1}{2}$.

3 Write $7 \times \frac{1}{2}$ as repeated addition.

____ + ____ + ____ + ____ + ____ + ____ + ____

4 Find $7 \times \frac{1}{2}$.

$7 \times \frac{1}{2} = \frac{\square}{\square} = \square\frac{\square}{\square}$

Solve.

5 Fill in the blanks to show different ways to write problems with the same product as $4 \times \frac{3}{8}$.

$\_\_\_\_\_ \times \frac{1}{8}$ $\quad$ $3 \times \frac{\square}{8}$

6 Draw a model to show $3 \times \frac{2}{6}$.

7 Look at the model you drew in problem 6. Write two different multiplication problems that have the same product.

____________ ____________

8 Solve the multiplication problems you wrote in problem 7. Explain why they have the same product as $3 \times \frac{2}{6}$.

____

____

____

Nadia made 4 loaves of bread. She used $\frac{3}{8}$ teaspoon of baking soda for each loaf.

9 Write a multiplication problem you could use to find how many teaspoons of baking soda Nadia used altogether.

____

10 Solve the multiplication problem.

____

Name: ______________________________

Solve Problems with Fraction Multiplication

Study the example problem that shows how to solve a word problem with fraction multiplication. Then solve problems 1–7.

Example

Henry doubled a cookie recipe to make two batches of cookies. The recipe calls for $\frac{7}{8}$ cup of flour for each batch. How much flour did Henry use for both batches of cookies?

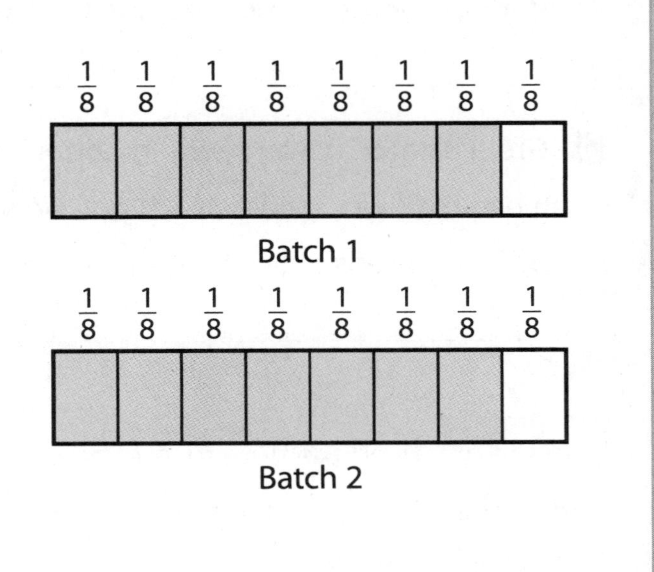

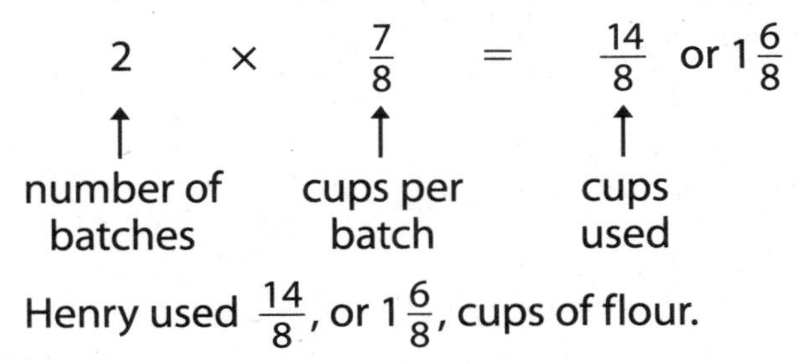

Henry used $\frac{14}{8}$, or $1\frac{6}{8}$, cups of flour.

1 Benson spent $\frac{5}{6}$ of an hour reading on each of 3 days this week. How long did Benson spend reading this week?

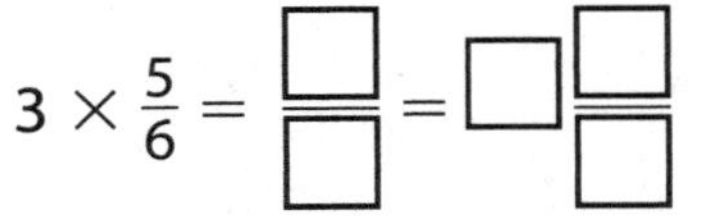

Benson spent __________ hours reading.

2 Show how to use repeated addition to check your answer in problem 1.

____

3 Sabrina rode her bike $\frac{3}{4}$ of a mile. Katrin rode her bike 4 times as far as Sabrina. How far did Katrin ride her bike?

____

Solve.

4 On Saturdays, Jorge coaches soccer for $\frac{1}{12}$ of the day. He also coaches tennis and swimming, each for the same amount of time as soccer. What fraction of the day does Jorge spend coaching on Saturdays?

____

5 Greta planted flower seeds in 12 pots. She used $\frac{2}{6}$ of a bag of flower seeds in each pot. How many bags of flower seeds did Greta use?

____

Leslie practiced the flute for $\frac{2}{6}$ of an hour 3 times this week. She practiced piano for $\frac{2}{3}$ of an hour 2 times this week.

6 Which expressions below can be used to show how much time Leslie spent practicing both the flute and piano this week? Circle the letter of all that apply.

A $\left(3 \times \frac{2}{6}\right) + \left(2 \times \frac{2}{3}\right)$

B $5 \times \left(\frac{2}{6} + \frac{2}{3}\right)$

C $\frac{2}{6} + \frac{2}{6} + \frac{2}{6} + \frac{2}{3} + \frac{2}{3}$

D $\frac{(3 \times 2)}{6} + \frac{(2 \times 2)}{3}$

7 Which did Leslie practice for a longer amount of time, the flute or the piano?

Show your work.

Solution: ______________________________

Name: ____________________

Multiply Fractions

Solve the problems.

1 Rick cut a sheet of paper into 4 strips. Each strip was $\frac{3}{4}$ of an inch wide. How wide was the paper Rick cut?

A $\frac{3}{16}$ inch

B $\frac{12}{16}$ inch

C $\frac{7}{4}$ inches

D $\frac{12}{4}$ inches

2 Diane walked her dog $\frac{4}{10}$ of a mile on 5 days this week. How far did Diane walk her dog this week?

A $\frac{20}{50}$ mile

B $\frac{9}{15}$ mile

C $\frac{20}{10}$ miles

D $\frac{40}{5}$ miles

Zoe chose **A**. How did she get that answer?

____

____

____

____

When you multiply a whole number by a fraction, do you multiply the whole number by the numerator or denominator?

3 Leo feeds his cat $\frac{2}{3}$ of a can of food 2 times a day. Leo is going out of town for 3 days. How many cans of food does Leo need to give a neighbor to feed his cat?

Show your work.

Solution: ____________________

What two numbers can you multiply to find how many times the neighbor needs to feed Leo's cat?

Solve.

4 Luke and Matt went fishing. Luke caught 4 fish, each weighing $\frac{7}{8}$ of a pound. Matt caught 6 fish, each weighing $\frac{3}{4}$ of a pound. Who caught more pounds of fish?

Show your work.

How do you figure out how many pounds each person caught?

Solution: ______________________________

5 Penny is training for a race. First she ran $\frac{1}{10}$ of a mile 4 times. Next she ran $\frac{1}{5}$ of a mile 3 times. Then she ran $\frac{3}{10}$ of a mile two times. How far did Penny run during her training?

Show your work.

Drawing a picture can help you decide which numbers to multiply and which numbers to add.

Solution: ______________________________

Dear Family,

Your child might see a problem such as $\frac{4}{10} + \frac{50}{100}$. One fraction in the problem has a denominator of 10. The other fraction has a denominator of 100.

Your child is learning how to write tenths fractions as equivalent hundredths fractions. $\frac{1}{10} = \frac{10}{100}$

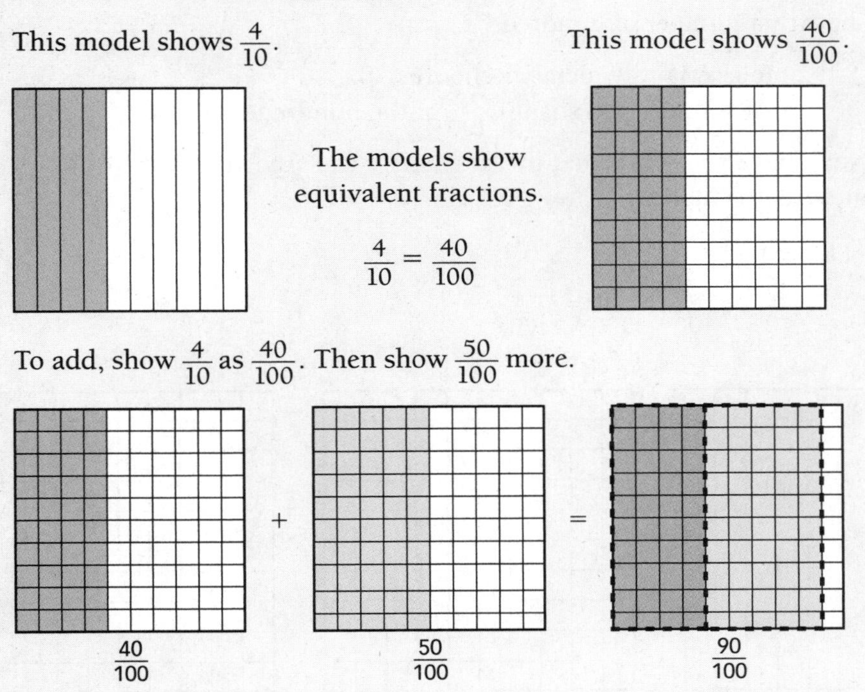

$\frac{40}{100} + \frac{50}{100} = \frac{90}{100}$ and $\frac{4}{10} + \frac{50}{100} = \frac{90}{100}$

Invite your child to share what he or she knows about fractions as tenths and hundredths by doing the following activity together.

Fractions as Tenths and Hundredths Activity

Do an activity with your child to explore tenths and hundredths fractions.

- Use the tenths and hundredths models below or create your own models using lined paper and grid paper.
- Have your child choose a number between 1 and 5. Shade the tenths model to show that number of tenths.

  Example: Your child chooses 4.
  Your child shades 4 tenths $\left(\frac{4}{10}\right)$ of the tenths model.
- Then have another family member choose a 2-digit number between 10 and 50. Your child shades the hundredths model to show that number of hundredths.

  Example: A family member chooses 28.
  Your child shades $\frac{28}{100}$ of the hundredths model.
- Next, have your child add the fractions. Shade the other hundredths model to show the sum.

  Example: $\frac{4}{10} + \frac{28}{100}$
  $\frac{40}{100} + \frac{28}{100} = \frac{68}{100}$

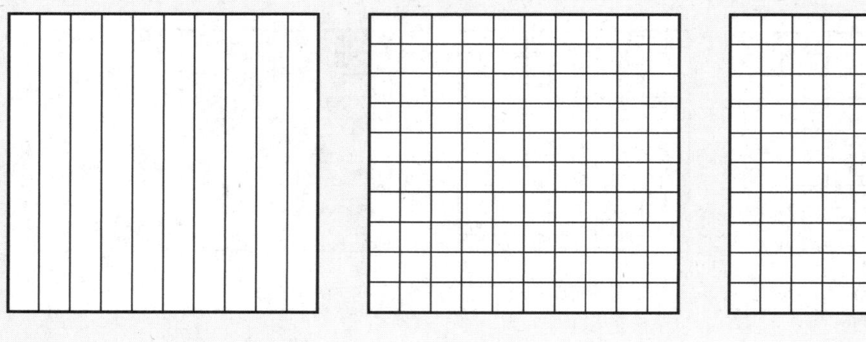

Fractions as Tenths and Hundredths

Name: ______________________

Prerequisite: Identify Equivalent Fractions

Study the example showing how to use a number line to find equivalent fractions. Then solve problems 1–8.

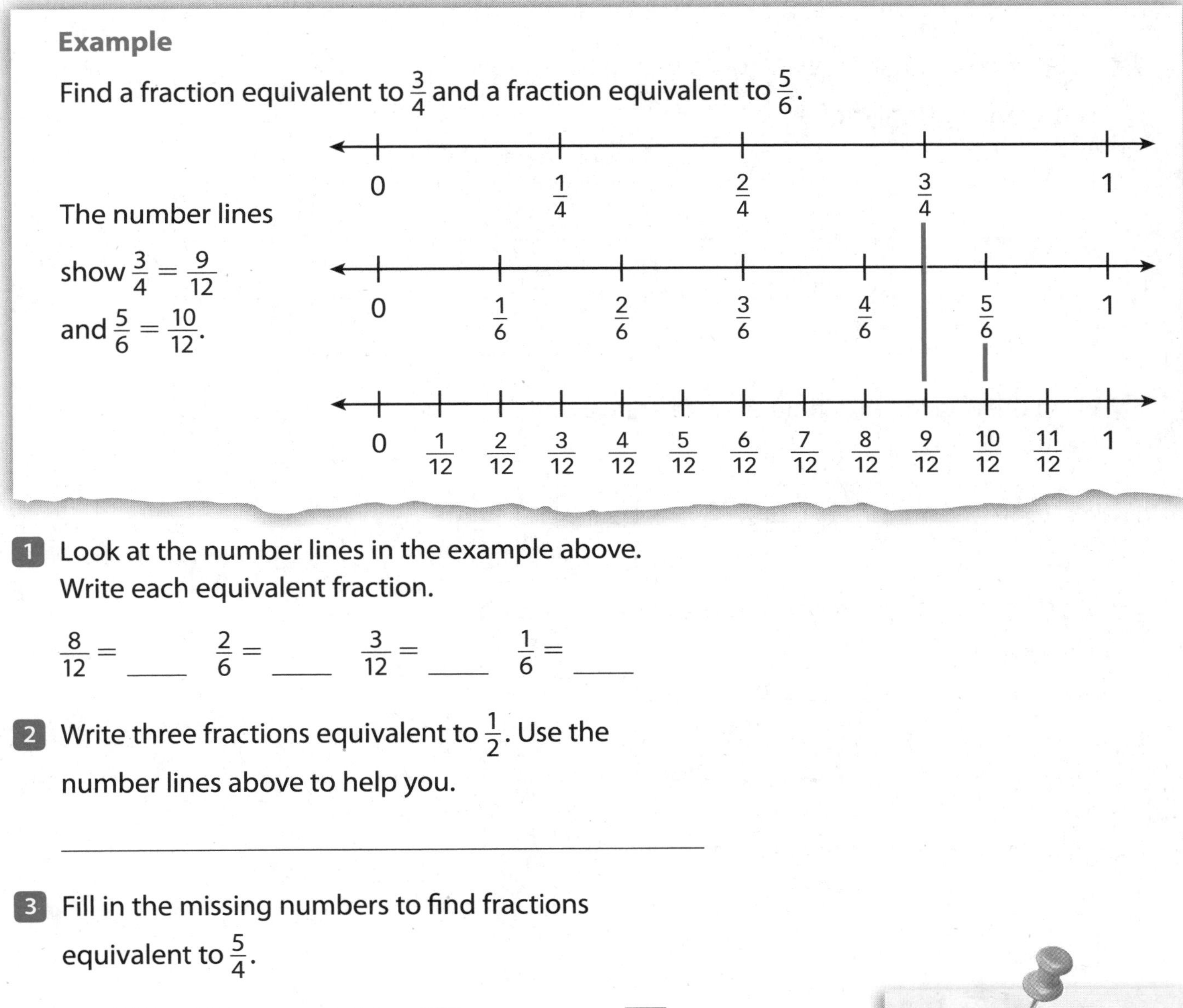

Example

Find a fraction equivalent to $\frac{3}{4}$ and a fraction equivalent to $\frac{5}{6}$.

The number lines show $\frac{3}{4} = \frac{9}{12}$ and $\frac{5}{6} = \frac{10}{12}$.

1 Look at the number lines in the example above. Write each equivalent fraction.

$\frac{8}{12} =$ ____ $\frac{2}{6} =$ ____ $\frac{3}{12} =$ ____ $\frac{1}{6} =$ ____

2 Write three fractions equivalent to $\frac{1}{2}$. Use the number lines above to help you.

____

3 Fill in the missing numbers to find fractions equivalent to $\frac{5}{4}$.

$\frac{5}{4} \times \frac{\square}{2} = \frac{\square}{8}$ $\frac{5}{4} \times \frac{\square}{\square} = \frac{\square}{16}$ $\frac{5}{4} \times \frac{10}{10} = \frac{\square}{40}$

Vocabulary

equivalent fractions two or more fractions that name the same part of a whole.

Solve.

4 Shade the model below to show $\frac{2}{3}$. Then divide the model to show $\frac{2}{3} = \frac{4}{6}$.

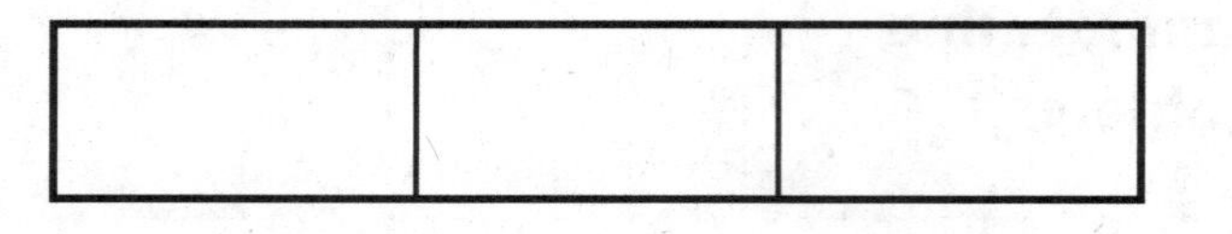

5 Look at problem 4. Explain how dividing the model shows the equivalent fractions $\frac{2}{3} = \frac{4}{6}$.

____

____

____

____

6 Fill in the missing numbers to write equivalent fractions.

$\frac{\square}{\square} \times \frac{2}{2} = \frac{2}{4}$ $\qquad \frac{\square}{3} \times \frac{\square}{\square} = \frac{8}{12}$ $\qquad \frac{\square}{\square} \times \frac{\square}{2} = \frac{10}{16}$

7 Shade the model to show $\frac{1}{2}$. Then divide the model to show $\frac{1}{2} = \frac{5}{10}$.

8 Fill in the missing numbers to show that $\frac{1}{2} = \frac{5}{10}$.

$\frac{1}{2} \times \frac{\square}{\square} = \frac{5}{10}$

Name: ____________________

Add Tenths and Hundredths Fractions

Study the example problem showing how to add tenths and hundredths fractions. Then solve problems 1–8.

Example

Jaden found $\frac{8}{10}$ of a dollar in change in his backpack.
He found $\frac{15}{100}$ of a dollar in change in his lunch bag.
What fraction of a dollar in change did he find altogether?

Multiply to find the hundredths fraction equivalent to $\frac{8}{10}$. $\frac{8}{10} = \left(\frac{8 \times 10}{10 \times 10}\right) = \frac{80}{100}$

Add the hundredths fractions. $\frac{80}{100} + \frac{15}{100} = \frac{95}{100}$

Jaden found $\frac{95}{100}$ of a dollar in change.

1 Write $\frac{2}{10}$ as an equivalent fraction with a denominator of 100.

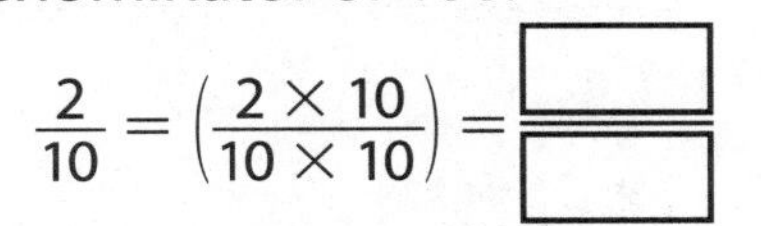

2 Fill in the blanks to show how to find the sum of $\frac{2}{10}$ and $\frac{10}{100}$.

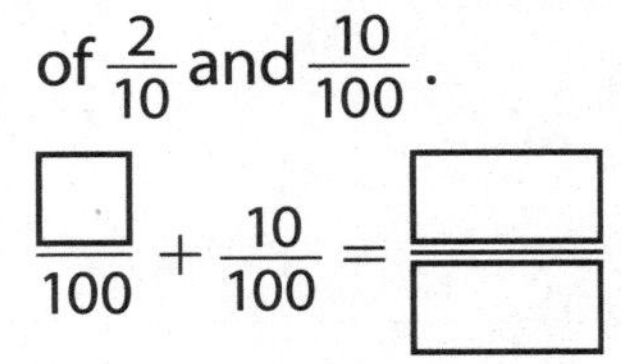

3 Look at problem 2. $\frac{10}{100} = \frac{1}{10}$. What is another way that you could show the sum of $\frac{2}{10}$ and $\frac{10}{100}$?

____

4 Look at problems 2 and 3. Are the sums equivalent? Explain.

____

____

Solve.

Mila has 100 math problems to finish this week. She solved $\frac{2}{10}$ of the problems on Monday and $\frac{25}{100}$ of the problems on Tuesday.

5 Did Mila solve more problems on Monday or on Tuesday? Explain.

Show your work.

Solution: ____________________

____

6 What fraction of the math problems for the week did Mila solve on Monday and Tuesday?

Show your work.

Solution: ____________________

7 Look at problem 6. Is the sum you found greater or less than $\frac{1}{2}$? Explain.

____

____

8 Has Mila completed more than half of her math problems for the week? Explain.

____

____

____

Name: ____________________

Fractions as Tenths and Hundredths

Solve the problems.

1 $\frac{3}{10} + \frac{3}{100}$ is equal to which of the following? Circle the letter for all that apply.

A $\frac{33}{100}$

B $\frac{6}{100}$

C $\frac{60}{100}$

D $\frac{30}{100} + \frac{3}{100}$

E $\frac{3}{10} + \frac{3}{10}$

How many hundredths are in 3 tenths?

2 Sylvia has $100. She spent $\frac{4}{10}$ of her money on a jacket and $\frac{20}{100}$ of her money on jeans. What fraction of her money did Sylvia spend?

A $\frac{60}{200}$

B $\frac{24}{100}$

C $\frac{6}{10}$

D $\frac{6}{20}$

Josh chose **B** as the correct answer. How did he get that answer?

____

____

____

____

There is more than one way to solve this problem.

3 Which is greater, $\frac{6}{10}$ or $\frac{6}{100}$? Explain.

____

____

____

____

You can compare the numerators or draw a model to solve this problem.

Solve.

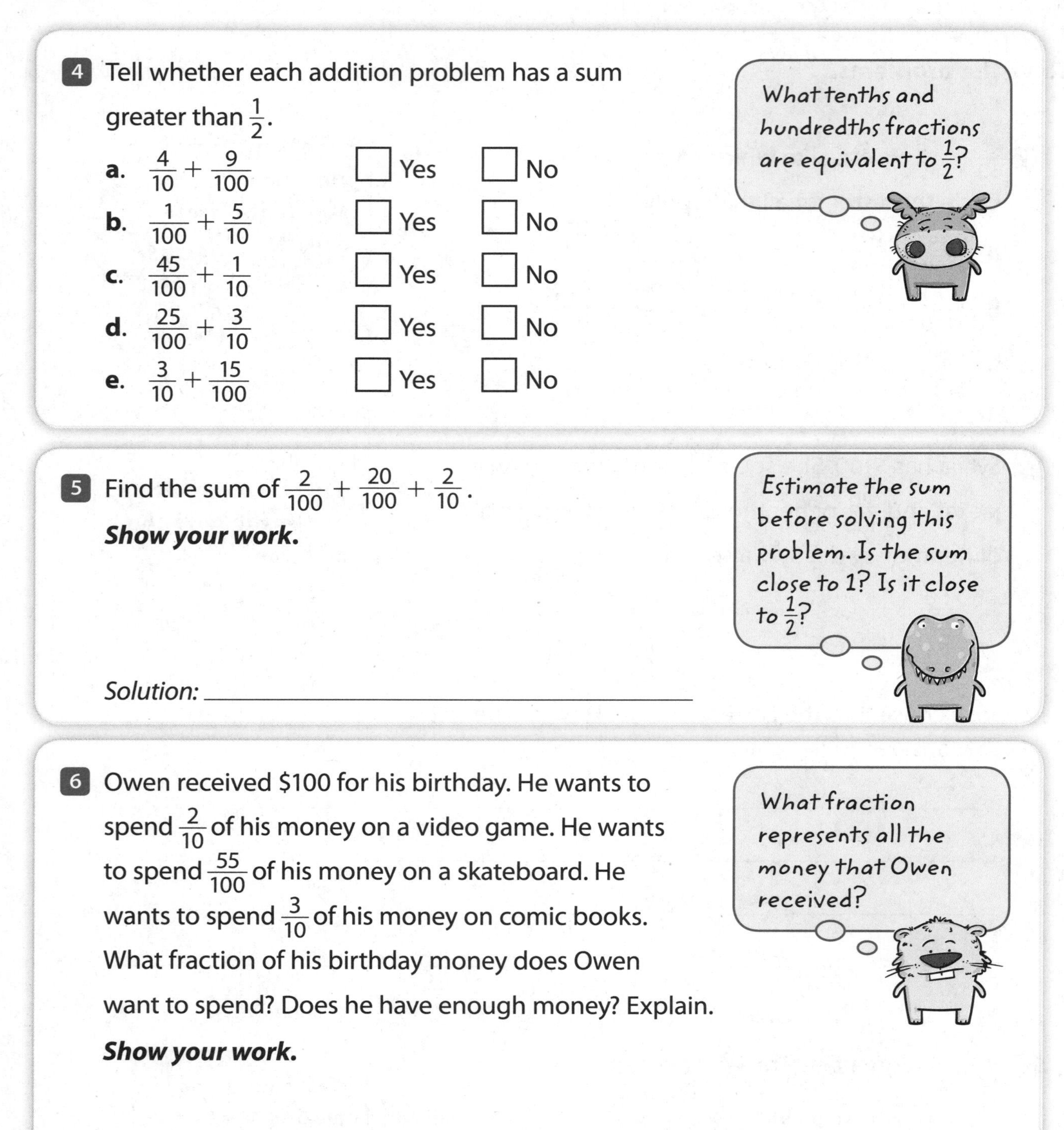

4 Tell whether each addition problem has a sum greater than $\frac{1}{2}$.

a. $\frac{4}{10} + \frac{9}{100}$ ☐ Yes ☐ No

b. $\frac{1}{100} + \frac{5}{10}$ ☐ Yes ☐ No

c. $\frac{45}{100} + \frac{1}{10}$ ☐ Yes ☐ No

d. $\frac{25}{100} + \frac{3}{10}$ ☐ Yes ☐ No

e. $\frac{3}{10} + \frac{15}{100}$ ☐ Yes ☐ No

5 Find the sum of $\frac{2}{100} + \frac{20}{100} + \frac{2}{10}$.

Show your work.

Solution: ______________________________

6 Owen received $100 for his birthday. He wants to spend $\frac{2}{10}$ of his money on a video game. He wants to spend $\frac{55}{100}$ of his money on a skateboard. He wants to spend $\frac{3}{10}$ of his money on comic books. What fraction of his birthday money does Owen want to spend? Does he have enough money? Explain.

Show your work.

Solution: ______________________________

____

____

Dear Family,

This week your child is learning about relating decimals and fractions.

Tenths and hundredths can be written as decimal fractions.

You can use models to show the fraction $\frac{48}{100}$ as the decimal 0.48.

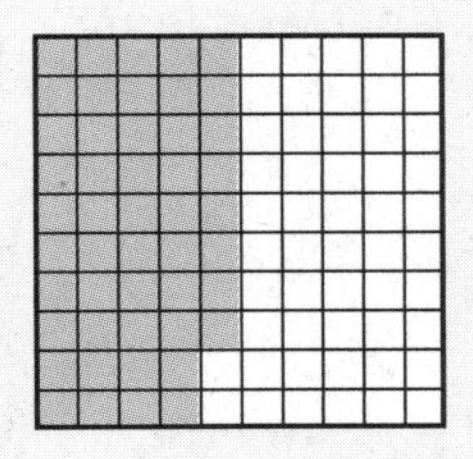

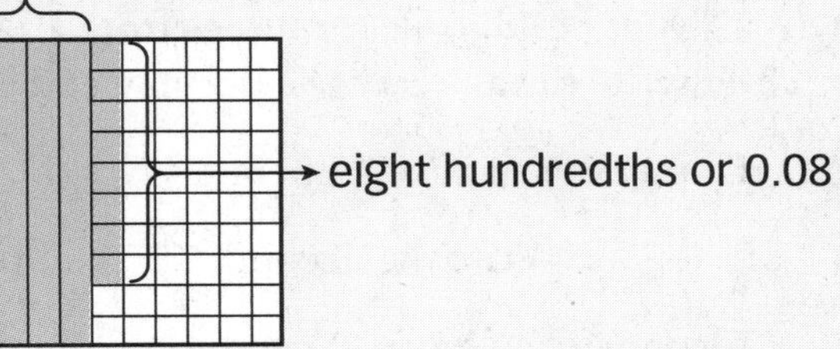

48 hundredths (0.48) is 4 tenths (0.4) and 8 hundredths (0.08).

To write the mixed number $2\frac{48}{100}$ as a decimal, use a place-value chart.

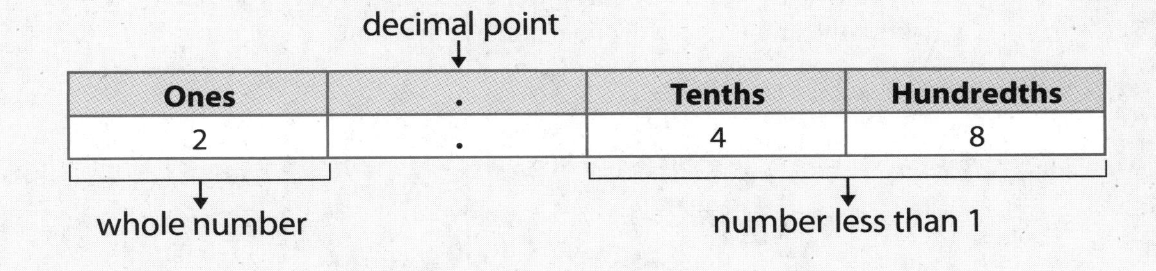

Ones	.	Tenths	Hundredths
2	.	4	8

Your child is learning to read the decimal 2.48:

1. Say the whole number part, if there is one. *two*
2. Say *and* for the decimal point. *and*
3. Read the rest of the digits as a whole number. *forty-eight*
4. Say the place-value name of the last digit. *hundredths*

Say: *two and forty-eight hundredths.*

Invite your child to share what he or she knows about relating decimals and fractions by doing the following activity together.

Relate Decimals and Fractions Activity

Do an activity with your child to relate decimals and fractions. You can use money to relate decimals and fractions because money is counted in tenths and hundredths. There are 100 pennies in 1 dollar, so one penny is 0.01, or $\frac{1}{100}$ of a dollar. There are 10 dimes in 1 dollar, so one dime is 0.1 (or 0.10), or $\frac{1}{10}$ of a dollar.

- With your child, collect pennies from around the house. Have your child write the amount as a decimal and as a fraction.

  Example: You have 23 pennies.

  Write the decimal 0.23 and the fraction $\frac{23}{100}$.

  Example: You have 30 pennies. Write the decimal 0.30 and the fraction $\frac{30}{100}$. Challenge your child to write the equivalent tenths decimal and fraction: 0.3 and $\frac{3}{10}$.

- Next, collect dimes from around the house and have your child write the amount as a decimal and as a fraction.

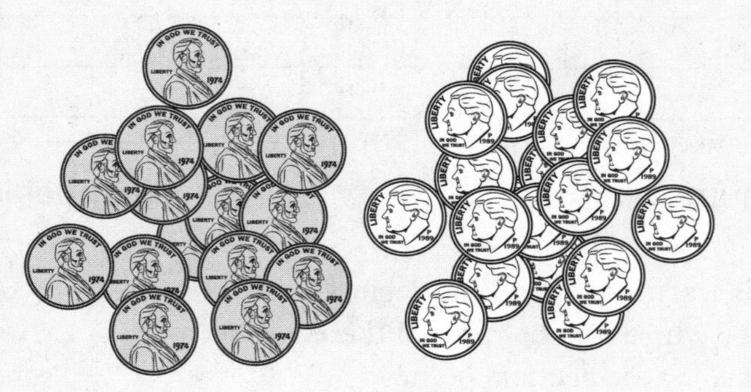

Look for other real-life opportunities to relate decimals and fractions with your child.

Relate Decimals and Fractions

Name: ____________________

Prerequisite: Find Equivalent Fractions

Study the example showing how to identify equivalent fractions with denominators of 10 and 100. Then solve problems 1–5.

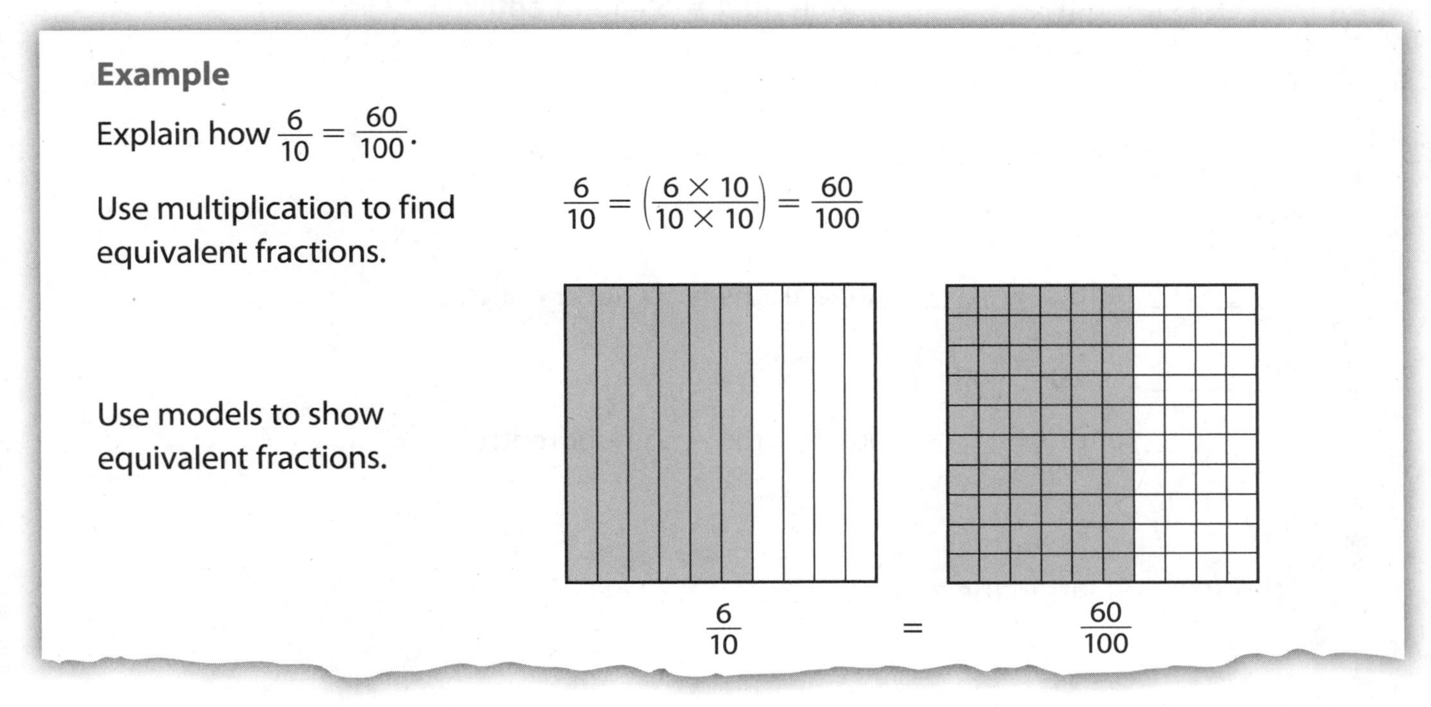

Example

Explain how $\frac{6}{10} = \frac{60}{100}$.

Use multiplication to find equivalent fractions.

$$\frac{6}{10} = \left(\frac{6 \times 10}{10 \times 10}\right) = \frac{60}{100}$$

Use models to show equivalent fractions.

$$\frac{6}{10} = \frac{60}{100}$$

1 Write the fractions that the models below show.

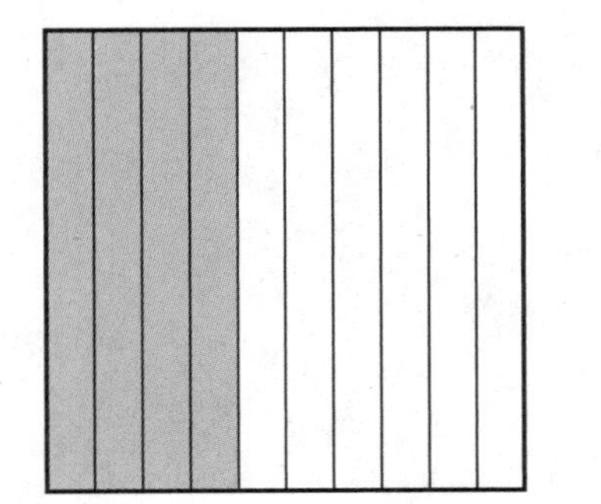

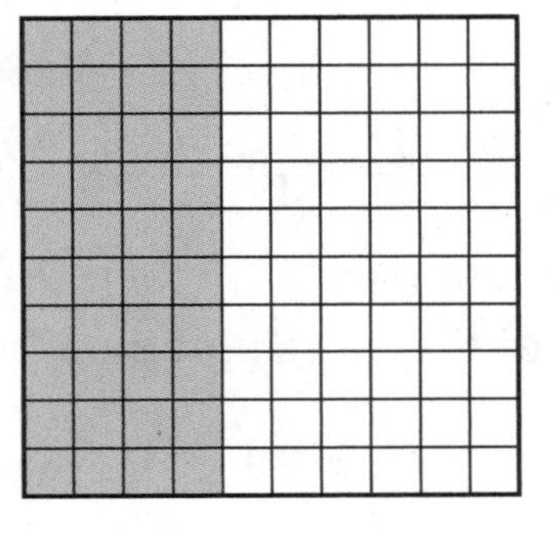

______ ______

2 Look at problem 1. Use multiplication to find the equivalent fractions.

____

Vocabulary

equivalent fractions two or more fractions that name the same part of a whole.

Solve.

3 Fill in the blanks with numbers and fractions to make true sentences.

a. ______ $+ \frac{15}{100} = \frac{55}{100}$

______ tenths + ______ hundredths = 55 hundredths.

b. ______ $+ \frac{4}{10} = \frac{55}{100}$

______ hundredths + ______ tenths = 55 hundredths.

c. ______ $+ \frac{5}{100} = \frac{55}{100}$

______ tenths + ______ hundredths = 55 hundredths.

d. ______ $+ \frac{25}{100} = \frac{55}{100}$

______ tenths + ______ hundredths = 55 hundredths.

Of the 100 students in the fourth grade, 70 students are girls.

4 Write a fraction in tenths and a fraction in hundredths to tell what fraction of the fourth-grade students are girls.

____

5 Write a fraction in tenths and a fraction in hundredths to tell what fraction of the fourth-grade students are boys.

____

Name: ____________________

Name the Same Amount

Study the example showing ways to name the same amount as a fraction and a decimal. Then solve problems 1–7.

Example

How do you write decimals equivalent to $\frac{7}{10}$ and $\frac{70}{100}$?

The model shows $\frac{7}{10}$.

The model shows $\frac{70}{100}$.

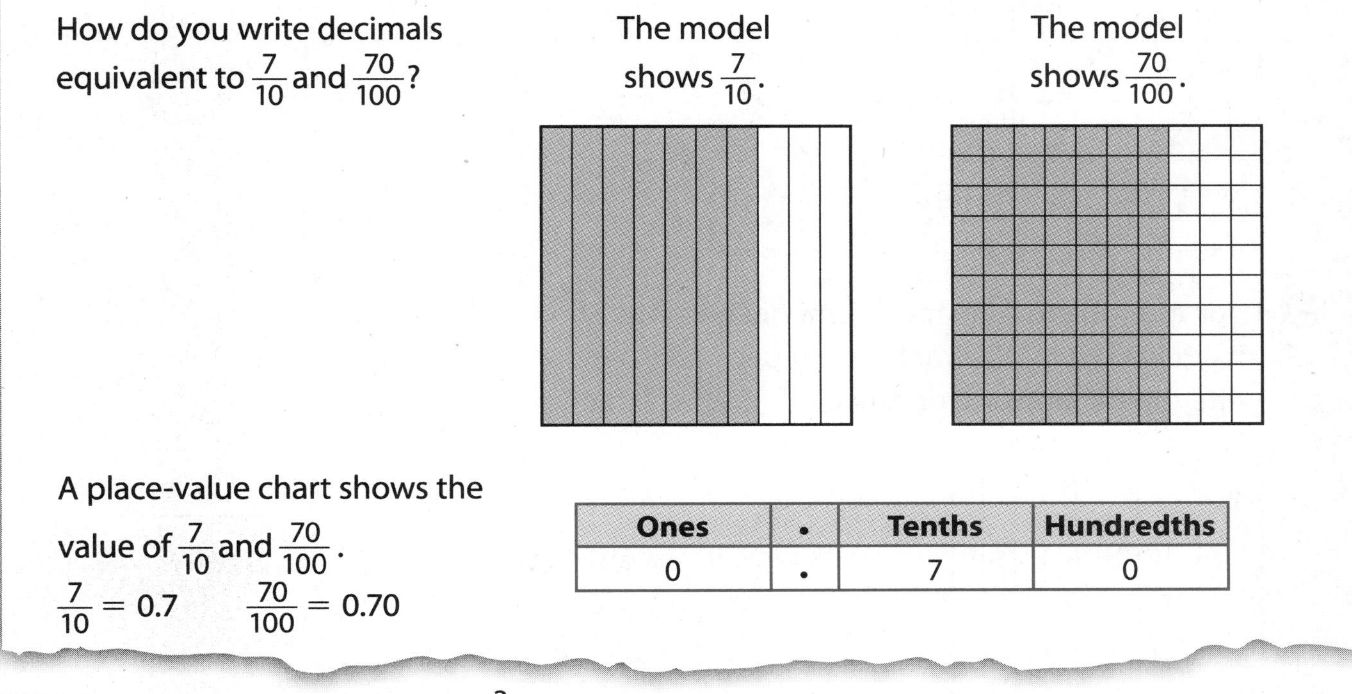

A place-value chart shows the value of $\frac{7}{10}$ and $\frac{70}{100}$.

$\frac{7}{10} = 0.7$ $\frac{70}{100} = 0.70$

Ones	•	Tenths	Hundredths
0	•	7	0

1 What decimal is equivalent to $\frac{3}{10}$?

Fill in the place-value chart to show the decimal.

Ones	•	Tenths
	•	

2 What decimal is equivalent to $\frac{55}{100}$?

Fill in the place-value chart to show the decimal.

Ones	•	Tenths	Hundredths
	•		

3 Write a decimal equivalent to $\frac{75}{100}$. __________

Vocabulary

decimal fraction (or decimal) a number containing a decimal point that separates a whole from fractional place values, such as tenths and hundredths.

0.7 and 0.70 are decimals.

Solve.

4 What decimal is equivalent to $\frac{80}{100}$? Shade the model below to show the fraction and the decimal. Then write the decimal.

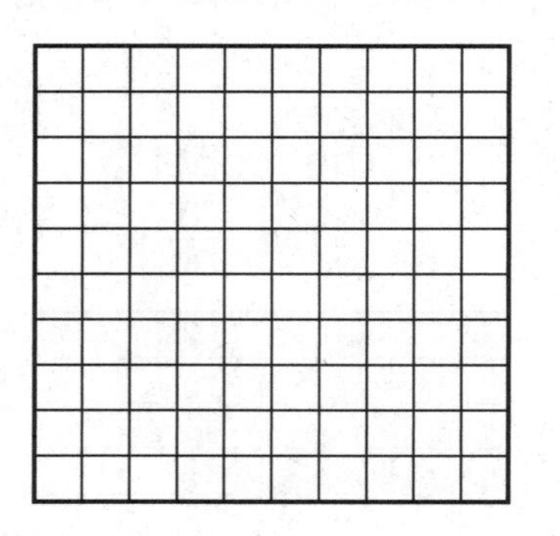

$\frac{80}{100}$ = ______

5 Look at problem 4. Shade the model below to show an equivalent tenths fraction and decimal. Then write the fraction and decimal.

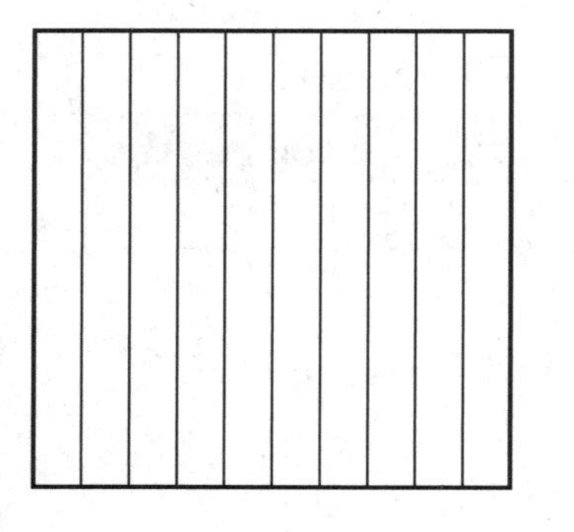

______ = ______

6 Use what you know about equivalent fractions to explain why 0.8 and 0.80 are equivalent.

____

____

7 Find the sum of $\frac{80}{100}$ and $\frac{20}{100}$. Then use what you know about equivalent fractions to explain why $0.8 + 0.2 = 1$.

____

____

____

Name: ______________________________

Write a Decimal as an Equivalent Fraction

Study the example problem showing how to write a decimal as an equivalent fraction. Then solve problems 1–8.

Example

Alanna has an assortment of books in her bookcase. 0.09 of her books are comic books. What fraction of the books are comic books?

Decimal: 0.09

Words: 9 hundredths

Fraction: $\frac{9}{100}$

$\frac{9}{100}$ of the books are comic books.

Ones	•	Tenths	Hundredths
0	•	0	9

1 Shade the model below to show 0.34.

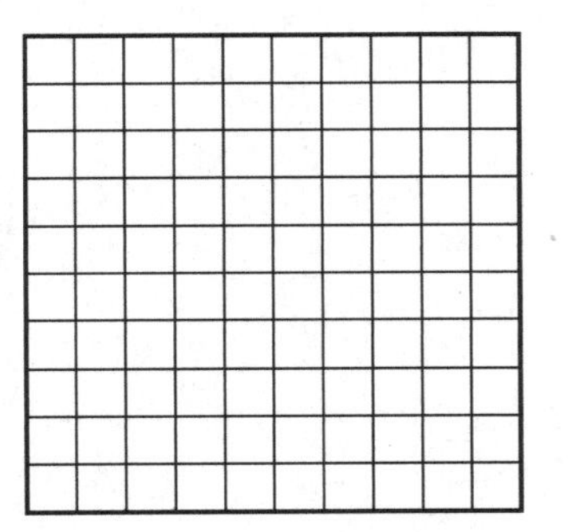

2 Show 0.34 in a place-value chart.

Ones	•	Tenths	Hundredths
	•		

3 Write 0.34 in words. ______________________________

4 Write 0.34 as a fraction. ____________________

Solve.

5 Tell whether each number sentence is *True* or *False*.

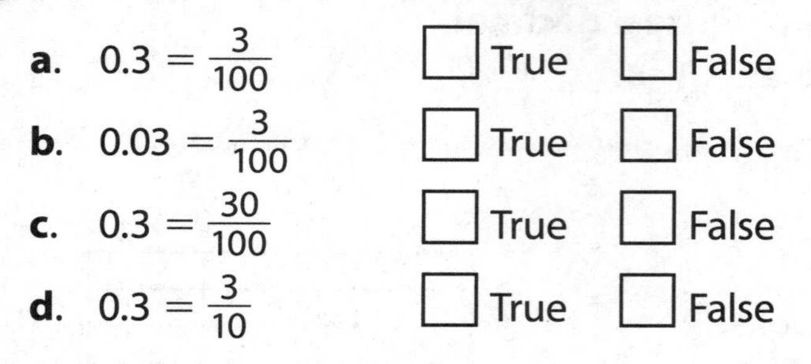

a. $0.3 = \frac{3}{100}$ ☐ True ☐ False

b. $0.03 = \frac{3}{100}$ ☐ True ☐ False

c. $0.3 = \frac{30}{100}$ ☐ True ☐ False

d. $0.3 = \frac{3}{10}$ ☐ True ☐ False

6 Write two equivalent fractions to 0.3.

____

7 Which of the following names the same number as 0.62? Circle the letter for all that apply.

A sixty-two hundredths

B six tenths and 2 hundredths

C $\frac{62}{10}$

D $\frac{62}{100}$

8 The number line below shows 1 whole divided into tenths. Write numbers in the boxes to label the missing fractions and decimal. Explain how you know what numbers to write.

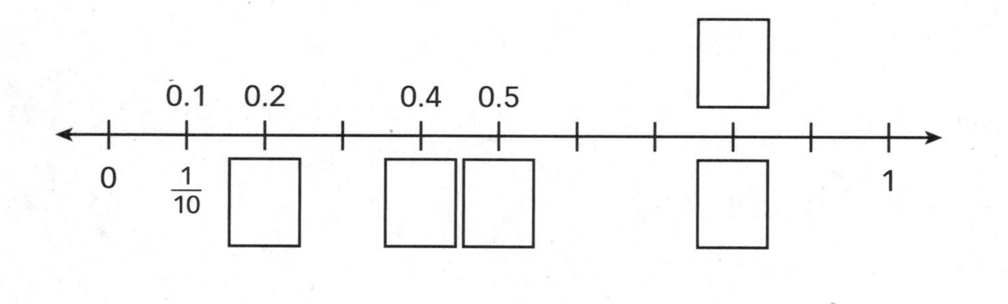

____

____

____

____

Name: ____________________

Relate Decimals and Fractions

Solve the problems.

1 What is 0.5 written as a fraction?
Circle the letter for all that apply.

How can you say the decimal in words?

A $\frac{5}{100}$

B $\frac{5}{10}$

C $\frac{50}{100}$

D $\frac{50}{10}$

2 Rita correctly answered 9 questions out of 10 on a test. What fraction of the test questions did Rita answer incorrectly?

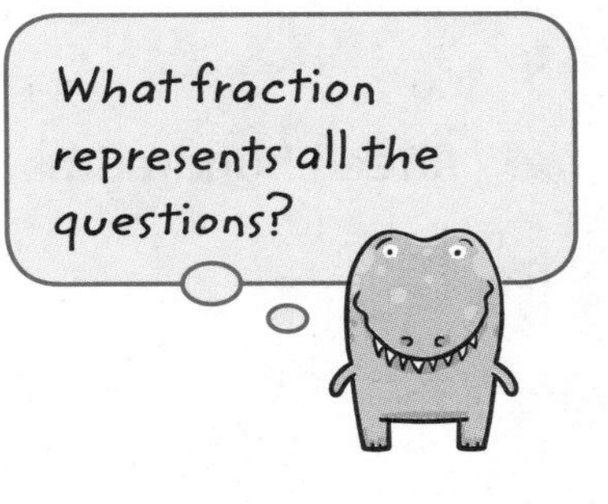

A $\frac{9}{10}$

B $\frac{9}{100}$

C $\frac{1}{10}$

D $\frac{1}{100}$

Patrick chose **A** as the correct answer. How did he get that answer?

____

____

____

____

____

____

Solve.

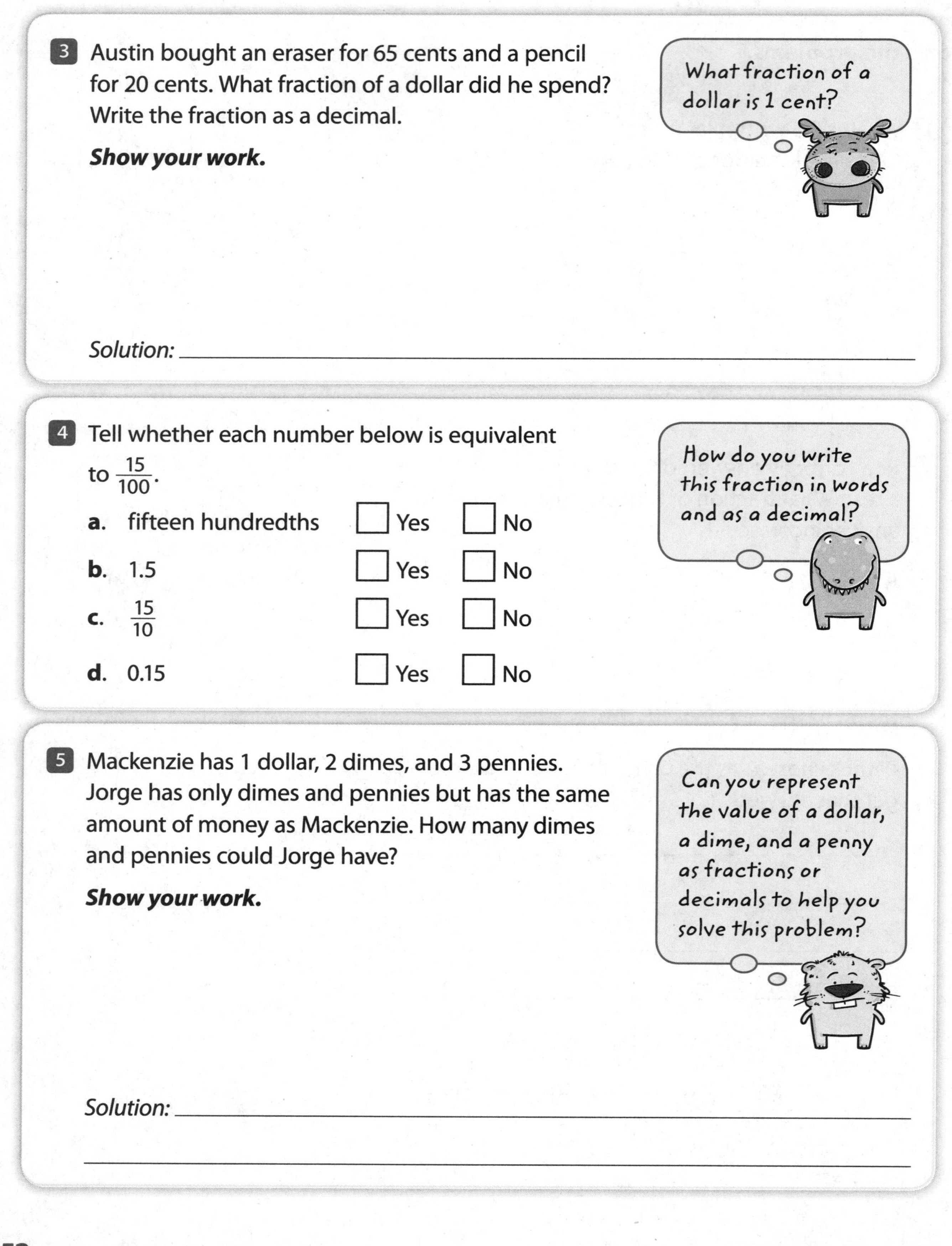

3 Austin bought an eraser for 65 cents and a pencil for 20 cents. What fraction of a dollar did he spend? Write the fraction as a decimal.

Show your work.

Solution: ______________________________

4 Tell whether each number below is equivalent to $\frac{15}{100}$.

a. fifteen hundredths ☐ Yes ☐ No

b. 1.5 ☐ Yes ☐ No

c. $\frac{15}{10}$ ☐ Yes ☐ No

d. 0.15 ☐ Yes ☐ No

5 Mackenzie has 1 dollar, 2 dimes, and 3 pennies. Jorge has only dimes and pennies but has the same amount of money as Mackenzie. How many dimes and pennies could Jorge have?

Show your work.

Solution: ______________________________

____

Dear Family,

This week your child is learning to compare decimals.

A model can help your child compare decimals when one decimal is in tenths and the other decimal is in hundredths.

The models show 0.75 and 0.8.

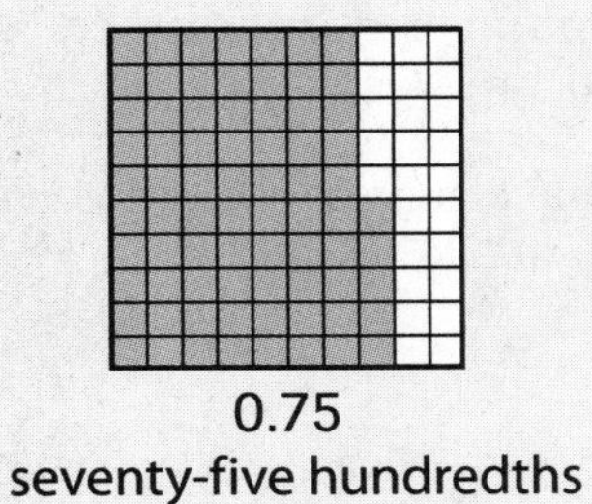

0.75
seventy-five hundredths

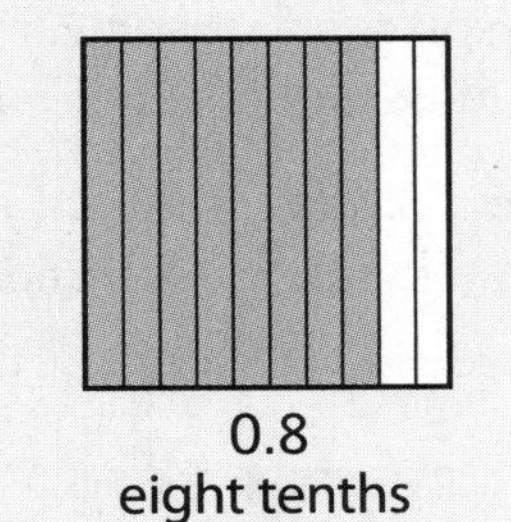

0.8
eight tenths

A greater area is shaded for 0.8 than for 0.75, so 0.8 is greater than 0.75.

Your child can also use a place-value chart to compare decimals in tenths and hundredths.

8 tenths equals 80 hundredths. $\frac{8}{10} = \frac{80}{100}$

Ones	.	Tenths	Hundredths
0	.	7	5
0	.	8	0

The place-value chart shows that eighty hundredths, or eight tenths, is greater than seventy-five hundredths. Compare the digits in the tenths place: $8 > 7$.

$0.80 > 0.75$ and $0.8 > 0.75$

Invite your child to share what he or she knows about comparing decimals by doing the following activity together.

Compare Decimals Activity

Do an activity with your child to compare decimals.

Materials: fliers for grocery, drug, or hardware stores (optional)

- Look for items around the house or look through the fliers to find at least 6 decimal numbers. Make a list of the numbers as you find them; do not include the units.

    Example: You have a box of crackers that is 6.75 ounces.

- Take turns. One person marks two decimal numbers for the other person to compare. Make and use place-value charts if needed.
- Challenge! Of all the decimal numbers you have compared, can you tell which is the greatest of all? Talk about how you know.

Look for other real-life opportunities to compare decimals with your child.

Compare Decimals

Name: ______________________

Prerequisite: Compare Fractions

Study the example showing ways to compare fractions. Then solve problems 1–6.

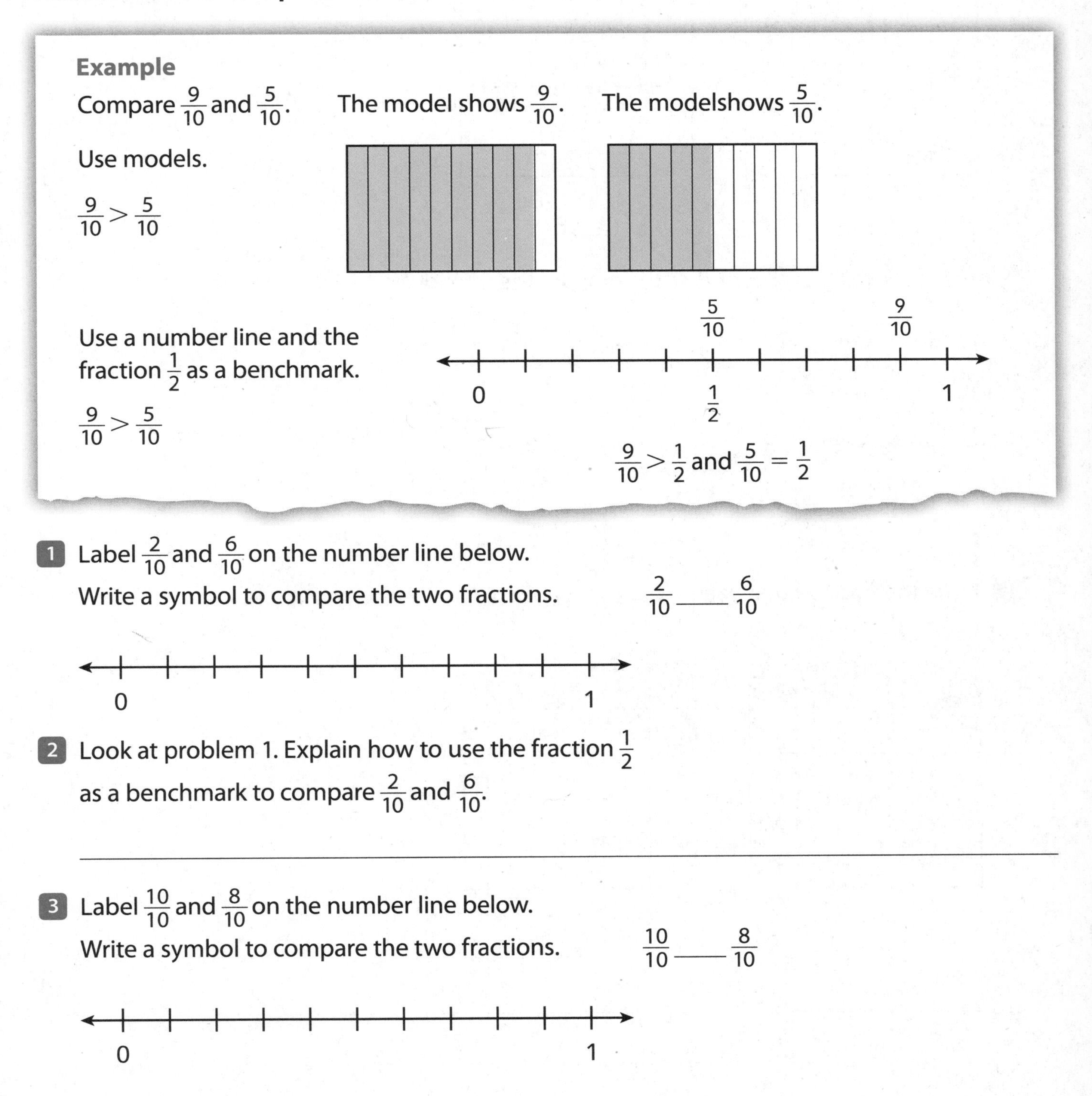

Example

Compare $\frac{9}{10}$ and $\frac{5}{10}$.

Use models.

$\frac{9}{10} > \frac{5}{10}$

The model shows $\frac{9}{10}$.

The modelshows $\frac{5}{10}$.

Use a number line and the fraction $\frac{1}{2}$ as a benchmark.

$\frac{9}{10} > \frac{5}{10}$

$\frac{9}{10} > \frac{1}{2}$ and $\frac{5}{10} = \frac{1}{2}$

1 Label $\frac{2}{10}$ and $\frac{6}{10}$ on the number line below.
Write a symbol to compare the two fractions.

$\frac{2}{10}$ ____ $\frac{6}{10}$

2 Look at problem 1. Explain how to use the fraction $\frac{1}{2}$ as a benchmark to compare $\frac{2}{10}$ and $\frac{6}{10}$.

____

3 Label $\frac{10}{10}$ and $\frac{8}{10}$ on the number line below.
Write a symbol to compare the two fractions.

$\frac{10}{10}$ ____ $\frac{8}{10}$

Solve.

4 Shade and label the models below to show $\frac{3}{10}$ and $\frac{3}{100}$.

Write a symbol to compare the fractions. $\frac{3}{10}$ _____ $\frac{3}{100}$

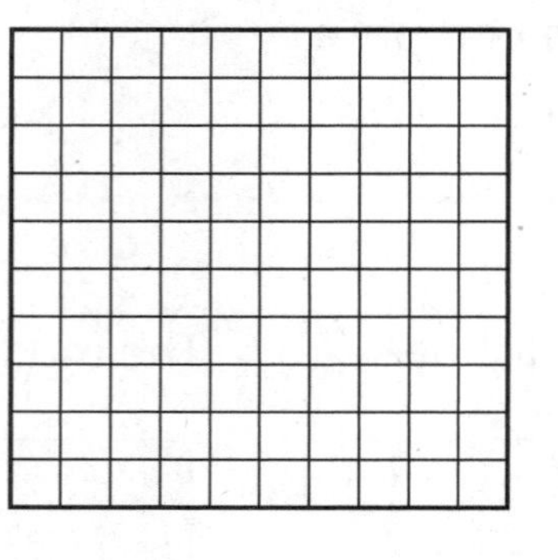

______ ______

5 Use the symbols $<$, $>$, and $=$ to compare the fractions.

a. $\frac{5}{10}$ _____ $\frac{50}{100}$

b. $\frac{4}{10}$ _____ $\frac{4}{100}$

c. $\frac{11}{10}$ _____ $\frac{12}{10}$

d. $\frac{62}{100}$ _____ $\frac{6}{10}$

e. $\frac{9}{100}$ _____ $\frac{9}{10}$

6 Write the fraction that each model shows. Explain which fraction is greater.

______ ______

____

____

Name: ____________________

Compare Hundredths Decimals

Study the example problem showing how to compare hundredths decimals to solve a problem. Then solve problems 1–7.

Example

Jacob bought an apple and a pear. The apple weighed 0.33 of a pound. The pear weighed 0.35 of a pound. Which piece of fruit weighed less?

Write equivalent fractions.
The denominators are the same.
Compare numerators. 33 < 35.

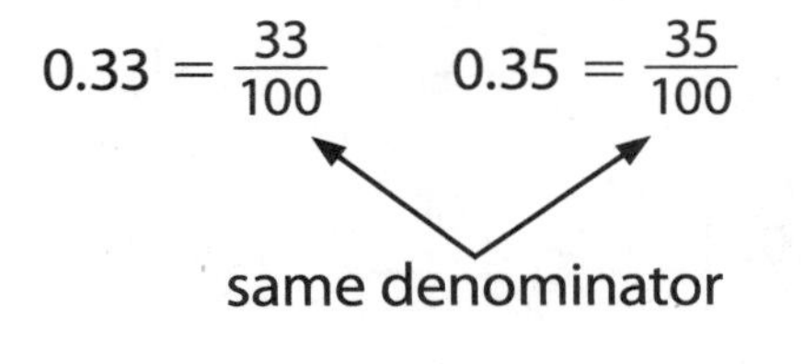

0.33 < 0.35
The apple weighed less than the pear.

1 Shade and label the models below to show 0.33 and 0.35.

________ ________

2 Explain how the models show which decimal is less. ____________________

____

3 Complete the place-value chart to show 0.33 and 0.35.

Ones	•	Tenths	Hundredths
	•		
	•		

4 Explain how the place-value chart shows which decimal is less. ____________________

____

Solve.

5 Use the digits in the tiles below to create decimals that make each inequality true.

a. $0.21 > 0.2\square$

b. $0.46 < 0.\square 6$

c. $0.99 < \square.00$

d. $0.7\square > 0.7\square$

6 Write the symbol ($>$, $<$, $=$) that makes each statement below true.

a. 0.85 ____ 0.82

b. 0.09 ____ 0.10

c. 0.45 ____ 0.54

d. 1.10 ____ 1.01

e. 0.30 ____ 0.3

7 Ryder bought 0.75 pound of turkey and 0.57 pound of cheese. Did he buy more turkey or cheese?

Show your work.

Solution: ______________________________

Name: ______________________

Compare Tenths and Hundredths Decimals

Study the example problem showing how to compare tenths and hundredths decimals. Then solve problems 1–6.

Example

Colin lives 0.6 mile from school and 0.65 mile from the park. Which place is closer to his home?

Write each decimal as an equivalent fraction. $0.6 = \frac{6}{10}$ $0.65 = \frac{65}{100}$

Write the tenths fraction as a hundredths fraction. $\frac{6}{10} = \frac{60}{100}$

Compare hundredths fractions. $\frac{60}{100} < \frac{65}{100}$

$0.6 < 0.65$

The school is closer to his home.

Lucas bought 0.6 pound of fish and 0.85 pound of shrimp to make a stew.

1 Shade the models below to compare 0.6 and 0.85.

2 Write a symbol to compare the decimals. 0.6 _____ 0.85

3 Did Lucas buy more fish or shrimp?
Use equivalent fractions to explain your answer.

____

____

Solve.

4 Compare 0.2 and 0.25 using >, =, or <. Use equivalent fractions to explain your answer.

5 Compare 0.09 and 0.1 using >, =, or <. Use a place-value chart to explain your answer.

Ones	•	Tenths	Hundredths
	•		
	•		

6 Write the decimals 1.00, 0.20, and 0.03 in the place-value chart below. Which number is the greatest? Which number is the least? Use equivalent fractions to explain.

Ones	•	Tenths	Hundredths
	•		
	•		
	•		

Name: ______________________

Compare Decimals

Solve the problems.

1 Which decimal is less than 0.35?

A 0.5
B 0.29
C 0.36
D 0.53

Do you compare the tenths or hundredths place?

2 Which is the greatest—0.19, 1.00, 0.91, or 0.02?

A 0.02
B 0.19
C 0.91
D 1.00

Sadie chose **B** as the correct answer. How did she get that answer?

____

____

____

____

A place-value chart can help you compare decimals.

3 Classify each decimal below as less than half, equal to half, or greater than half, by writing each decimal in the correct column of the chart.

0.05 0.52 0.25 0.48 0.9 0.50 0.6 1.05

Less than Half	Equal to Half	Greater than Half

You can think about half as the benchmark fraction $\frac{1}{2}$ to help solve this problem.

Solve.

4 Milk costs \$0.50 and juice costs \$0.55. Which costs less, milk or juice?

Show your work.

Solution: ______________________________

5 Julie has 2 dollars to spend on lunch. A slice of pizza is \$2.25. A sandwich is \$2. A bowl of soup is \$1.95. What can Julie buy for lunch? Explain your answer.

Show your work.

Think of each price as a decimal. Then compare each price to the amount of money Julie has.

Solution: ______________________________

____

Unit 4 Game

Name: ____________________

Fraction Sums

What you need: Recording Sheet, two 1–6 number cubes

Directions

- Players each choose a denominator from the list on the Recording Sheet. Players write their numbers in the Denominator Choice column of the Recording Sheet.
- Player A rolls the number cubes and makes two fractions using the numbers rolled as the numerators along with the chosen denominator.
- Player A writes and solves an addition problem with the two fractions on the Recording Sheet.
- Player B takes a turn following the same steps as Player A.
- Players compare the two fraction sums. The player with the greater sum wins the round.
- In each round, players choose a denominator that they have not used yet. The player with more wins after 5 rounds wins the game.

Name: Maya

Fraction Sums Recording Sheet

Denominators		Denominators	
2 3 ~~4~~ 6 8		2 3 4 6 ~~8~~	
Maya		Isaac	
Player A Name		Player B Name	
Denominator Choice	Equation	Denominator Choice	Equation
1. 4	$\frac{3}{4} + \frac{4}{4} = \frac{7}{4}$	1. 8	$\frac{4}{8} + \frac{6}{8} = \frac{10}{8}$
2.		2.	

I chose fourths. $\frac{3}{4} + \frac{4}{4} = \frac{7}{4}$. That's the same as $\frac{14}{8}$. I win this round because $\frac{14}{8}$ is more than your sum of $\frac{10}{8}$.

Name: ____________________

Fraction Sums Recording Sheet

Denominators

2 3 4 6 8

Denominators

2 3 4 6 8

____

Player A Name

Denominator Choice	Equation
1. ________	____________
2. ________	____________
3. ________	____________
4. ________	____________
5. ________	____________

Final Score Player A [ ]

____

Player B Name

Denominator Choice	Equation
1. ________	____________
2. ________	____________
3. ________	____________
4. ________	____________
5. ________	____________

Final Score Player B [ ]

Unit 4 Practice

Name: ______________________

Fractions

In this unit you learned to:	Lesson
find equivalent fractions, for example: $\frac{2}{3} = \frac{4}{6}$.	13A
write whole numbers as fractions and write mixed numbers as improper fractions.	13B
compare fractions with unlike denominators, for example: $\frac{2}{5} > \frac{3}{10}$.	14
add and subtract fractions with like denominators; add and subtract mixed numbers, for example: $\frac{2}{6} + \frac{3}{6} = \frac{5}{6}$.	15, 16, 17
multiply a fraction by a whole number, for example, $3 \times \frac{1}{2} = \frac{3}{2}$.	18, 19
write a decimal as a fraction, for example: $0.4 = \frac{4}{10}$.	20, 21
compare decimals, for example: $0.65 < 0.7$.	22

Use these skills to solve problems 1–5.

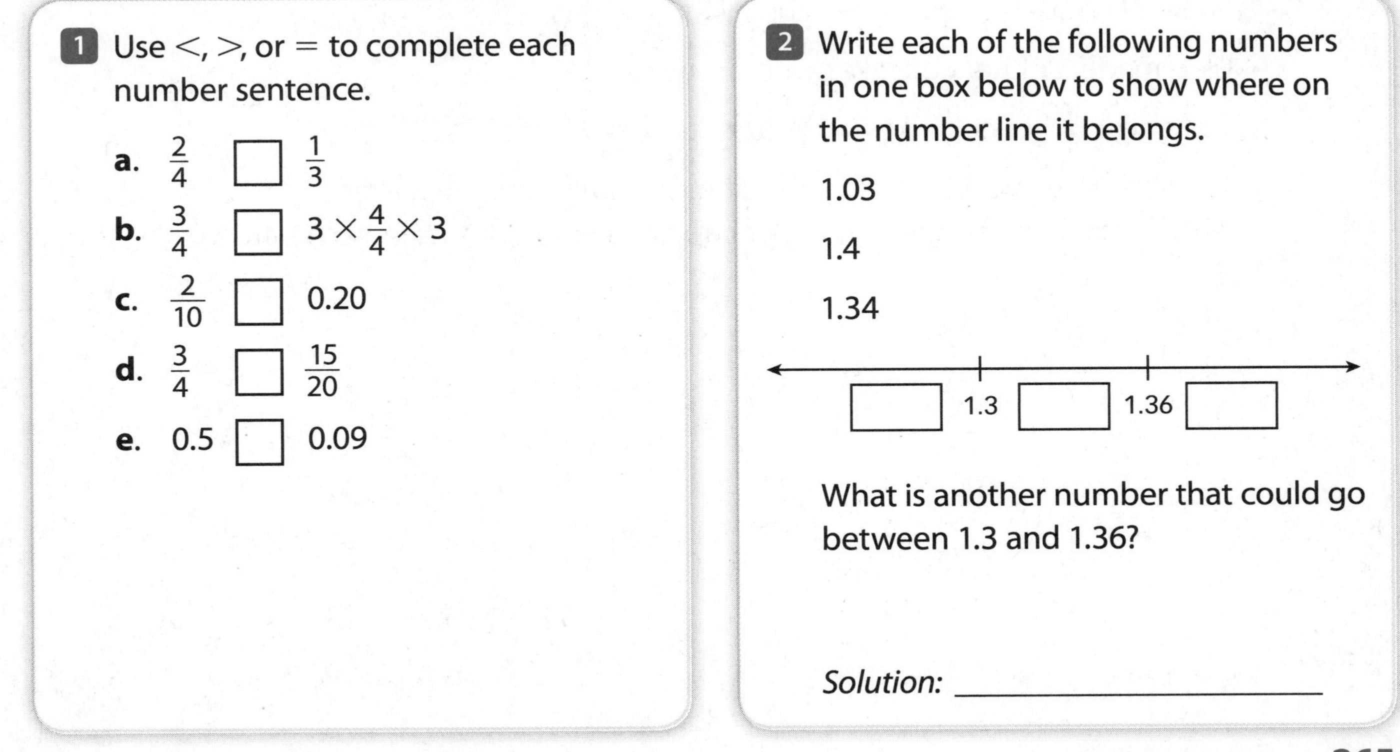

1 Use $<$, $>$, or $=$ to complete each number sentence.

a. $\frac{2}{4}$ ☐ $\frac{1}{3}$

b. $\frac{3}{4}$ ☐ $3 \times \frac{4}{4} \times 3$

c. $\frac{2}{10}$ ☐ 0.20

d. $\frac{3}{4}$ ☐ $\frac{15}{20}$

e. 0.5 ☐ 0.09

2 Write each of the following numbers in one box below to show where on the number line it belongs.

1.03

1.4

1.34

What is another number that could go between 1.3 and 1.36?

Solution: ______________________

Solve.

3 Diego wants to ride a bike path that is 10 miles long. He bikes $3\frac{3}{10}$ miles and stops for a rest. Then he goes another $3\frac{5}{10}$ miles and stops for lunch. How many more miles does Diego have to ride? Write your answer as a decimal.

Show your work.

Solution: ______________________

4 Alicia and Gwen need to find 12 different leaves for a science project. Alicia has found $\frac{2}{3}$ of her leaves. Gwen has found $\frac{3}{4}$ of her leaves.

Who has collected more leaves? How do you know?

____

____

____

____

____

____

____

5 Cleo and Li both made a dozen cupcakes.

- Cleo made 3 of her cupcakes without nuts.
- Li made 4 of her cupcakes without nuts.

In the space below, draw pictures of the two batches of cupcakes.
Use numbers to show the fraction of cupcakes without nuts in each batch.

Unit 4 Performance Task

Name: ______________________

Answer the questions and show all your work on separate paper.

A grocery store sells fruit salad made with pineapples, strawberries, raspberries, blueberries, blackberries, and grapes. The store sells three different kinds of salad:

The Hawaiian: More than $\frac{1}{2}$ of the salad is made of pineapple. The rest is made of grapes and blueberries.

The Red Rose: Less than $\frac{1}{2}$ of the salad is made of red grapes. The rest is made of strawberries and raspberries.

The Berry Basket: The salad has equal parts of strawberries, blueberries, raspberries, and blackberries.

Make an ingredient list for each of the salads. Write a fraction for the fruits that are included in each salad. Explain why your lists fit the description of each salad.

Checklist

Did you . . .

- ☐ meet the given conditions?
- ☐ check your work?
- ☐ reread your explanation to see if it makes sense?

The Hawaiian	The Red Rose	The Berry Basket
$\frac{\square}{8}$ ________	$\frac{\square}{8}$ ________	$\frac{\square}{8}$ ________
$\frac{\square}{8}$ ________	$\frac{\square}{8}$ ________	$\frac{\square}{8}$ ________
$\frac{\square}{8}$ ________	$\frac{\square}{8}$ ________	$\frac{\square}{8}$ ________
		$\frac{\square}{8}$ ________

Reflect on the Process Standards

After you complete the task, choose one of the following questions to answer.

 **Make Sense of Problems** How did you know which fraction to find first for The Hawaiian and The Red Rose salads?

2 **Use Structure** How did you decide which fractions to use after you found the first fraction?

Performance Task Tips

Word Bank Here are some words that you might use in your answer.

more	fraction	add
greater than	whole	equal
less	part	equivalent
less than	sum	

Models Here are some models that you might use to find the solution.

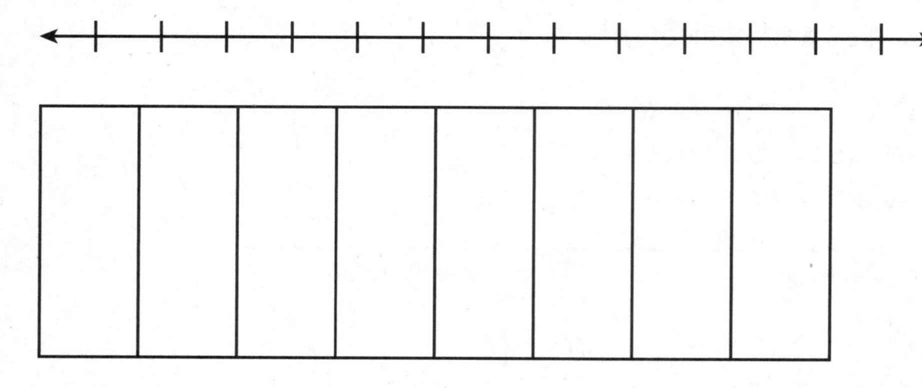

Sentence Starters Here are some sentence starters that might help you write an explanation.

The fractions ______________________________

An equivalent fraction ______________________________

______________ is greater than ______________

______________ is less than ______________

Unit 4 Vocabulary

Name: ___________________

My Examples

fraction

a number that names part of a whole

numerator

the number above the line in a fraction; it tells how many equal parts are described

denominator

the number below the line in a fraction; it tells how many equal parts are in a whole

equivalent fractions

two or more fractions that name the same part of a whole

My Examples

mixed number

a number with a whole number part and a fractional part

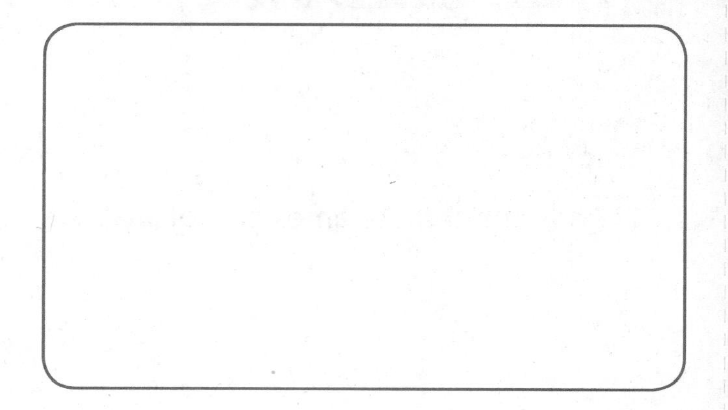

decimal fraction (or decimal)

a number containing a decimal point that separates a whole from fractional place values, such as tenths and hundredths

compare

to decide if one number is greater than, less than, or equal to another number

greater than (>)

a comparison that says one number has greater value than another number

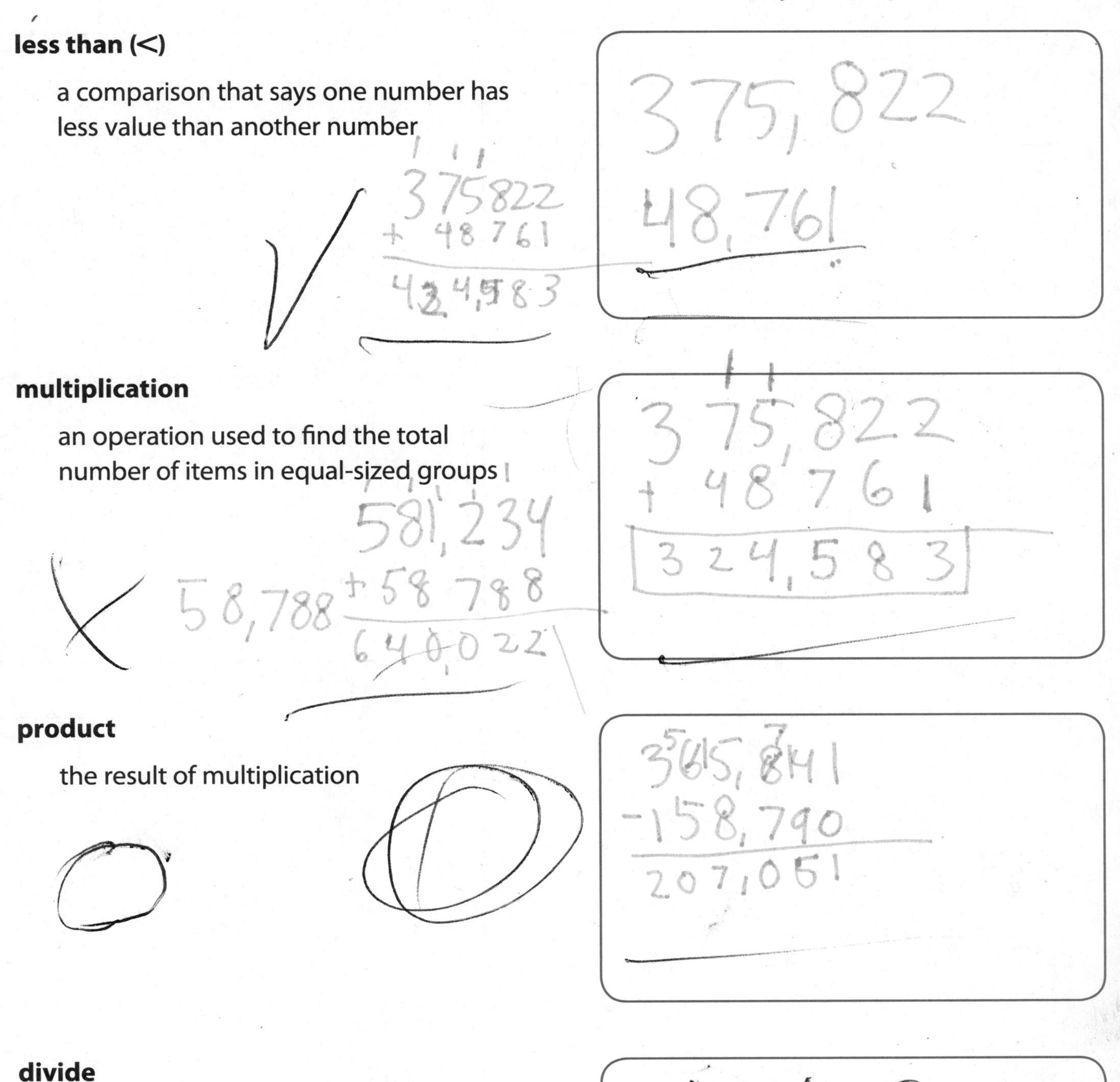

My Examples

less than (<)

a comparison that says one number has less value than another number

multiplication

an operation used to find the total number of items in equal-sized groups

product

the result of multiplication

divide

to separate an amount into equal groups and find the number in each group or the number of groups

My Words
My Examples

Dear Family,

This week your child is learning to convert measurements.

When you convert from a larger unit, such as a pound, to a smaller unit, such as an ounce, you use multiplication.

Knowing that there are 16 ounces in one pound, you multiply by 16 to find the number of ounces in any number of pounds. For example, to find how many ounces are in 12 pounds, you multiply 12 by 16.

When your child is converting larger units to smaller units, he or she is not only becoming more familiar with the relative sizes of units, but is also getting good practice with multiplication!

Sometimes it's convenient to use a table to convert measurements. The diagram below shows that each pound is the same as 16 ounces.

12 pounds (lb)

1 lb	1 lb	1 lb	1 lb	1 lb	1 lb	1 lb	1 lb	1 lb	1 lb	1 lb	1 lb
16 oz	16 oz	16 oz	16 oz	16 oz	16 oz	16 oz	16 oz	16 oz	16 oz	16 oz	16 oz

192 ounces (oz)

The table below shows exactly how many ounces are in any number of pounds.

Pounds (lb)	1	2	3	4	5	6	7	8	9	10	11	12
Ounces (oz)	16	32	48	64	80	96	112	128	144	160	176	192

When your child writes $p \times 16$ to tell how many ounces are in p pounds, he or she is applying the skill of writing an expression. The expression gives the formula for converting any number of pounds to ounces.

Invite your child to share what he or she knows about converting measurements by doing the following activity together.

Converting Measurements Activity

Do an activity with your child to convert measurements.

Materials: ruler or yardstick

Measure the stride of your child. Put a mark at your child's toe to create a "starting point."

- Ask your child to take a long step and put another mark at the heel of the foot taking the step.
- Measure the distance *in feet* between the marks.
- Now, find the measure of your child's stride in inches by converting feet to inches. There are 12 inches in one foot.
- Talk with your child about different ways you could convert the measurement, such as using a bar model or a table, drawing a picture, or writing an expression. How could you use a different way to convert the measurement?
- Next, measure the stride of another family member. First find the measure in feet and then convert it to inches. Compare the length of this stride to the length of your child's stride. Who has a longer stride? Who has a shorter stride?

Convert Measurements

Name: ______________________________

Prerequisite: Multiply with Measurements

Study the example showing how to use multiplication to solve a measurement problem. Then solve problems 1–5.

Example

Kian filled 5 pitchers with water. Each pitcher holds 2 liters. How many liters of water did Kian use to fill the pitchers?

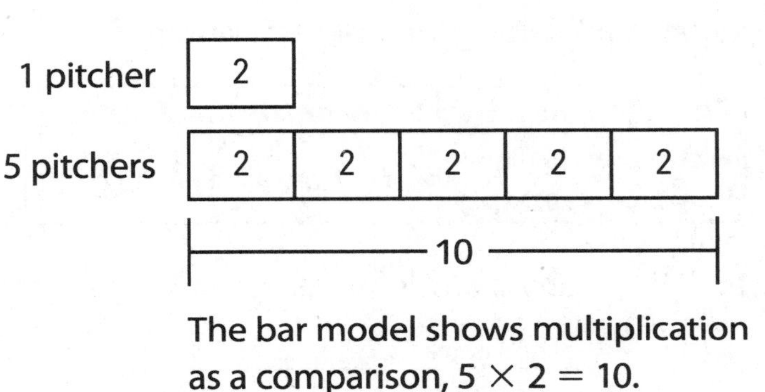

The picture shows that $2 + 2 + 2 + 2 + 2 = 10$.

Kian used 10 liters of water.

The bar model shows multiplication as a comparison, $5 \times 2 = 10$.

1 Yvonne's house has 4 bedrooms. It takes 1 gallon of paint to paint each bedroom. How many gallons of paint are needed to paint all 4 bedrooms? Show how to add or multiply to find the answer.

____

2 One granola bar has 5 grams of protein. A package has 6 granola bars. How many grams of protein are in a package? Draw a bar model to show how to find the answer.

Solution: ______________________________

Solve.

3 Miranda's family brought 3 large coolers full of lemonade to the family picnic. Each cooler contains 8 liters of lemonade. How much lemonade did the family bring to the picnic?

Show your work.

Solution: The family brought ____________ of lemonade.

4 The table below shows the number of grams of sugar in a 1-cup serving of each kind of fruit.

Fruit	Strawberries	Apples	Bananas
Grams of sugar in a 1-cup serving	7 g	13 g	18 g

a. How many grams of sugar are in 3 cups of strawberries?

____

b. How many grams of sugar are in 2 cups of apples?

____

c. Are there more grams of sugar in 3 cups of strawberries or 2 cups of apples? Explain.

____

____

5 Look at the table in problem 4. Madeleine made a strawberry-banana smoothie to share with her friends. She put 4 cups of strawberries and 2 cups of bananas in a blender. How many total grams of sugar are in the smoothie?

Show your work.

Solution: ______________________________

Name: ____________________

Convert Units of Weight and Mass

Study the example showing how to convert from a larger unit to a smaller unit of weight and mass. Then solve problems 1–7.

Example

Eleanor bought a 3-pound watermelon and 32 ounces of strawberries. How much more does the watermelon weigh than the strawberries?

1 pound (lb) = 16 ounces (oz)

Write an expression to convert pounds to ounces. Let p stand for the number of pounds.

$p \times 16$

Find the weight of the watermelon in ounces. The watermelon weighs 48 ounces.

Substitute 3 for p.
$3 \times 16 = 48$

$48 - 32 = 16$

The watermelon weighs 16 ounces more than the strawberries.

1 John has a watermelon with a mass of 3 kilograms. Complete the bar model. Then write the mass of the watermelon in grams.

3 kilograms (kg)

1 kg	1 kg	
1,000 g	1,000 g	

________ grams (g)

2 Write an expression that shows how to convert kilograms to grams. Use K to stand for the number of kilograms.

____

3 Convert the units of mass.

2 kg = ________ g   4 kg = ________ g

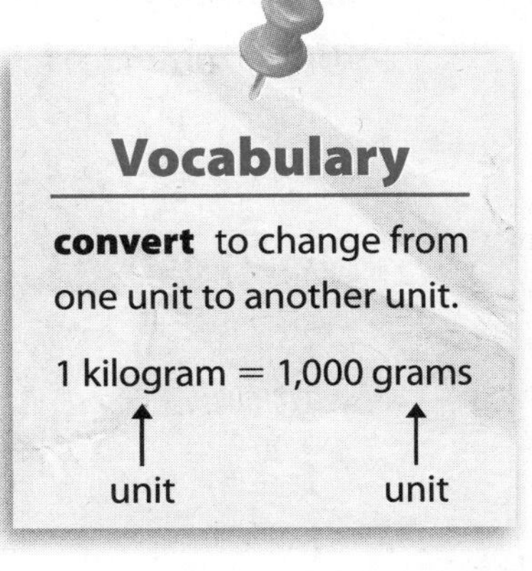

Solve.

4 Complete the table to convert from a larger unit to a smaller unit of weight.

Pounds (lb)	1	2	3	4	5	6	7
Ounces (oz)	16		48				112

5 Neil brought 2 pounds of grapes for fruit salad at the class picnic. There are 8 ounces of grapes left. How many ounces of grapes were used? Look at the table in problem 4 to help you answer the question.

Show your work.

Solution: ______________________________

6 Choose *Yes* or *No* to tell whether the given weight is equal to 6 pounds.

a. 22 ounces ☐ Yes ☐ No

b. 96 ounces ☐ Yes ☐ No

c. 4 pounds, 32 ounces ☐ Yes ☐ No

d. 5 pounds, 16 ounces ☐ Yes ☐ No

7 An adult bottlenose dolphin has a mass of 200 kilograms. What is the mass of an adult bottlenose dolphin in grams?

1 kilogram = 1,000 grams

Show your work.

Solution: ______________________________

Name: ____________________

Convert Units of Liquid Volume

Study the example showing how to convert from a larger unit to a smaller unit of liquid volume. Then solve problems 1–7.

Example

Josie made 4 quarts of iced tea for a family picnic. Her sister made 14 cups of punch for the picnic. Who made a greater amount of beverages?

Use a table to convert quarts to cups.

Quarts	1	2	3	4	5
Cups	4	8	12	16	20

1 quart = 4 cups

Josie made 4 quarts, or 16 cups of iced tea.
$16 > 14$

Josie made a greater amount of beverages.

1 The soccer coach has a container that holds 5 liters of water. How many milliliters of water does the container hold?

Fill in the table to answer the question.

Liters (L)	1	2	3	4	5
Milliliters (mL)	1,000		3,000		

The container holds ____________________ of water.

2 Write an expression that shows how to convert liters to milliliters. Use *L* to stand for the number of liters.

____

3 Convert the units of liquid volume.

6 L = __________ mL $\frac{1}{2}$ L = __________ mL

Vocabulary

convert to change from one unit to another unit.

1 liter = 1,000 milliliters
↑ unit   ↑ unit

Solve.

4 Carla had 2 liters of juice to share. She and her 3 friends each drank an equal amount of the juice. How many milliliters of juice did each friend have?

1 liter = 1,000 milliliters

Show your work.

Solution: ______________________

5 Theo filled up a 3-liter watering can to water the garden. He has 750 milliliters of water left in the watering can. How many milliliters of water did Theo use?

Show your work.

Solution: ______________________

6 A small bottle contains 2 cups of juice. Do 5 small bottles of juice have a greater amount of juice than a 1-quart bottle of juice? Explain.

1 quart = 4 cups

____

____

____

____

7 Rachel has a 4-liter jug of water. She fills 3 small vases each with 900 mL of water. How much water did she use? How much water is left in the jug?

Show your work.

Solution: ______________________

Name: ______________________

Convert Measurements

Solve the problems.

1 How many weeks are in 2 years?

A 26 weeks

B 52 weeks

C 54 weeks

D 104 weeks

There are 52 weeks in a year.

2 How many cups of milk are in 8 quarts?

A 2 cups

B 12 cups

C 16 cups

D 32 cups

1 quart = 4 cups

Which is the larger unit, quarts or cups?

Jeff chose **A** as the correct answer. How did he get that answer?

____

____

____

3 Stacia buys 6 yards of ribbon to make a costume. She has 2 feet of ribbon left over. How many feet of ribbon did Stacia use to make the costume?

Show your work.

1 yard = 3 feet

You can write an equation to show the relationship between yards and feet.

Solution: ______________________

Solve.

4 Which of the following is equal to 2 days, 12 hours? Circle the letter for all that apply.

A 48 hours

B 60 hours

C 1 day, 36 hours

D 1 day, 24 hours

5 Jason is 5 foot 11 inches tall. Amy is 63 inches tall. Who is taller and by how much?

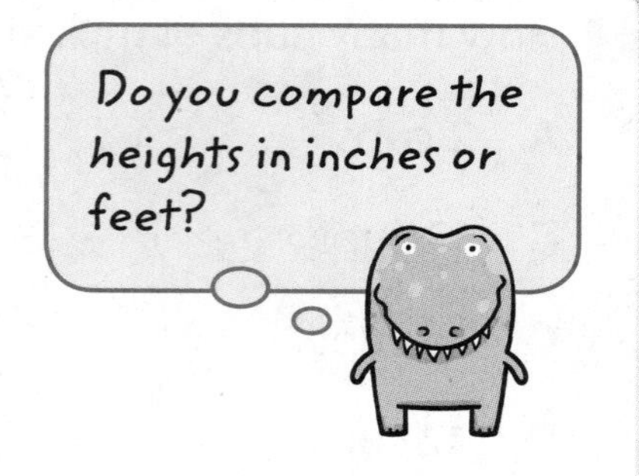

1 foot = 12 inches

Show your work.

Solution: ______________________________

6 How many 250 mL glasses can be filled with 2 L of water?

1 liter = 1,000 milliliters

Show your work.

Solution: ______________________________

Dear Family,

This week your child is learning about converting units of time and money.

Your child is learning different ways to solve multi-step problems converting larger units to smaller units for time and money. Here's a time problem your child might see.

> Penny has 2 hours to complete her chores. She spends 15 minutes putting away her clean clothes. She spends 45 minutes cleaning her closet. It takes her 40 minutes to clean the bathroom. How much time does Penny have left to give her dog a bath?

Since the problem has information in both minutes and hours, the first step is to convert the hours to minutes. There are 60 minutes in one hour, so multiply by 2 to convert 2 hours to minutes: $2 \times 60 = 120$.

Then, one way to solve the problem is to show the information on a number line.

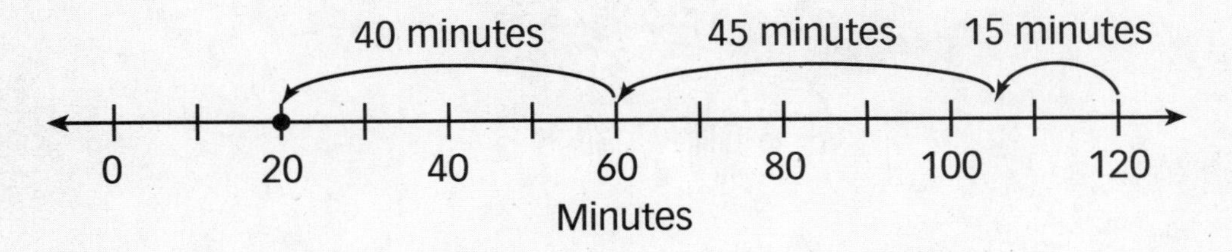

Only 20 minutes are left for the dog bath!

Other ways to solve a problem like this include writing an equation, such as $d = 120 - 15 - 45 - 40$, where d is the time left for the dog bath. Ask your child to compare the equation and the number line diagram to see how they are similar.

Invite your child to share what he or she knows about converting units to solve multi-step problems about time and money by doing the following activity together.

Converting Time and Money Activity

Do an activity with your child to convert units of time and money.

Make up multi-step problems about time and money that might occur in everyday life. Here are some examples you might use:

- Pete bought 4 rolls of tape and 2 packages of markers for his project. The tape cost $0.75 a roll, and the markers cost $1.25 for each package. Pete gave the clerk a $10 bill. How much change did Pete receive? ($4.50)
- Marta wanted to spend one hour gardening. She spent 30 minutes planting flowers. Then she spent 10 minutes watering the flowers and 15 minutes pruning roses. Did Marta spend more or less time than she wanted to spend gardening? (She spent less time. There are 60 minutes in an hour and she spent 55 minutes in all.)

- Talk with your child about how to solve the problem.
- Ask your child if he or she could solve the problem another way. (Ways to solve the problem include using a bar model, a number line, a picture, or an equation.)

Look for other real-life opportunities to practice converting units of time and money with your child.

Time and Money

Name: ____________________

Prerequisite: Solve Problems About Money and Time

Study the example showing how to solve a word problem about money. Then solve problems 1–5.

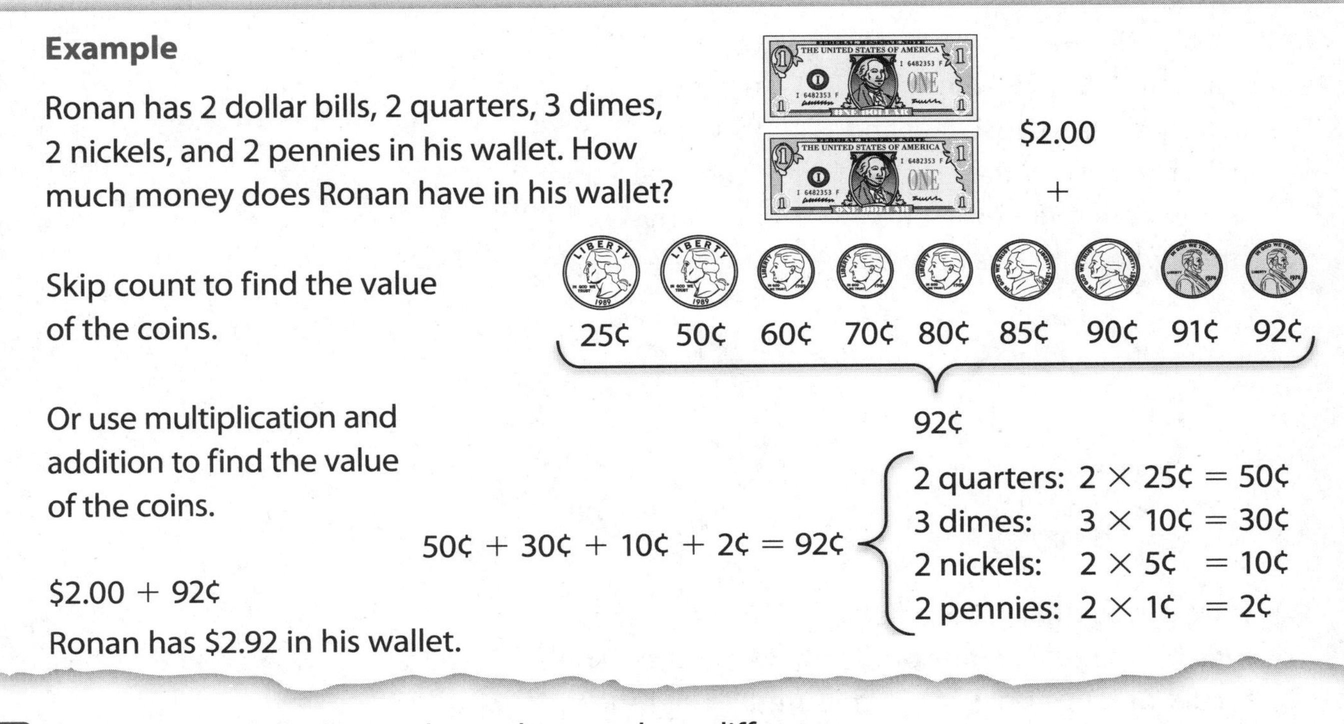

Example

Ronan has 2 dollar bills, 2 quarters, 3 dimes, 2 nickels, and 2 pennies in his wallet. How much money does Ronan have in his wallet?

$2.00 +

Skip count to find the value of the coins.

25¢ 50¢ 60¢ 70¢ 80¢ 85¢ 90¢ 91¢ 92¢

92¢

Or use multiplication and addition to find the value of the coins.

2 quarters: 2 × 25¢ = 50¢
3 dimes: 3 × 10¢ = 30¢
2 nickels: 2 × 5¢ = 10¢
2 pennies: 2 × 1¢ = 2¢

50¢ + 30¢ + 10¢ + 2¢ = 92¢

$2.00 + 92¢

Ronan has $2.92 in his wallet.

1 Fill in the blanks below with numbers to show different ways to make 50 cents with quarters, dimes, and nickels.

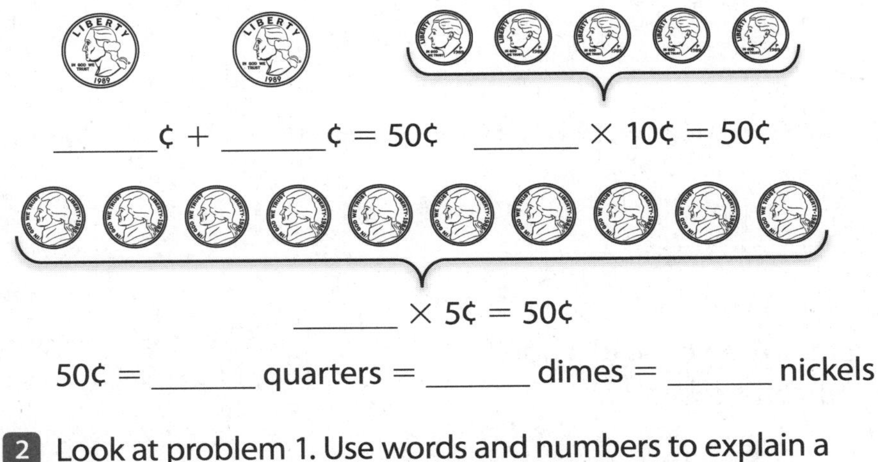

______¢ + ______¢ = 50¢ ______ × 10¢ = 50¢

______ × 5¢ = 50¢

50¢ = ______ quarters = ______ dimes = ______ nickels

2 Look at problem 1. Use words and numbers to explain a different way to make 50 cents with a quarter, dimes, and nickels.

____

____

Solve.

3 Daphne woke up at 7:15. It took her 15 minutes to dress and brush her teeth. She ate breakfast for 20 minutes. Then it took 5 minutes for her to walk to the bus stop and wait for the bus to arrive. What time did the bus arrive?

The clock below shows the start time at 7:15 when Daphne woke up. Draw and label arrows on the clock to show how to find the end time when the bus arrived.

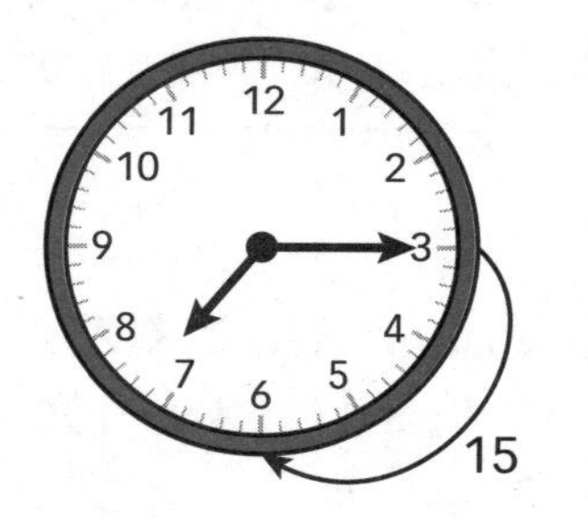

Draw hands on the clock below to show the end time when the bus arrived.

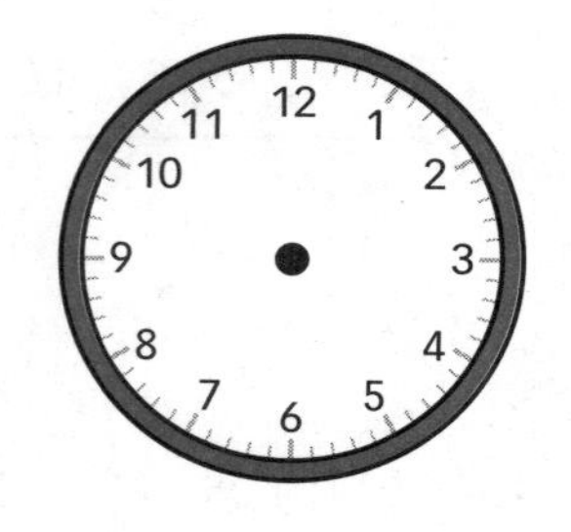

4 Evan got to the practice field at 8:00. He stretched for 15 minutes. He did sprints for 30 minutes. Then he did practice drills for 25 minutes. What time did Evan finish practice drills? Complete and label the jumps on the number line to find the end time.

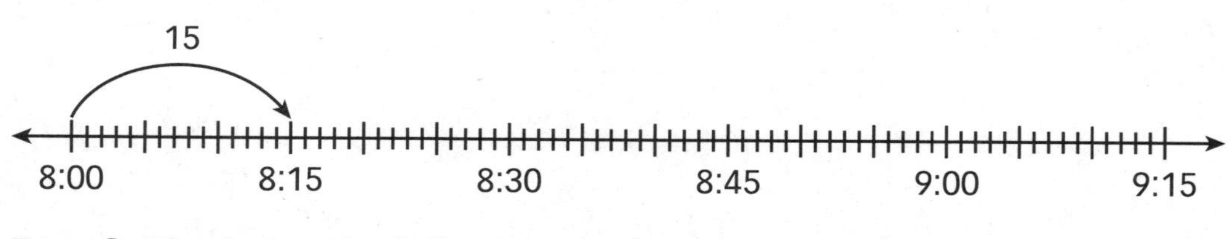

Evan finished practice drills at ____________.

5 Kurt got home at 4:00. He did homework for 25 minutes and played outside for 20 minutes. Then he read a book for 15 minutes before dinner. What time was dinner?

Show your work.

Solution: ____

Name: ______________________

Solve Problems About Time

Study the example showing how to solve a problem about time. Then solve problems 1–6.

Example

Amy had 1 hour to do activities. She talked on the phone for 5 minutes. She rode her bike for 15 minutes. She played a game with her brother for 25 minutes. How much time did Amy have left to spend painting a picture?

Amy had 60 minutes to do activities. 1 hour = 60 minutes

Add the minutes for the known activities. $5 + 15 + 25 = 45$ minutes

Write an equation to find how much time Amy had left to paint a picture. $45 + P = 60$ or $P = 60 - 45$; $P = 15$ $P = 15$

Amy had 15 minutes left to paint a picture.

1 Complete the labels on the number line to represent the example problem.

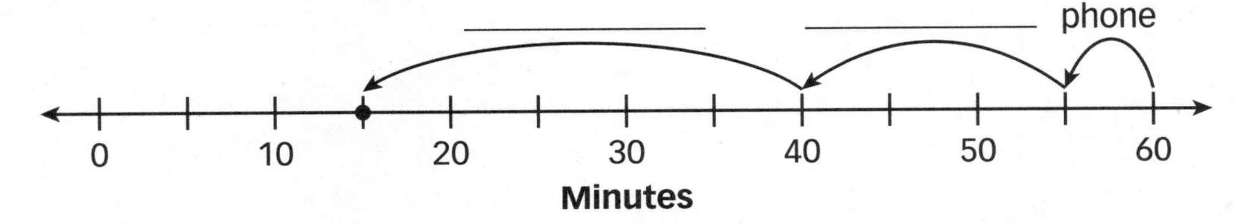

2 Look at the number line in problem 1. What does the dot at 15 represent?

____

3 Milo visited an amusement park for 3 hours. He rode rides for 50 minutes, played carnival games for 40 minutes, and ate food for 30 minutes. He spent the rest of the time waiting in lines. How much time did Milo spend waiting in lines? Write and solve an equation to find the answer.

3 hours = ______ minutes

Known activities = ______ + ______ + ______ = ______ minutes

Equation: ______________________

Milo spent ______ minutes waiting in lines.

Solve.

4 Tell whether each amount of time is equivalent to 2 hours and 10 minutes.

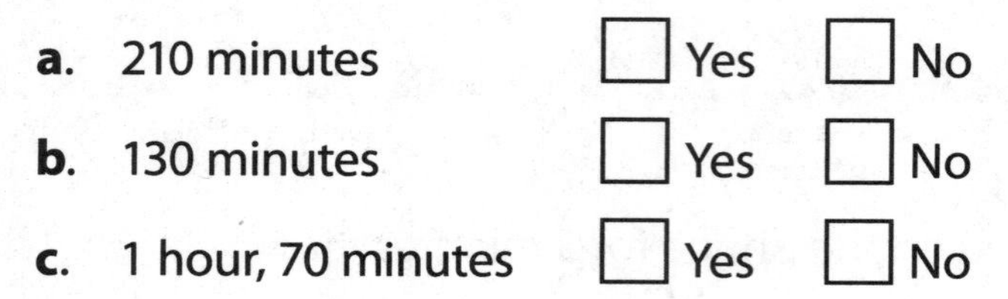

a. 210 minutes ☐ Yes ☐ No

b. 130 minutes ☐ Yes ☐ No

c. 1 hour, 70 minutes ☐ Yes ☐ No

5 One of the fastest times for a 1,500-meter race is 3 minutes and 34 seconds. How many seconds is this time?

Show your work.

Solution: ____________________

6 Bennett spent 4 hours at school today. He attended three 70-minute classes. There is a 5-minute break between classes. Then he ate lunch before going home. How long did Bennett spend eating lunch?

Show your work.

Solution: ____________________

Name: ____________________

Solve Problems About Money

Study the example showing how to solve a problem about money. Then solve problems 1–7.

Example

Rita bought milk for \$0.50, a sandwich for \$2.50, and a fruit salad for \$1.25. She paid for her lunch with a \$5.00 bill. How much change did Rita get?

$1.00 = 100 cents
$5.00 = 500 cents

Rita spent: 50 + 250 + 125 = 425 cents

500 cents − 425 cents = 75 cents

Rita got 75 cents, or \$0.75, in change.

1 The picture below shows that \$5.00 is the same as \$3.00 in bills plus 8 quarters. Cross out the bills and coins to show the amount that Rita spent on lunch in the example above.

1 dollar = 4 quarters
1 quarter = 25 cents

2 How can you find the change Rita gets by looking at the picture above? Explain. ____________________

____

____

3 Josh bought 4 movie tickets and 2 large popcorns. Each movie ticket is \$8. Each popcorn is \$5. How much money did Josh spend?

Tickets: ____________ Popcorn: ____________

Tickets and popcorn: ____________

Josh spent ____________.

Solve.

4 Mandy has a total of $2.00 in change in her purse. Complete each set of coins below to show amounts equivalent to $2.00.

a. 4 quarters, 5 dimes, ______ nickels

b. 10 pennies, ______ dimes, 3 quarters, 5 nickels

c. 2 quarters, 12 dimes, 3 nickels, ______ pennies

d. ______ quarters, 4 dimes, 6 nickels, 5 pennies

5 A pound of apples costs $1.30. Sawyer bought $2\frac{1}{2}$ pounds of apples. How much did Sawyer pay?

Show your work.

Solution: ______________________________

6 Brie earns $3,000 a month. Every month, she spends $1,400 on rent and bills, $700 on groceries, $200 on a car payment, and $100 on gas. She saves the rest. How much money does Brie save?

Show your work.

Solution: ______________________________

7 Regular bananas cost $0.20 each at the supermarket. Organic bananas cost $0.30 each. If you have $3.00, how many more regular bananas than organic bananas can you buy?

Show your work.

Solution: ______________________________

Name: ______________________

Time and Money

Solve the problems.

1 How many days are in 1 year and 5 weeks?

A 372 days

B 378 days

C 400 days

D 1,825 days

There are 365 days in a year. There are 7 days in a week.

2 Rowan bought 2 comic books for $2.50 each, a fiction book for $7, and a poster for $1.25 at the book fair. Rowan paid with a $20.00 bill. How much change did he get?

A $6.75

B $12.75

C $13.25

D $17.75

Courtney chose **C** as the correct answer. How did she get that answer?

____

____

____

3 How many minutes are there in one day?

Show your work.

Solution: ______________________

Solve.

4 A private music lesson at Parker Music costs $40 for 1 hour. A private music lesson at Joelle Music costs $25 for 30 minutes. How much more does a 1-hour private lesson cost at Joelle Music than at Parker Music?

Show your work.

Solution: ____________________

5 Susan bought 4 boxes of granola bars and 2 cartons of milk. Each box of granola bars cost $2.50 and each carton of milk cost $2.75, including tax. Susan gave the clerk a $20.00 bill. What did she get in change? List two different ways Susan could have received change.

Show your work.

Solution: bills: ____________ coins: ____________

bills: ____________ coins: ____________

Dear Family,

This week your child is learning to convert units of length, liquid volume, and mass.

Your child is learning different ways to solve multi-step problems converting larger units to smaller units for measurements of length, liquid volume, and mass. Here's a liquid volume problem your child might see.

> Ethan, Dave, and Robert are making punch for a party. They combine 1 liter of lemonade, a 2-liter bottle of sparkling water, and 450 milliliters of fruit juice. How many milliliters of punch do the boys make for the party?

One way to help solve the problem is to use a picture to think about the size of the measurements.

Since the problem is in liters and milliliters, the first step is to convert the liters to milliliters. Then combine the milliliters to find the total. You can show the measurements with a bar model like the one below.

1 liter	2 liters	450 milliliters
↓	↓	↓
1,000 milliliters	2,000 milliliters	450 milliliters

1 liter is the same as 1,000 milliliters.

Multiply 2 by 1,000 to convert 2 liters to milliliters: $1{,}000 \times 2 = 2{,}000$. Add all the milliliter measurements to find the total:
$1{,}000 + 2{,}000 + 450 = 3{,}450$ milliliters.

Invite your child to share what he or she knows about converting units to solve multi-step problems by doing the following activity together.

Converting Units of Length Activity

Do an activity with your child to convert units of length.

Materials: ruler

- Each person uses a ruler to measure the lengths of three household items. Measure the length of each item in feet and inches, to the nearest whole inch.

- List the three items along with their measurements on a sheet of paper.

  Examples: Picture frame: 9 inches

  Table top: $1\frac{1}{2}$ feet

  Door: 2 feet 8 inches

- Exchange papers and find the total length, in inches, of the three items on the other person's list. Remember, there are 12 inches in 1 foot.

  Example: Picture frame: 9 inches

  Table top: $1\frac{1}{2}$ feet $=$ 18 inches

  Door: 2 feet 8 inches $=$ 32 inches

  Total: $9 + 18 + 32 = 59$ inches

- The person whose measured items add up to a total length closest to 100 inches wins.

Look for other real-life opportunities to practice converting units of length, as well as units of liquid volume and mass, with your child.

Length, Liquid Volume, and Mass

Name: ______________________

Prerequisite: Convert Measurements

Study the example problem showing how to convert from a larger to a smaller unit of length. Then solve problems 1–7.

Example

Tess needs 75 inches of ribbon for a project. She has 6 feet of ribbon. Does she have enough ribbon? How much extra ribbon does she have or how much more ribbon does she need?

Use a table to convert from the larger unit, feet, to the smaller unit, inches.

1 foot = 12 inches

Feet (ft)	1	2	3	4	5	6
Inches (in)	12	24	36	48	60	72

The table shows that 6 feet = 72 inches.
Since 72 < 75, Tess does not have enough ribbon.

75 − 72 = 3, so Tess needs 3 more inches of ribbon.

1 A concrete walkway is 6 meters long. How many centimeters long is the walkway?

Fill in the missing numbers in the table. Circle the numbers that show how many centimeters are equal to 6 meters.

Meters (m)	1	2				
Centimeters (cm)	100					

The walkway is ______ centimeters long.

2 Explain how to use multiplication to solve problem 1.

____

____

____

____

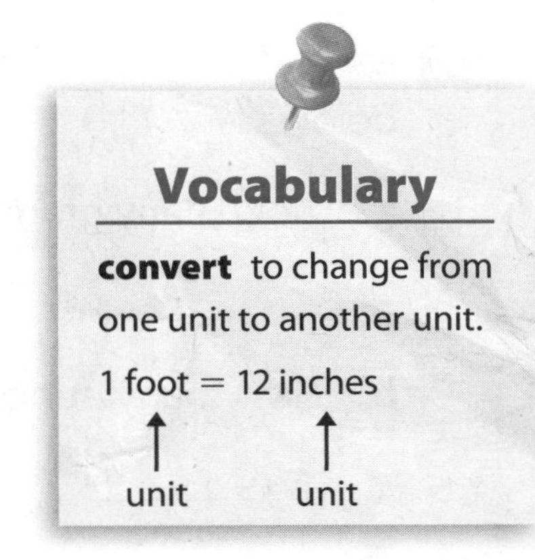

Solve.

3 The cooler at a softball game holds 5 quarts of sports drink. How many cups of sports drink does the cooler hold?

1 quart = 4 cups

Show your work.

Solution: ______________________

4 Mark brought 2 1-liter bottles of water to basketball practice. He drank 1,500 milliliters of water during practice. How many milliliters of water does he have left?

1 liter = 1,000 milliliters

Show your work.

Solution: ______________________

5 Write an expression to convert kilograms to grams. Let K stand for kilograms.

1 kilogram = 1,000 grams

Expression: ______________________

6 Write an expression to convert pounds to ounces.

Let p stand for pounds.

1 pound = 16 ounces

Expression: ______________________

7 Look at problems 5 and 6 to answer the questions below.

a. How many grams are in 4 kilograms?

____

b. How many ounces are in 7 pounds?

____

Name: ______________________

Solve Length Problems

Study the example problem showing how to solve a multi-step problem about length. Then solve problems 1–5.

Example

Wendy has a fence that is 10 feet long. Vines cover a section of fence that is $\frac{5}{6}$ foot long. Wendy and 4 friends will each paint an equal length of the rest of the fence. How long is the section of fence that each friend will paint?

1 foot = 12 inches

Length of fence

Length with vines

Each length to paint

Length of fence: 10 feet = 120 inches

Length covered with vines: $\frac{5}{6} \times 12$ inches = 10 inches

Length to paint: 120 − 10 = 110 inches

Length of each section: 110 ÷ 5 = 22 inches

The section of fence each friend will paint is 22 inches.

1 Nestor needs 750 centimeters of rope. Rope comes in lengths of $4\frac{1}{2}$ meters and 9 meters at the hardware store. Which length of rope should Nestor buy?

1 meter = 100 centimeters

$4\frac{1}{2}$ meters = ______ centimeters

9 meters = ______ centimeters

a. Which length is greater than 750 centimeters? ______ centimeters

b. Nestor should buy rope with a length of __________.

2 Which length is greater, $\frac{1}{2}$ meter or 240 centimeters? Explain.

____

____

____

Solve.

3 Jorge is playing football. He carries the ball forward $5\frac{2}{3}$ yards and then moves backward 1 foot. How far forward is the ball, in feet, from where Jorge started carrying the ball?

1 yard = 3 feet

Show your work.

Solution: ______________________________

4 Last summer, Marion was $3\frac{1}{2}$ feet tall. She was 4 inches taller than her brother Elijah. She was $1\frac{1}{4}$ feet shorter than her sister Lorie. How tall were Elijah and Lorie last summer?

1 foot = 12 inches

Show your work.

Solution: Elijah: ______________ Lorie: ______________

5 Paula has $4\frac{2}{3}$ yards of ribbon. She cuts 4 inches off each end of the ribbon to remove the frayed ends. She divides the remaining ribbon into 16 equal pieces to make bows. What is the length of ribbon, in inches, used to make each bow?

Show your work.

Solution: ______________________________

Name: ______________________

Solve Liquid Volume Problems

Study the example showing how to solve a liquid volume problem. Then solve problems 1–5.

Example

Naomi has a container of water. She uses 4 liters to water her vegetable garden. She uses $3\frac{1}{2}$ liters to water flowers. She uses the remaining 500 milliliters in the container to fill up a bird bath. How many milliliters of water did Naomi have in the container?

1 liter (L) = 1,000 milliliters (mL)

Write an equation to find the total amount of water. $W = 4\text{ L} + 3\frac{1}{2}\text{ L} + 500\text{ mL}$

Convert liters to milliliters.
$4 \times 1{,}000\text{ mL} = 4{,}000\text{ mL}$
$3 \times 1{,}000\text{ mL} = 3{,}000\text{ mL}$ and $\frac{1}{2} \times 1{,}000\text{ mL} = 500\text{ mL}$

Write the equation using milliliters and solve.
$W = 4{,}000\text{ mL} + 3{,}500\text{ mL} + 500\text{ mL}$
$W = 8{,}000\text{ mL}$

Naomi had 8,000 milliliters of water in the container.

Benny has two small fish tanks with one fish in each tank. One tank has $3\frac{1}{2}$ quarts of water. The other tank has 12 cups of water. Benny combines the water into one large fish tank with both fish in the large tank.

1 quart = 4 cups

1 How many cups of water are in the large tank?

$3\frac{1}{2}$ quarts: 3×4 cups = ______ cups and $\frac{1}{2} \times 4$ cups = ______ cups

$3\frac{1}{2}$ quarts = ______ cups; ______ cups + ______ cups = ______ cups

There are ____________ of water in the large tank.

2 At least 5 cups of water are needed for each fish in a tank. How many more fish would Benny be able to put in the large tank? Explain.

____

____

Solve.

3 Tamara prepared fruit punch for a party. She used $\frac{3}{4}$ gallon of pineapple juice, 2 quarts of lemonade, and $1\frac{1}{4}$ gallons of orange juice. How many quarts of punch did Tamara prepare?

1 gallon = 4 quarts

Show your work.

Solution: ____________________

4 Sharon and her cousin are making milkshakes at a family reunion. Sharon brought $2\frac{1}{2}$ gallons of milk. Her cousin brought 2 quarts of milk. The girls used 8 quarts of milk for the milkshakes. How much milk is left? There may be more than one correct answer. Circle the letter for all that apply.

A 4 quarts

B 6 quarts

C $\frac{1}{2}$ gallon

D 1 gallon

E $1\frac{1}{2}$ gallons

5 Rob has 6 quarts of apple cider for the fall fair. He pours the cider into glasses to set on picnic tables. He pours 6 ounces of cider into each glass. How many glasses of cider does Rob set on the tables?

1 quart = 4 cups 1 cup = 8 ounces

Show your work.

Solution: ____________________

Name: ____________________

Solve Mass and Weight Problems

Study the example problem showing how to solve a mass and weight problem. Then solve problems 1–5.

Example

The softball coach has a box filled with softballs. The weight of the empty box is 3 pounds. When it is filled with softballs, the box weighs 12 pounds. Each softball has a weight of 6 ounces. How many softballs are in the box?

1 pound = 16 ounces

Find the weight of the softballs in ounces.

$S = 12 \text{ pounds} - 3 \text{ pounds} = 9 \text{ pounds}$

$S = 9 \times 16 \text{ ounces} = 144 \text{ ounces}$

12 pounds

Weight of softballs (S)	3 pounds

S = Weight of 1 softball (6 ounces) × number of softballs (n)

Weight of empty container

Find the number of softballs.

$S = 6 \times n$

$144 = 6 \times n$

$24 = n$

There are 24 softballs in the box.

1 Look at the example above. Explain why you need to find the weight of the softballs in the box in ounces.

____

____

____

2 Tyson's baby brother weighed 7 pounds, 3 ounces when he was born. The baby lost 9 ounces after a few days, and then gained 1 pound, 6 ounces by the end of the week. How much did the baby weigh at the end of the week?

Show your work.

Solution: ______________________________

Solve.

3 A large truck that moves cars can carry a maximum load of 15,720 pounds. The table below shows the weight of each kind of car that could be loaded onto the truck.

1 ton = 2,000 pounds

Kind of Car	Compact	Mid-size	Full-size
Weight (in tons)	$1\frac{1}{2}$	$2\frac{1}{4}$	3

Choose *Yes* or *No* to tell whether the truck is able to carry each load of cars below.

a. 2 full-size cars, 1 compact car ☐ Yes ☐ No

b. 2 compact cars, 2 full-size cars ☐ Yes ☐ No

c. 2 mid-size cars, 2 compact cars ☐ Yes ☐ No

d. 4 mid-size cars ☐ Yes ☐ No

4 Melinda donated fudge for the school bake sale. She wrapped 80 pieces of fudge. Each piece of fudge weighed 1 ounce. How many pounds of fudge did Melinda wrap?

1 pound = 16 ounces

Show your work.

Solution: ______________________________

5 A paper clip has a mass of 1 gram. A box of paper clips has 100 paper clips. Which equation below can be used to find the number of boxes of paper clips that will have a mass of 1 kilogram? Let *n* be the number of boxes. Circle the letter for all that apply.

1 kilogram = 1,000 grams

A $100 = 1{,}000 \div n$

B $n = 1{,}000 \times 100$

C $n = 1{,}000 \div 100$

D $1{,}000 = n \times 100$

Name: ____________________

Length, Liquid Volume, and Mass

Solve the problems.

1 Miguel and his brother put two 8-foot tables end to end for a graduation party. The tablecloth they plan to use is 5 yards in length. Is the tablecloth long enough to cover both tables?

A Yes, because 8 feet $<$ 10 yards.

B Yes, because the tables are 8 feet long and the tablecloth is 15 feet long.

C No, because the tables are 16 feet long and the tablecloth is 15 feet long.

D No, because 8 feet $>$ 5 yards.

2 Patel bought a 2-pound bag of trail mix. He poured $\frac{1}{2}$ pound of the mix into a bowl and divided the remaining amount into bags. Each bag had 2 ounces of trail mix. How many bags did Patel use?

1 pound = 16 ounces.
How many ounces of trail mix is he dividing into bags?

A 20 bags

B 16 bags

C 12 bags

D 8 bags

Jen chose **A** as the correct answer. How did she get that answer?

____

____

____

____

Solve.

3 Marcus poured an equal amount of milk into 4 bottles. He started with 1 quart of milk. After pouring, he had $\frac{1}{4}$ of a quart of milk left. How many ounces of milk did Marcus pour into each bottle?

Show your work.

1 quart = 4 cups.
1 cup = 8 ounces.
There are two steps in this problem.

Solution: ______________________________

4 Maya cut a length of wood into strips to make 5 small picture frames. She used 14 inches of wood for each frame. For another project, she cut another length of wood into 3 strips of 1 foot each and 4 strips of $\frac{1}{6}$ foot each. How much wood, in inches, did Maya use in all?

Show your work.

1 foot = 12 inches.
You can use multiplication and addition to solve this problem.

Solution: ______________________________

Dear Family,

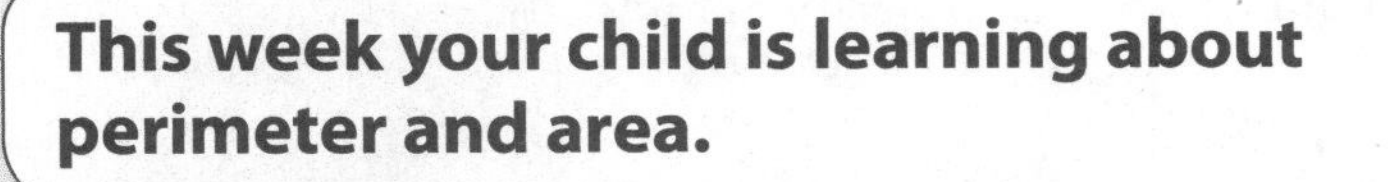

Some real-world situations that involve perimeter and area are installing a fence around a yard and determining how much flooring is needed for a room.

To find perimeter, find the total length of all the sides of a rectangle. One way to do this is by adding together the lengths of all the sides.

For example, to find the length of fencing that is needed to enclose a rectangular yard like the one shown below, add the 4 side lengths.

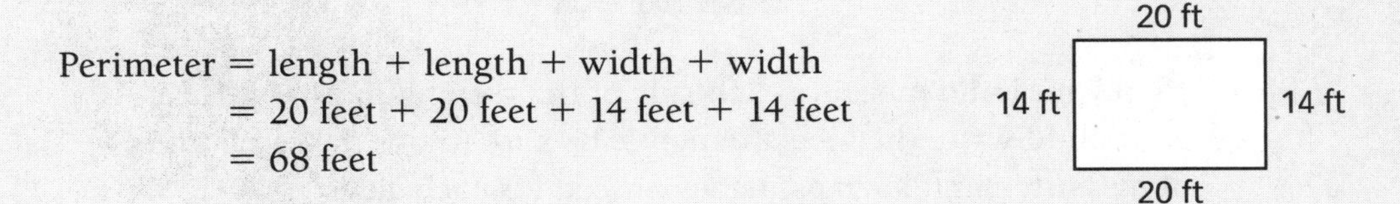

Perimeter = length + length + width + width
= 20 feet + 20 feet + 14 feet + 14 feet
= 68 feet

Another way to find the perimeter of a rectangle is to use a formula. P stands for perimeter, l stands for length, and w stands for width.

$P = 2l + 2w$ or $P = 2(l + w)$
$= 2(20) + 2(14)$ $= 2(20 + 14)$
$= 40 + 28$ $= 2 \times 34$

$P = 68$ feet

You need 68 feet of fencing to enclose the yard.

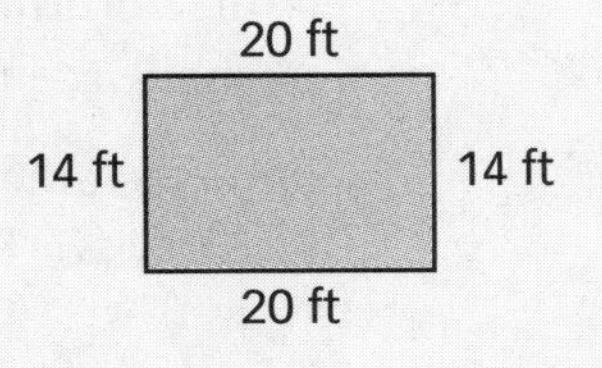

To find the area of a rectangle, use the area formula.
Area = length × width $A = l \times w$

The area of the rectangle at the right is:
14 feet × 20 feet = 280 square feet

If you were covering the rectangular yard with pavers, you would need enough pavers to cover 280 square feet.

Invite your child to share what he or she knows about perimeter and area by doing the following activity together.

NEXT

Perimeter and Area Activity

Do an activity with your child to find perimeter and area.

Materials: ruler or yardstick

- Look around the house for items that are shaped like a rectangle.

  Examples: a TV or computer screen, a table top, a rug, the floor of a room

- Help your child measure each side of the rectangular item. Have your child write the measurements. Be sure to use the same units of measurement, such as inches or feet, for each side.
- Have your child use the measurements to find the perimeter of the item.
- Now measure a different rectangular-shaped item and find its perimeter. Is the perimeter greater or less than the perimeter of the first item you measured?
- Next, find area. Suppose you want to cover a window in your home with a shade. Choose a window and measure each side. Have your child find the area and tell how many square inches or square feet of shade are needed to cover the window.
- Find the area of other items in your home, such as different-size windows or floors.

Look for other real-life opportunities to practice finding perimeter and area with your child.

Perimeter and Area

Name: ______________________

Prerequisite: Connect Area and Perimeter

Study the example showing how to find the area and perimeter of a rectangle. Then solve problems 1–7.

Example

Find the area and perimeter of the rectangle at right.

Area
Count square units or multiply side lengths.
The rectangle is 4 units by 10 units.
$4 \times 10 = 40$ square units

Area = 40 square units

Perimeter
Add the lengths of all the sides.
$4 + 10 + 4 + 10 = 28$ units

Perimeter = 28 units

1 Find the area and perimeter of the rectangle at right.

Area = _______ square units Perimeter = _______ units

2 Look at the rectangle in problem 1. Draw a rectangle with the same area but a different perimeter.

What is the perimeter of the rectangle you drew?

____

3 Look at the rectangle in problem 1. Draw a rectangle with the same perimeter but a different area.

What is the area of the rectangle you drew?

____

Solve.

4 Look at the shape below. Find the area and perimeter of the shape.

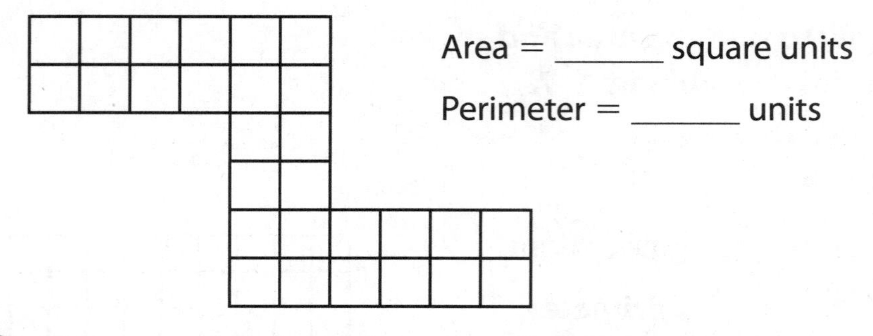

Area = ______ square units

Perimeter = ______ units

5 What is the area and perimeter of a square with side lengths of 4 units? Draw the square below.

Area = ______ square units

Perimeter = ______ units

6 Look at the square you drew in problem 5.

a. Draw a rectangle with the same area as the square and a different perimeter than the square.

b. What is the perimeter of the rectangle you drew? Is it equal to, greater than, or less than the perimeter of the square you drew in problem 5? Explain.

____

____

____

7 The perimeter of each triangle below is 12 centimeters. Write the missing side length on each triangle.

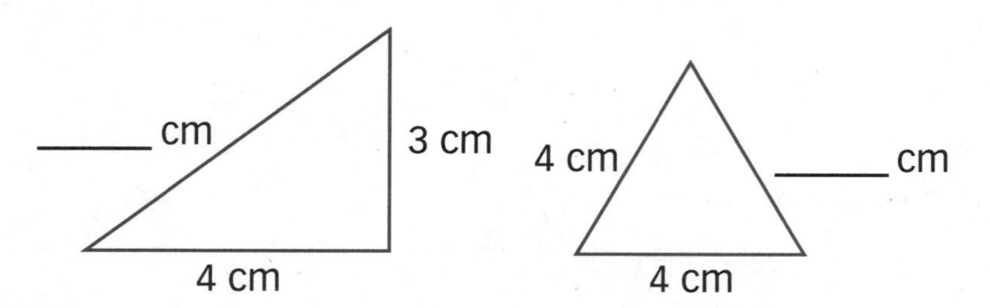

Name: ____________

Solve Perimeter Problems

Study the example problem showing how to solve a problem about perimeter. Then solve problems 1–6.

Example

The community center has a rectangular kiddie pool. The length of the pool is 25 feet. The width is 15 feet. What is the perimeter of the kiddie pool?

Use a formula for the perimeter of a rectangle.

$P = 2l + 2w$	$P = 2\,(l + w)$
$= (2 \times 25) + (2 \times 15)$	$= 2\,(25 + 15)$
$= 50 + 30$	$= 2\,(40)$
$= 80$	$= 80$

25 ft

15 ft

The perimeter of the pool is 80 feet.

1 A rectangular photograph has a length of 10 inches and a width of 8 inches. Fill in the numbers in the formulas below to show two ways to find the perimeter of the photograph.

$P = 2l + 2w$	$P = 2(l + w)$
$P = (2 \times$ ____ $) + (2 \times$ ____ $)$	$P = 2\,($ ____ $+$ ____ $)$
$=$ ____ $+$ ____	$= 2\,($ ____ $)$
$=$ ____	$=$ ____

The perimeter is ______ inches.

2 Jason's rectangular computer screen is 50 centimeters across and 36 centimeters high. What is the perimeter of Jason's computer screen?

Show your work.

Solution: P = ______ centimeters

Solve.

3 A rectangular garden has a width of 90 feet. The perimeter is 500 feet. What is the length of the garden?

$500 = (2 \times l) + (\_\_\_\_\_ \times \_\_\_\_\_)$

$500 = 2l + \_\_\_\_\_$

$\_\_\_\_\_ = 2l$

$\_\_\_\_\_ \div 2 = l$

$\_\_\_\_\_ = l$

The length of the garden is ______ feet.

4 What is the perimeter of a square with side lengths of 3 inches?

Show your work.

Solution: ____________________________________

5 Amy has a ribbon that is 36 inches long. Choose *Yes* or *No* to tell whether she has enough ribbon to wrap around the perimeter of a picture frame for each frame with the given shape and size.

a. square, side lengths of 9 inches ☐ Yes ☐ No

b. rectangle, 18 inches by 10 inches ☐ Yes ☐ No

c. rectangle, 12 inches by 24 inches ☐ Yes ☐ No

d. square, side lengths of 6 inches ☐ Yes ☐ No

6 The square and the rectangle at the right each have a perimeter of 200 centimeters. What are the side lengths of the square and rectangle?
(Hint: First find the side length of the square.)

Show your work.

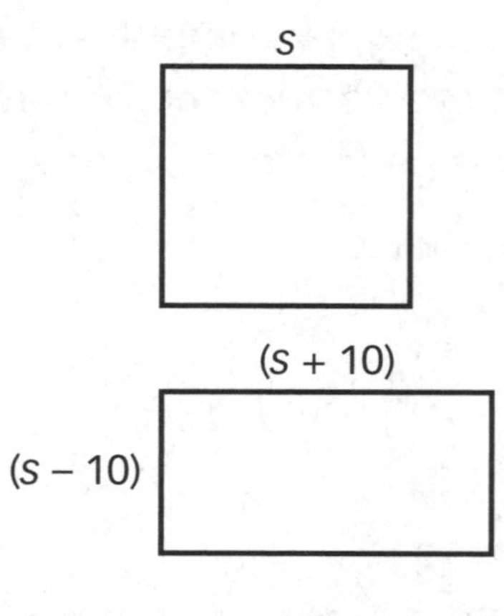

Square: side length ______ cm Rectangle: length ______ cm width ______ cm

Name: ______________________

Solve Area Problems

Study the example showing how to solve a problem about area. Then solve problems 1–6.

Example

Michelle wants to use bricks to make a rectangular patio. She has enough bricks to cover an area of 135 square feet. She wants the length of the patio to be 15 feet. How wide should she make the patio?

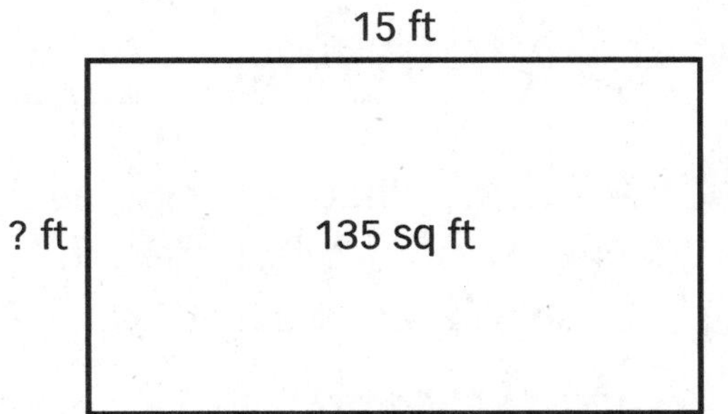

Write an equation to represent the area of a rectangle: $A = l \times w$

$$A = 15 \times w$$
$$135 = 15 \times w$$
$$135 \div 15 = w$$
$$9 = w$$

Michelle should make the patio 9 feet wide.

1 Juan is installing new flooring in a large entryway. The picture at the right shows the length and width of the entryway. How many square feet of flooring does Juan need?

30 ft

25 ft

$A =$ ______ $\times$ ______

$A =$ ______

Juan needs ______ square feet of flooring.

2 Look at the picture at the right. Alyssa wants to tile a room with an area of 480 square feet. The width of the room is 12 feet. What is the length of the room?

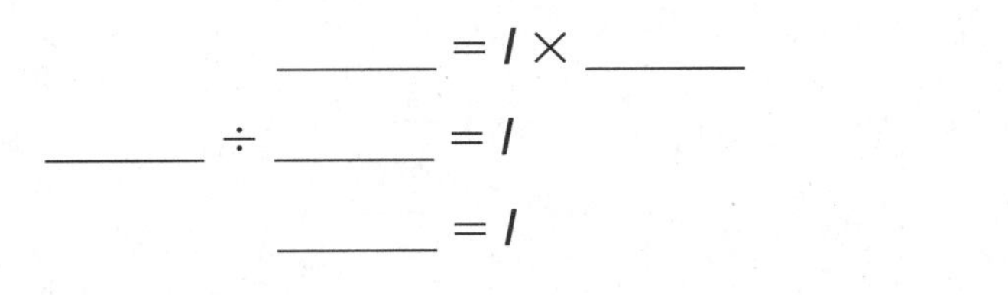

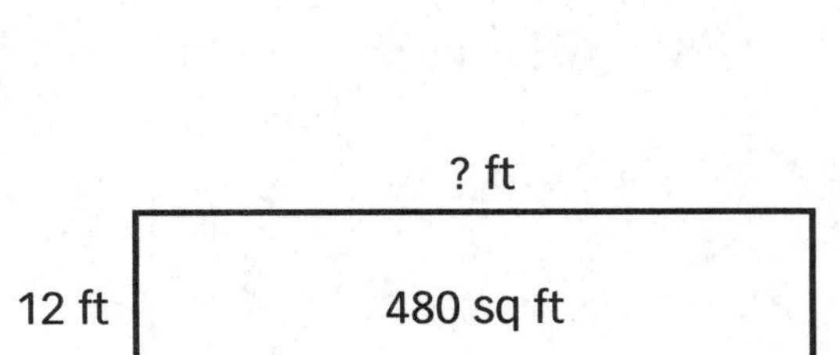

The length of the room is ______ feet.

Solve.

3 Jim is painting the surface of a picnic table. The surface has an area of 2,160 square inches. The width of the table is 30 inches. What is the length of the table?

Show your work.

Solution: ______________________________

4 An Olympic floor exercise mat has an area of 144 square meters. Its length is 12 meters. What is the width of the mat?

Show your work.

Solution: ______________________________

5 Look at problem 4. What is the shape of the floor exercise mat? Explain how you know.

____

____

6 Melissa has enough paint to cover an area of 250 square feet. She wants to paint two walls. The rectangular wall is 9 feet high and 20 feet wide. The square wall has a height of 9 feet. Does Melissa have enough paint to cover the area of both walls?

Show your work.

Solution: ______________________________

Name: ____________________

Solve Perimeter and Area Problems

Solve the problems.

1 The area of a rectangle is 40 square feet. What could be the perimeter of the rectangle? Circle the letter for all that apply.

A 82 ft

B 44 ft

C 40 ft

D 28 ft

E 26 ft

$A = l \times w$
$P = 2(l + w)$
Find the length and width. Then find the perimeter.

2 Trish had a square garden with side lengths of 8 feet. She expanded her garden to 10 feet by 8 feet. By how many square feet did she expand the area of her garden?

A 144 sq ft

B 80 sq ft

C 64 sq ft

D 16 sq ft

Kerry chose **A** as the correct answer. How did she get that answer?

____

____

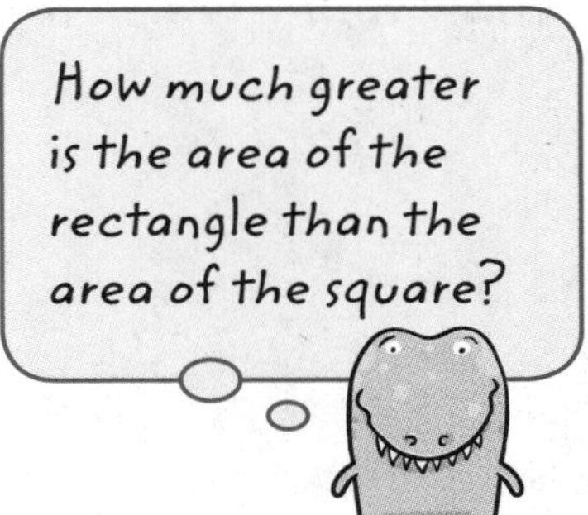

3 Layla painted the walls of a rectangular room. Two walls are 9 feet by 12 feet. The other two walls are 9 feet by 20 feet. What is the total area of wall that Layla painted?

Show your work.

Solution: ____________________

Solve.

4 Olivia is putting decorations around the photo in the picture frame shown below. What is the area of the frame that she can decorate?

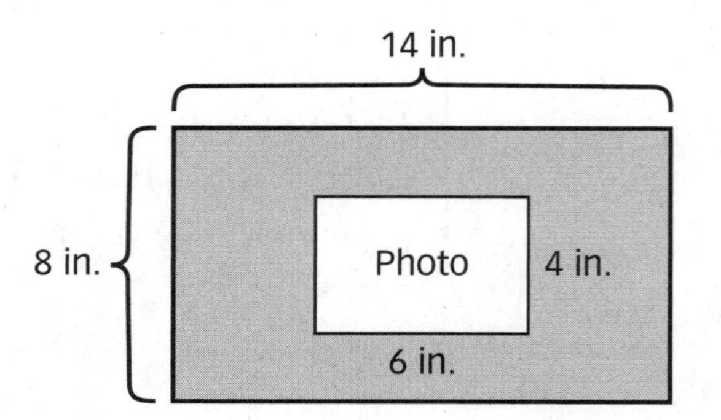

You can find the difference between the area of the larger rectangle and the area of the smaller rectangle.

Show your work.

Solution: ______________________

5 A painter needs a piece of glass to protect a painting. He is also putting wooden strips around the perimeter to make a frame for the painting. The painting is 85 centimeters by 62 centimeters. How many square centimeters of glass does he need to cover the area of the painting? What is the total length of wooden strips that he needs to frame the perimeter of the painting?

You need to find both the area and the perimeter.

Show your work.

Solution: Glass: ______________________

Wooden strips: ______________________

Dear Family,

This week your child is learning to use line plots to solve problems.

A line plot is a way to organize a group of data, such as a set of measurements. A line plot gives a visual view of the data.

The line plot below shows the lengths of different pieces of yarn. Each X represents a piece of yarn. Since there are 9 Xs, there are 9 pieces of yarn.

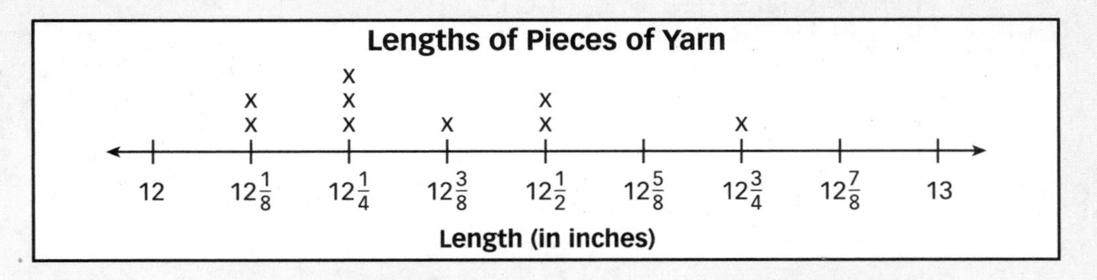

Xs that are one above another show pieces of yarn that have the same length. You can see at a glance that:

- 2 pieces of yarn are $12\frac{1}{8}$ inches long.
- the longest piece of yarn is $12\frac{3}{4}$ inches.

To find the total length of all the pieces of yarn, add the individual lengths. For each X on the line plot, write a length. Then add the lengths.

$12\frac{1}{8}$	$12\frac{1}{8}$	$12\frac{1}{4}$	$12\frac{1}{4}$	$12\frac{1}{4}$	$12\frac{3}{8}$	$12\frac{1}{2}$	$12\frac{1}{2}$	$12\frac{3}{4}$

In order to add, all the fractions must have the same denominator. Write the fractions as eighths. For example, write $12\frac{1}{4}$ as $12\frac{2}{8}$.

Add the whole numbers: $12 + 12 + 12 + 12 + 12 + 12 + 12 + 12 + 12 = 108$.

Add the fractions: $\frac{1}{8} + \frac{1}{8} + \frac{2}{8} + \frac{2}{8} + \frac{2}{8} + \frac{3}{8} + \frac{4}{8} + \frac{4}{8} + \frac{6}{8} = \frac{25}{8}$.

$108 + \frac{25}{8} = 108 + 3\frac{1}{8} = 111\frac{1}{8}$

The total length of all the pieces of yarn is $111\frac{1}{8}$ inches.

Invite your child to share what he or she knows about using line plots to solve problems by doing the following activity together.

Line Plot Activity

Do an activity with your child to use a line plot to solve the problem below. Then have your child answer the questions below using the line plot you make.

Steve took 12 nails out of a toolbox. He measured the length of each nail. This is what he wrote:

- 1 nail measures $\frac{1}{8}$ inch.
- 4 nails measure $\frac{3}{8}$ inch.
- 3 nails measure $\frac{1}{2}$ inch.
- 3 nails measure $\frac{5}{8}$ inch.
- 1 nail measures $\frac{7}{8}$ inch.

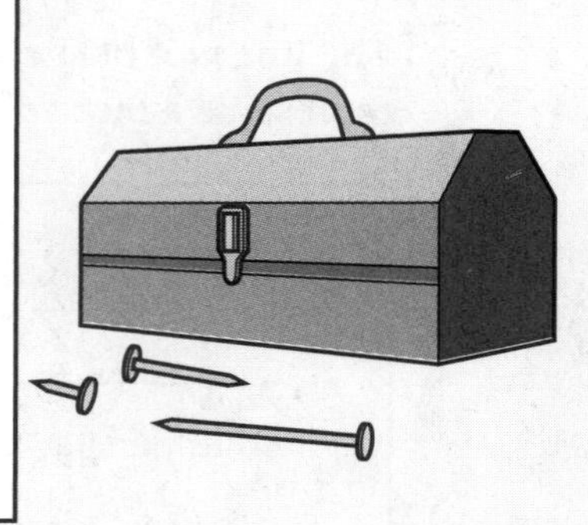

- Make a line plot to show the lengths of the nails. Use a blank number line. Label it with eighths fractions from 0 through 1.
- Write a title for the line plot, such as "Lengths of Nails from the Toolbox." Be sure to write a label below the number line, such as "Lengths (in inches)."
- Mark Xs on the line plot to show the data.
- Ask questions and have your child use the line plot to find the answers.

  Examples:

  Which length of nail is there the greatest number of? $\left(\frac{3}{8}\right)$

  What is the difference between the lengths of the longest nail and the shortest nail? $\left(\frac{6}{8}, \text{ or } \frac{3}{4} \text{ inch}\right)$

  How would the line plot change if there was another nail that measures $1\frac{1}{4}$ inches? $\left(\text{Add eighths labels through } 1\frac{2}{8} \text{ and mark an X above } 1\frac{2}{8}.\right)$

Line Plots

Name: ____________________

Prerequisite: Display Data on a Line Plot

Study the example problem showing how to display data on a line plot. Then solve problems 1–6.

Example

Ginny measured the heights of tomato seedlings in her garden. The heights are shown in the table below. Make a line plot to represent the data.

Seedling Heights							
Seedling	A	B	C	D	E	F	G
Height (in inches)	$1\frac{1}{4}$	$\frac{3}{4}$	$1\frac{1}{4}$	2	$1\frac{3}{4}$	$1\frac{1}{2}$	$\frac{1}{2}$

Use a number line with a scale of $\frac{1}{4}$ inch.

For each seedling, put an X on the line plot above its height.

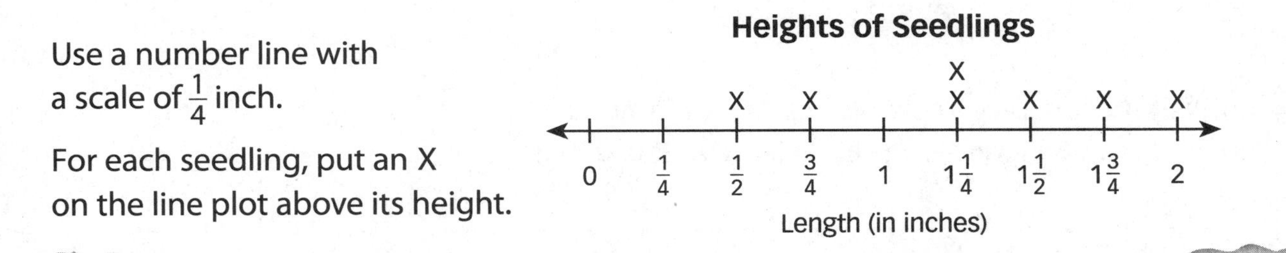

For problems 1–3, use the line plot in the example above.

1 Explain how to use the line plot to find how many seedlings Ginny measured.

____

____

2 What are the heights of the shortest seedling and the tallest seedling? Explain how you know.

Shortest seedling: __________ Tallest seedling: __________

____

____

3 Two seedlings have the same height. What is the height? Explain how you know. ______________________________

____

Solve.

4 The lengths of snakes at a zoo are shown in the table below.

Snake Lengths

Snake	A	B	C	D	E	F	G	H
Length (in inches)	9	$7\frac{1}{4}$	$8\frac{1}{4}$	$7\frac{1}{4}$	8	7	$7\frac{3}{4}$	$8\frac{1}{4}$

Complete the line plot below to represent the data in the table.

Lengths of Snakes

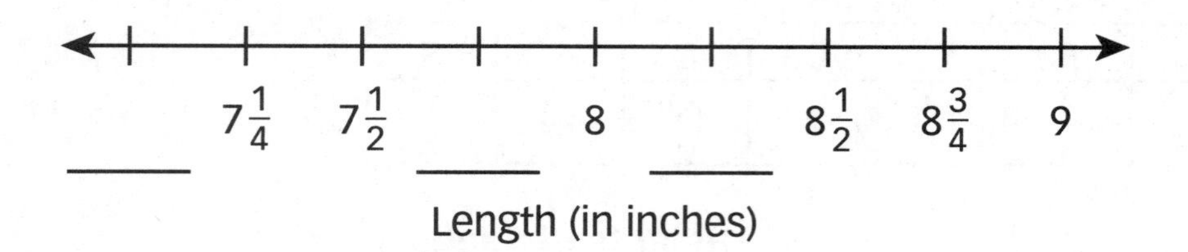

5 Look at the line plot in problem 4. How many snakes are less than 8 inches long? Explain how you know.

____

____

____

6 Sally measured the width of seashells she collected. The table below shows the data.

Seashell Widths

Seashell	A	B	C	D	E	F	G	H
Width (in inches)	2	$\frac{3}{4}$	$1\frac{3}{4}$	$\frac{1}{2}$	$1\frac{1}{4}$	$\frac{1}{4}$	$\frac{3}{4}$	$1\frac{3}{4}$

Draw a line plot to represent the data in the table.

Widths of Seashells

Name: ______________________

Represent Data on a Line Plot

Study the example problem showing how to make a line plot. Then solve problems 1–5.

Example

Students in science class measured the widths of butterfly wingspans in inches. The widths are shown in the table. Make a line plot to represent the data.

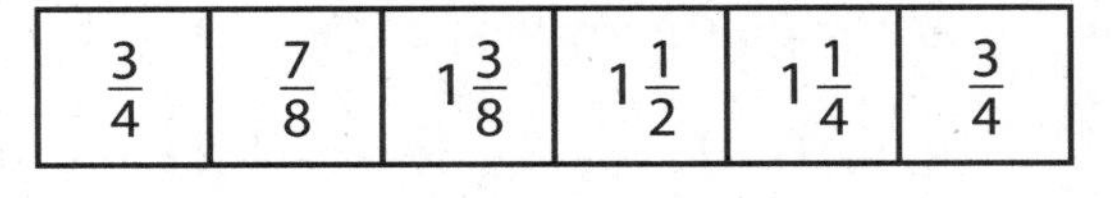

$\frac{3}{4}$	$\frac{7}{8}$	$1\frac{3}{8}$	$1\frac{1}{2}$	$1\frac{1}{4}$	$\frac{3}{4}$

Write equivalent fractions.

$\frac{1}{4} = \frac{2}{8}$ $\frac{1}{2} = \frac{4}{8}$ $\frac{3}{4} = \frac{6}{8}$

Draw and label a number line by eighths.
Put an X above each butterfly wingspan width.

Butterfly Wingspan Widths

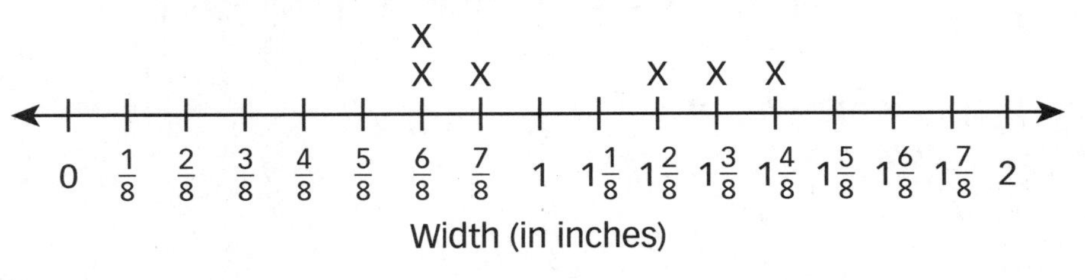

The height of fourth graders was measured on the first day of school and on the last day of school. The growth in inches of some students is listed below.

$3, 1\frac{3}{4}, 2\frac{1}{4}, 1\frac{1}{2}, 2\frac{1}{4}, 2\frac{7}{8}$

1 Write the data in eighths, by using equivalent fractions.

3, ________, ________, ________, ________, $2\frac{7}{8}$

2 Complete the line plot below to represent the data.

Growth of Students

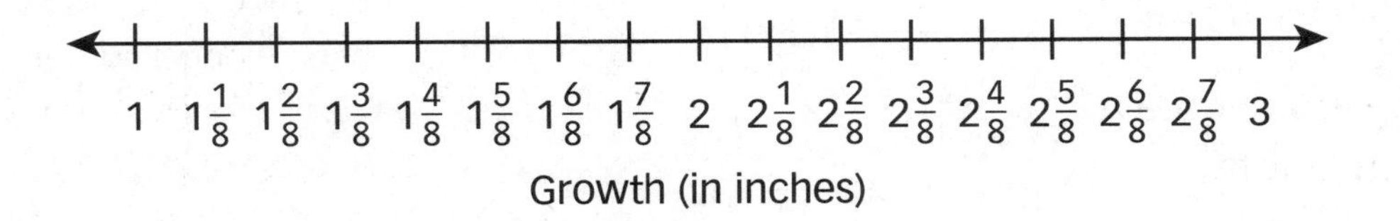

Solve.

3 Look at the measurements in inches listed below. What fractions could be labeled on a number line with a line plot of the data? Circle all that apply.

$$10\frac{1}{4}, 10\frac{1}{2}, 11, 11\frac{3}{4}$$

A Halves

B Thirds

C Fourths

D Eighths

Micah's dog has 8 puppies. The length in inches of each puppy is listed below.

$$4, 4\frac{3}{4}, 4\frac{3}{8}, 4\frac{1}{2}, 4\frac{1}{2}, 4\frac{7}{8}, 4\frac{1}{4}, 4$$

4 Draw a line plot to represent the data.

5 Use the line plot to answer the questions.

a. How many measurements are recorded? ____________

b. What is the longest length of a puppy? ____________

c. What is the shortest length of a puppy? ____________

d. How many puppies are less than or equal to $4\frac{1}{2}$ inches in length? ____________

e. How many puppies are greater than $4\frac{1}{2}$ inches in length? ____________

Vocabulary

line plot a graph using marks along a number line to show how many objects are in a set.

Name: ____________________

Solve Addition Problems with Line Plots

Study the example showing how to solve an addition problem with a line plot. Then solve problems 1–5.

Example

Ashley is decorating a frame with seashells. She wants to know if all the shells will fit along the edge of a 16-inch wide frame. She measures the width of each shell and records the information in a line plot. If Ashley puts all the shells in a row, will the total width of the shells fit on the frame?

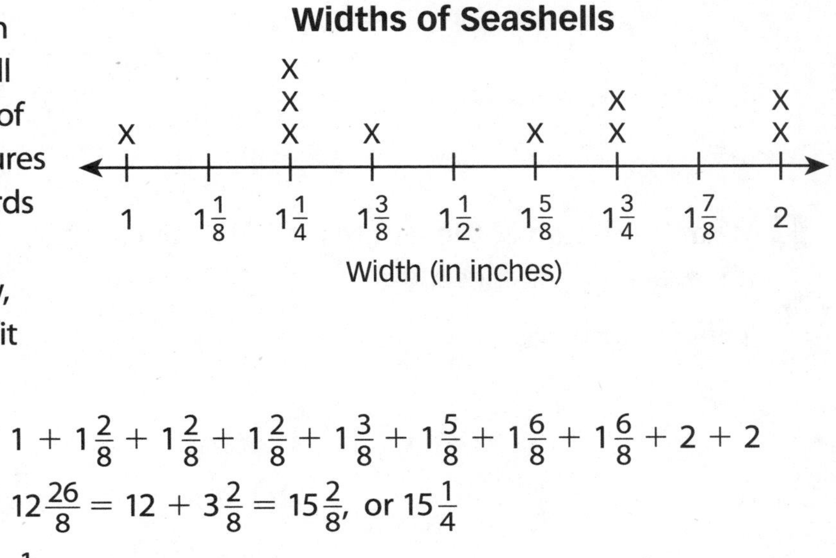

Write the fractions in eighths. $1 + 1\frac{2}{8} + 1\frac{2}{8} + 1\frac{2}{8} + 1\frac{3}{8} + 1\frac{5}{8} + 1\frac{6}{8} + 1\frac{6}{8} + 2 + 2$

Then add. $12\frac{26}{8} = 12 + 3\frac{2}{8} = 15\frac{2}{8}$, or $15\frac{1}{4}$

The total width of the shells is $15\frac{1}{4}$ inches.

$15\frac{1}{4} < 16$, so the shells will fit on the frame.

1 Look at the line plot in the example. Ashley decides to glue the five largest shells along the edge of another frame. The shells fit exactly. How wide is the other frame?

Show your work.

Solution: ____________________

2 Ashley puts the $1\frac{1}{4}$ inch shells onto a string. What is the total width of the shells on the string?

Show your work.

Solution: ____________________

Vocabulary

line plot a graph using marks along a number line to show how many objects are in a set.

Solve.

A standard-sized brick should be $7\frac{5}{8}$ inches long. The line plot shows the actual lengths of 12 different bricks.

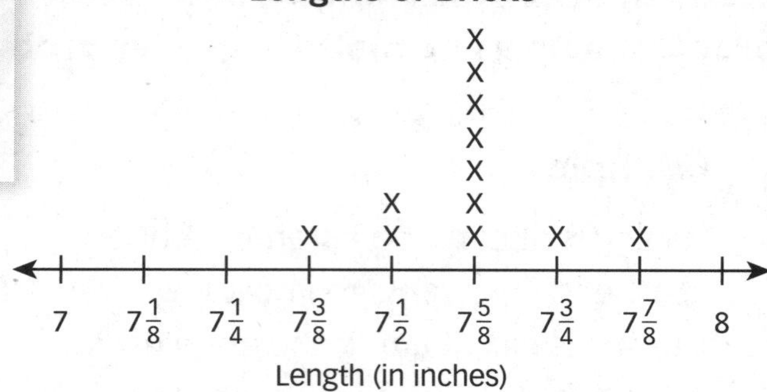

3 What is the sum of the lengths of all the bricks that are exactly $7\frac{5}{8}$ inches long?

Show your work.

Solution: ____________________

4 What is the sum of the lengths of all the bricks that are less than $7\frac{5}{8}$ inches long?

Show your work.

Solution: ____________________

5 What is the sum of the lengths of all the bricks that are greater than $7\frac{5}{8}$ inches long?

Show your work.

Solution: ____________________

Name: ______________________

Solve Subtraction Problems with Line Plots

Study the example showing how to solve a subtraction problem with a line plot. Then solve problems 1–5.

Example

The monthly rainfall in inches for one city is shown in the line plot. What is the difference in inches of rain between the month with the greatest amount of rain and the month with the least amount of rain?

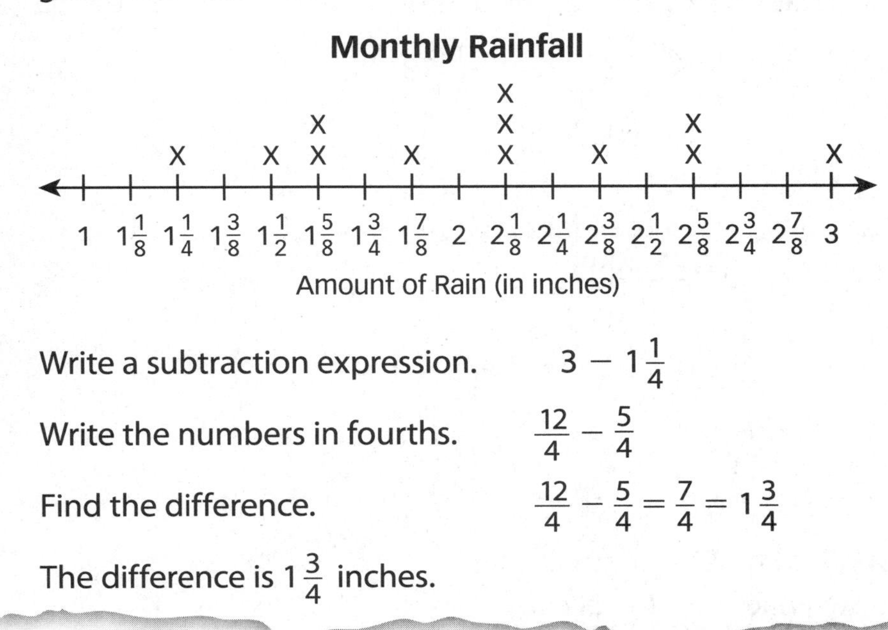

Write a subtraction expression. $3 - 1\frac{1}{4}$

Write the numbers in fourths. $\frac{12}{4} - \frac{5}{4}$

Find the difference. $\frac{12}{4} - \frac{5}{4} = \frac{7}{4} = 1\frac{3}{4}$

The difference is $1\frac{3}{4}$ inches.

1 Which questions below can be answered using the line plot in the example above? Circle all that apply.

A In 3 months, it rained the same amount. What is the difference between that amount and the amount in the month when it rained the most?

B What was the total amount of rainfall for the year?

C In how many months did it rain more than 2 inches?

D How much rainfall occurred in January?

2 Look at the choices you circled in problem 1. Which can be solved using subtraction? What is the solution? Explain.

____

____

Solve.

Marine biologists caught fish for research. They measured the sea bass they caught and recorded the lengths in the line plot below.

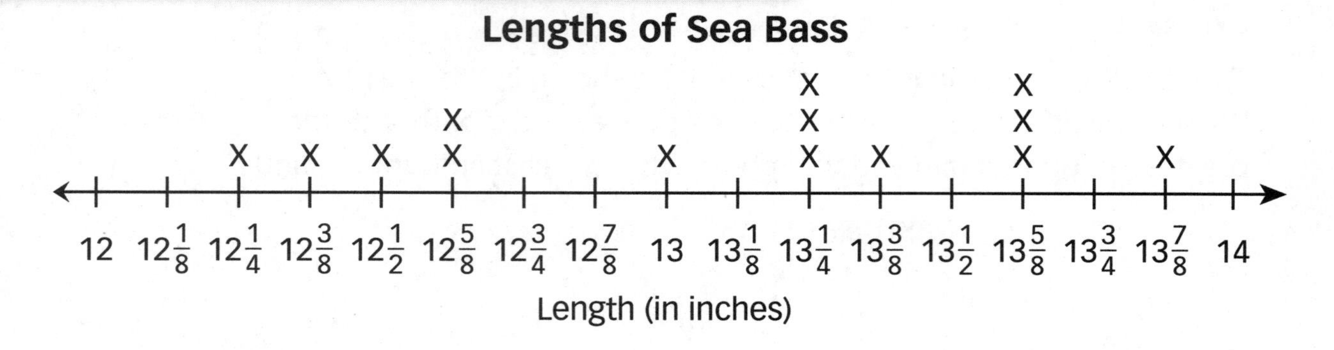

3 What is the difference in length between the longest and shortest sea bass that the biologists caught?

Show your work.

Solution: ______________________________

4 Sea bass that are caught and that have a length less than 13 inches must be thrown back into the ocean. How many more inches does the shortest fish need to grow before it can be taken out of the ocean?

Show your work.

Solution: ______________________________

5 Sea bass can grow to a maximum length of 23 inches. How much more would the longest fish caught need to grow in order to reach the maximum length?

Show your work.

Solution: ______________________________

Name: ____________________

Solve Problems with Line Plots

Solve the problems.

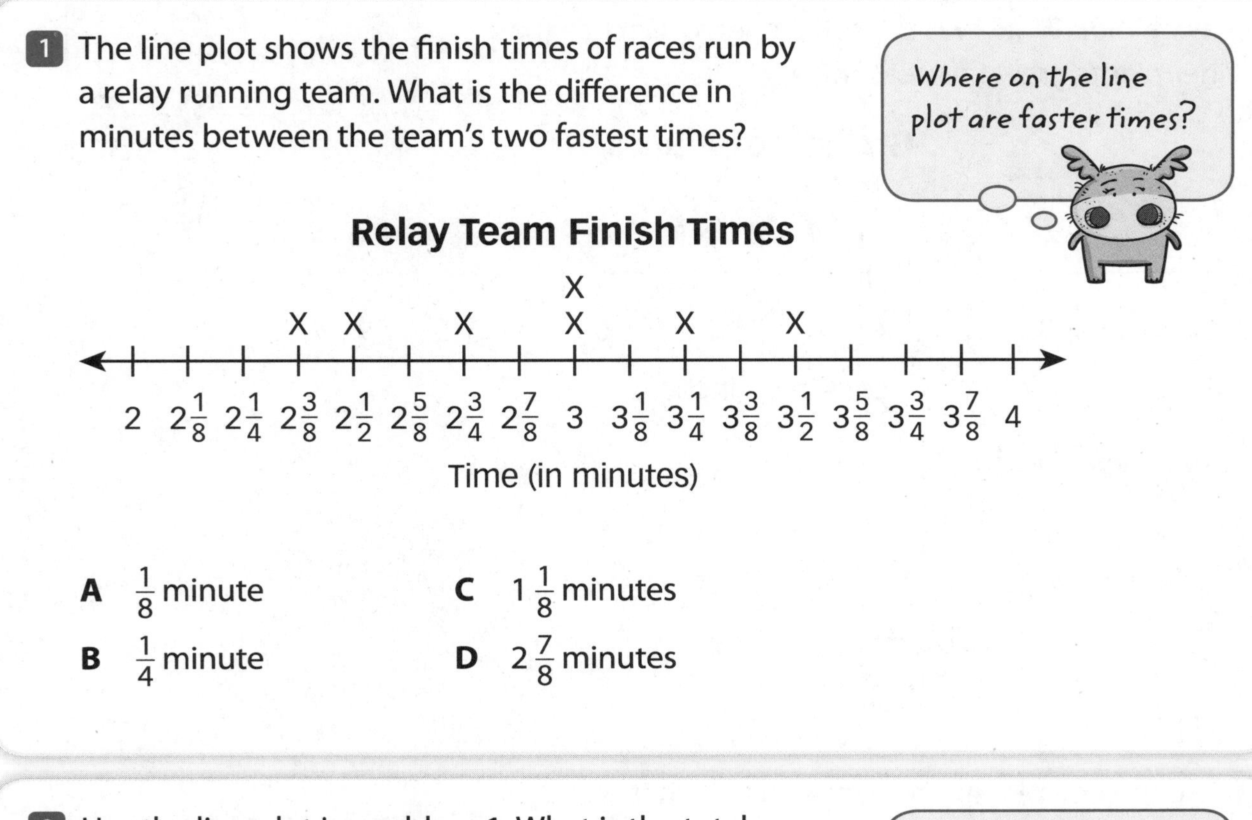

1 The line plot shows the finish times of races run by a relay running team. What is the difference in minutes between the team's two fastest times?

A $\frac{1}{8}$ minute

B $\frac{1}{4}$ minute

C $1\frac{1}{8}$ minutes

D $2\frac{7}{8}$ minutes

2 Use the line plot in problem 1. What is the total amount of time the team spent running in relay races?

A 17 minutes

B $17\frac{3}{8}$ minutes

C 20 minutes

D $20\frac{3}{8}$ minutes

Miriam chose **B** as the correct answer. How did she get that answer?

____

____

____

Solve.

3 Ginny recorded how much her tomato plants grew this season. She plotted the growth of each plant in a line plot. What was the total length in inches that her plants grew this season?

What operation do you use to find the combined length?

Growth of Plants

Length (in inches)	4	$4\frac{1}{8}$	$4\frac{1}{4}$	$4\frac{3}{8}$	$4\frac{1}{2}$	$4\frac{5}{8}$	$4\frac{3}{4}$	$4\frac{7}{8}$	5	$5\frac{1}{8}$	$5\frac{1}{4}$	$5\frac{3}{8}$	$5\frac{1}{2}$	$5\frac{5}{8}$	$5\frac{3}{4}$	$5\frac{7}{8}$	6
Plants					X				X	X		X			X X		X

Length (in inches)

Show your work.

Solution: ______________________

4 Use the line plot in problem 4 to tell whether each sentence is *True* or *False*.

Plants that grew a greater number of inches are farther to the right on the number line in the line plot.

a. The difference between the plant that grew the most and least is $2\frac{1}{2}$ inches. ☐ True ☐ False

b. Two plants that grew the most have a combined growth of $10\frac{1}{2}$ inches. ☐ True ☐ False

c. Two plants that grew the least have a combined growth of $9\frac{1}{2}$ inches. ☐ True ☐ False

d. Two plants grew the same amount. The combined growth of these two plants is $11\frac{1}{2}$ inches. ☐ True ☐ False

Dear Family,

This week your child is interpreting data shown on circle graphs.

A **circle graph** shows data divided into sections of a circle, showing how each data category is related to the whole and to other data categories. The circle graph below shows the kinds of instruments played by members of a school band.

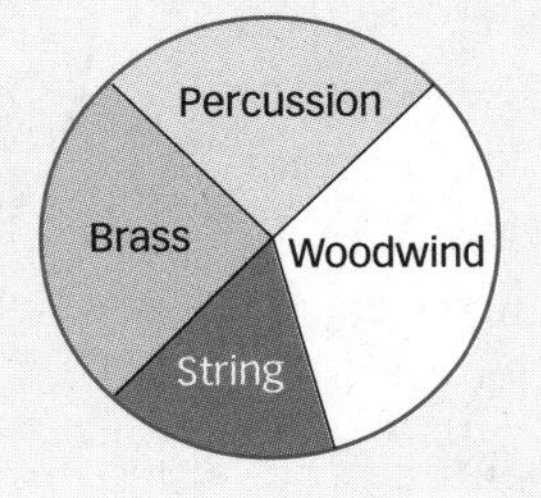

One way to solve problems using a circle graph is to compare the sizes of sections to each other.

For example, use the graph above to determine what kind of instrument is played by the fewest students.

Identify the smallest section of the circle graph: string. Therefore, string instruments are played by the fewest students.

Another way to solve problems is to compare the size of a section to the whole circle.

To determine what fraction of the band plays percussion instruments, for example, you can divide the circle into familiar fractions, such as quarters. Percussion is represented by one quarter of the circle, so $\frac{1}{4}$ of the band plays percussion.

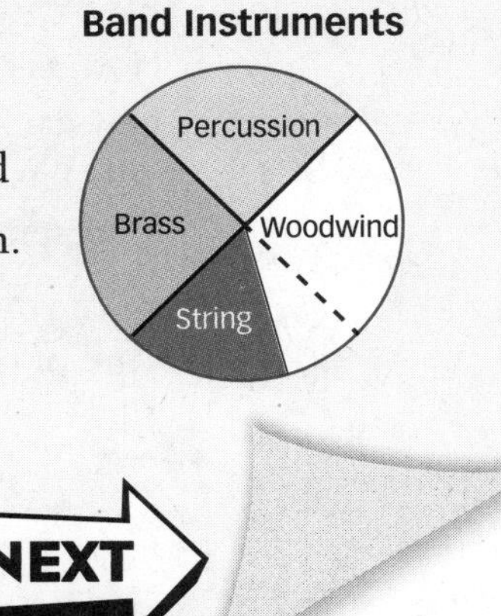

Invite your child to share what he or she knows about interpreting circle graphs by doing the following activity together.

NEXT

Using Familiar Fractions with a Circle Graph Activity

Materials: ruler or straight edge, pencil

Do this activity with your child to practice dividing a circle graph into familiar fractions.

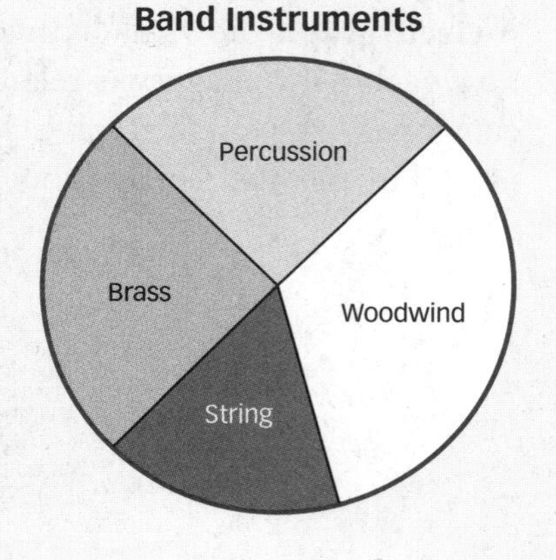

- Ask your child if he or she can tell the fraction of students that play each instrument by looking at the graph.
- Have your child point to the line that splits the circle into halves.
- Next, ask your child to identify the line that can be extended to split the circle into 4 equal parts, or quarters. (Between Brass and Percussion) Extend this line across the circle using the ruler and pencil.
- Work together again to extend the remaining line between the String and Woodwind across into the Percussion section.
- Have your child split the String section in half by drawing a line across the whole circle.
- Point out that the Percussion and String sections of the graph are now split into equal parts of the same size.
- Have your child continue splitting the circle graph into parts of this size. Help your child divide the *Brass* section into 3 equal parts and extend those lines across the circle.
- Ask your child if the circle graph is now divided into equal parts. Together, count the total number of parts and the number of parts in each section.
- Now ask your child if he or she can tell the fraction of students that play each instrument. Your child should recognize that he or she now has the information needed to determine the exact fraction represented by each section.
- Have your child identify the fraction of students that play each kind of instrument.

Interpret Circle Graphs

Name: ______________________

Prerequisite: Interpret a Bar Graph

Study the example showing how to interpret a bar graph. Then solve problems 1–6.

Example

Mr. Perry gave his students a math assignment with 3 problems. The bar graph shows the number of problems students solved correctly. What fraction of students correctly solved 2 or 3 problems?

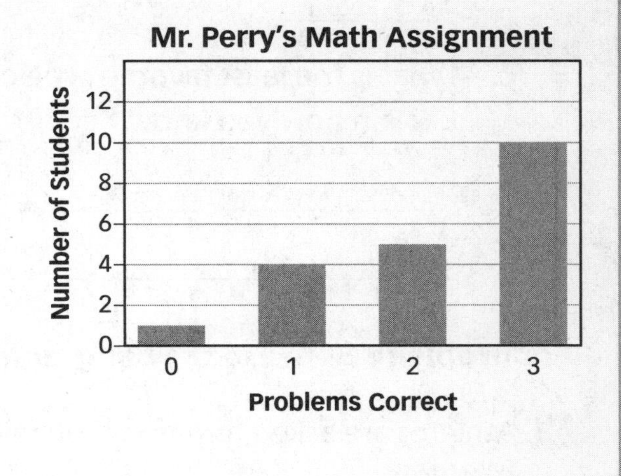

Determine the total number of students who completed the assignment: $1 + 4 + 5 + 10 = 20$.

5 students solved 2 problems correctly.

10 students solved 3 problems correctly.

So, 15 students solved 2 or 3 problems correctly.

$\frac{15}{20}$ or $\frac{3}{4}$ of students in the class correctly solved 2 or 3 problems.

For problems 1–3, use the bar graph in the example above.

1 How many students solved 1 problem correctly? ______

2 What fraction of students solved 1 problem correctly? __________

3 Mr. Perry says that $\frac{1}{4}$ of students solved 2 problems correctly. Is this true? Explain.

____

____

Solve.

4 A class made a survey of their favorite type of shoes. Name the fraction of the circle graph represented by Sneakers. Then compare the sections.

a. The Sneakers section is _______ of the circle.

b. Did more students choose Sandals or Boots?

____

c. What is the least favorite type of shoe? Explain how you know.

____

____

For problems 5–6, use the bar graph.

5 Athletes are asked to name their favorite event in a triathlon.

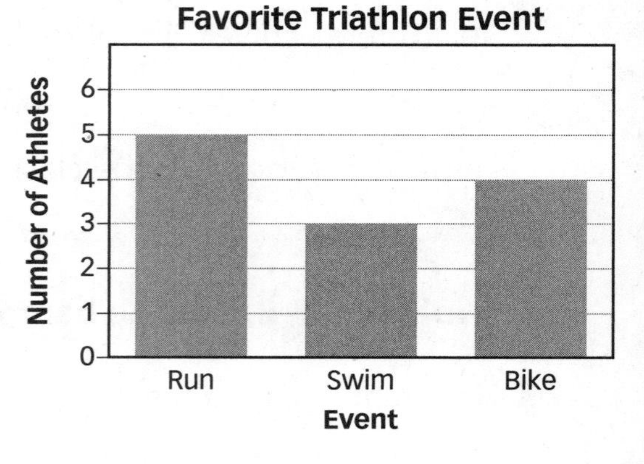

a. How many athletes were surveyed? _______

b. Did more than or less than half of the athletes say running is their favorite event? _______________

6 Identify the fraction of athletes that chose each event. Describe what part of a circle would be represented by each fraction.

Run: ____

____

Swim: ____

____

Bike: ____

____

____

Name: ______________________

Read Circle Graphs

Study the example showing how to interpret a circle graph. Then solve problems 1–6.

Example

The circle graph shows the kinds of instruments played by students in a middle school band. What kind of instrument is played by $\frac{1}{3}$ of the band?

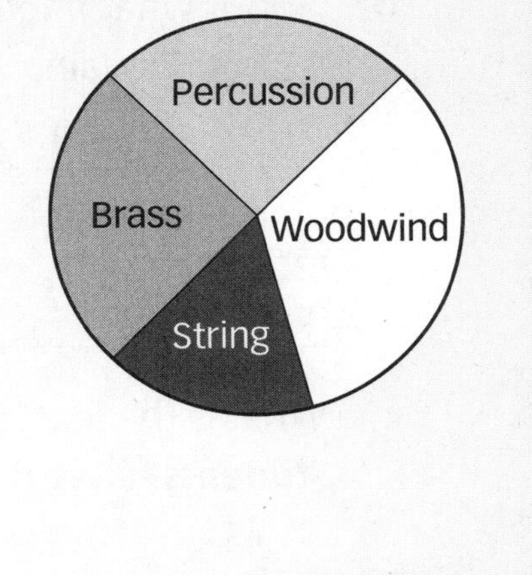

Look for a section that is close to $\frac{1}{3}$ of a circle.

$\frac{1}{3}$ is greater than $\frac{1}{4}$ and less than $\frac{1}{2}$.

The woodwind section is greater than a quarter of the circle but less than half of the circle.

Woodwind instruments are played by $\frac{1}{3}$ of the band.

A group of fourth grade students were asked to name their favorite season. The results are shown in the circle graph. Use the circle graph for problems 1–3.

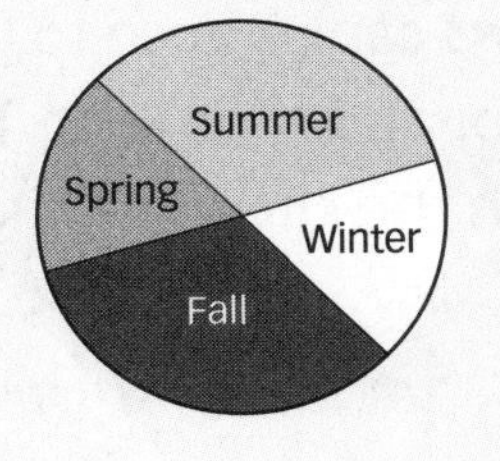

1 Which two seasons are the most popular?

____

2 Are any seasons equal in popularity? If so, which seasons? ______________________

3 About what fraction of students said summer is their favorite season? How do you know?

____

____

____

Vocabulary

circle graph a graph that shows data divided into sections of a circle, showing how each data category is related to the whole and to other data categories.

Solve.

4 A group of fourth grade students were asked how many pets they have at home. The results are shown in the circle graph.

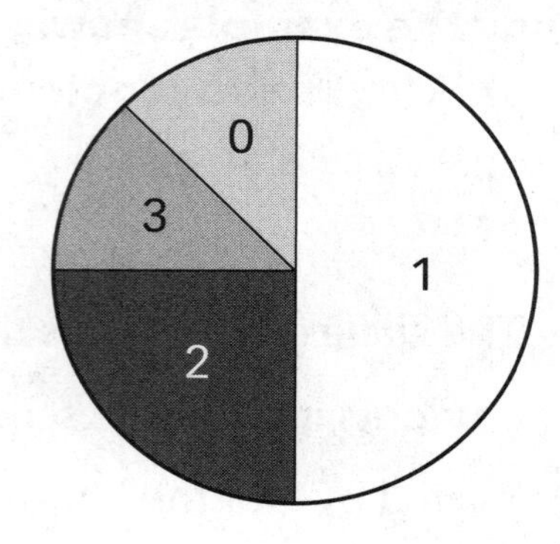

a. About what fraction of the students have 1 pet?

____

b. About what fraction of the students have 2 pets? Explain.

____

____

____

c. What is the least common number of pets that students have? Explain.

____

____

Students in an art class can choose to use colored pencils, markers, or crayons for an art project. The materials selected by students are shown in the circle graph. Use this graph for problems 5 and 6.

5 Write the materials selected by the students in order from least used to most used.

____

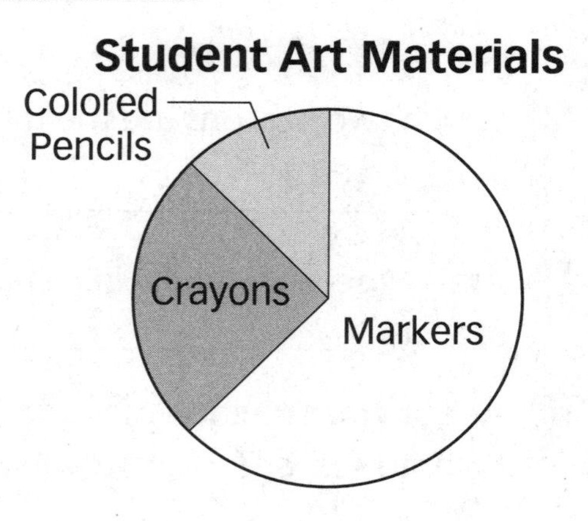

6 How does the number of students who used crayons compare to the number of students who used colored pencils? Explain.

____

____

____

____

Name: ______________________

Interpret Circle Graphs

Solve the problems.

1 Students in gym class complete a one-mile run. The circle graph summarizes the finish times. About what fraction of students completed the run in 8 minutes or under?

Mile Run Times

8 minutes or under

over 8 min.

Imagine dividing the circle into familiar fractions.

______

2 The circle graph shows the flower sales at a local nursery. Which statement is true? Circle the letter of the correct answer.

Flower Sales

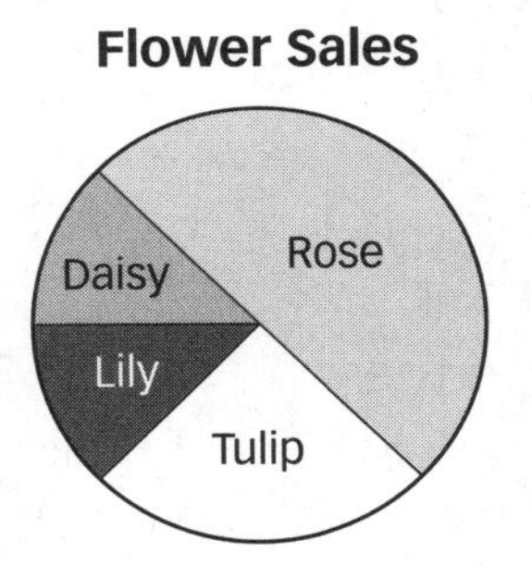

Determine the fraction represented by each section of the circle. The sum of the fractions is 1.

A About $\frac{1}{3}$ of the flowers sold are roses.

B The nursery sells more tulips than daisies and lilies combined.

C Twice as many roses are sold as tulips.

D The nursery sells more daisies than lilies.

Brianne chose **B** as the correct answer. How did she get that answer?

____

____

Solve.

3 A group of college students are asked what electronic device they use most often. The results are shown in the circle graph. Compare the use of computers with the use of tablets.

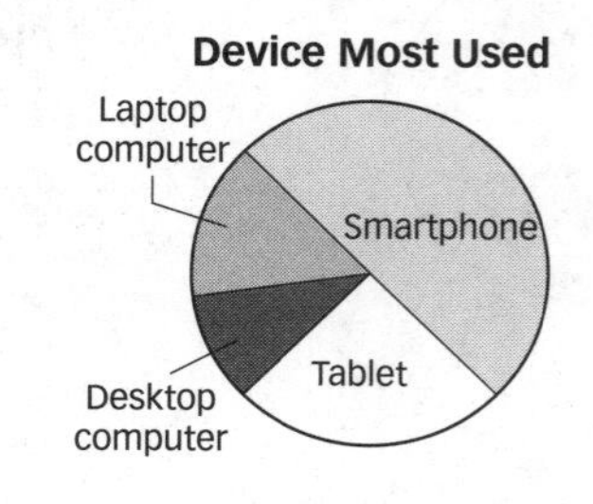

____

____

____

____

4 A group of fourth graders are asked to name their favorite school subject. The results are shown in the circle graph. Complete the following statements so they are true.

How can you compare the sizes of different sections in the circle graph?

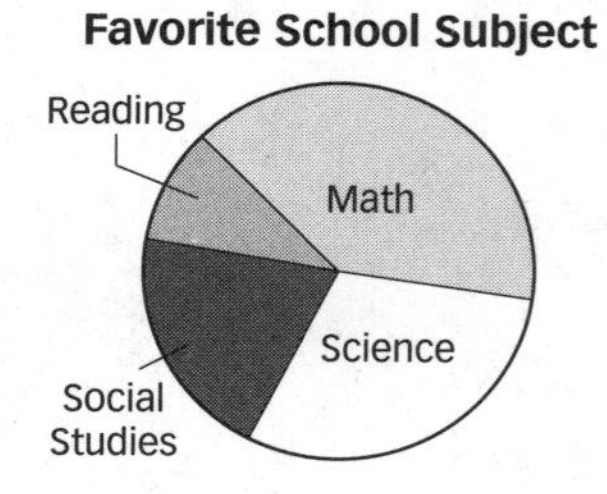

Almost $\frac{1}{2}$ of students said their favorite subject is ____________.

Exactly __________ of students said their favorite subject is science or social studies.

Science is as popular as ________________ and ________________ combined.

Dear Family,

This week your child is learning to collect and represent data.

One way to learn more about a topic is to ask a question that can be answered by collecting data about the topic. In order to collect data, it is important that answers to the question will vary.

"What pizza topping is the favorite among students in the class?" This question can be answered by collecting data because various answers are possible: pepperoni, mushrooms, and so on.

"What day does the cafeteria serve pizza?" This question has a single answer; it will not generate a set of data.

Before collecting data to answer a question, determine the best way to collect the data. There are three methods for data collection:

observation: a method of collecting data by watching people or events in a natural setting.

survey: a method of gathering information by asking questions.

experiment: a procedure that can be repeated to collect data.

The best method for collecting data depends on the question that is being asked. For instance, you can observe the kinds of pizza your classmates buy from the cafeteria, however there is no guarantee the pizza has their favorite topping. In this case, a survey that asks students to name their favorite pizza topping is the best way to collect this data.

A **frequency table** can be used to represent a set of data. This is a table that identifies how many times each piece of data occurs. Data can also be displayed in a line plot or a bar graph.

Invite your child to share what he or she knows about collecting and representing data by doing the following activity together.

Collecting and Representing Data Activity

Collect and represent a set of data with your child. You may organize your information in a table like the one below.

- Think of a topic you are interested in learning more about. Write a question on this topic that can be answered by collecting a set of data. Make sure the topic and question is something for which you can easily gather data.
- Determine the method you should use to collect the data: observation, survey, or experiment.
- Using the appropriate method, collect data that can be used to answer the question. Aim to collect 15–20 pieces of data.
- Represent the data using a frequency table.
- Summarize the data. What is the answer to the question you wrote?

Question:	
Data Collection Method:	
Data:	
Frequency Table:	
Summary of Data (2–3 sentences):	

Collecting and Representing Data

Name: ____________________

Prerequisite: Create and Interpret Line Plots and Bar Graphs

Study the example showing how to interpret a bar graph. Then solve problems 1–5.

Example

Athletes are asked to name their favorite event in a triathlon. What is the most popular event? What is the least popular event?

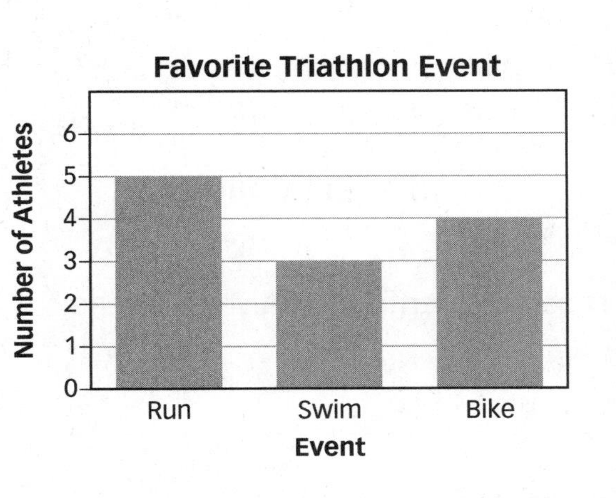

The tallest bar indicates the event named the most frequently. The run is the most popular event.

The shortest bar indicates the event named the least frequently. The swim is the least favorite event.

1 In the example above, how many more athletes named the most popular event than the least popular event? ____________________

2 Create a line plot that represents the same data.

The line plot shows the finish times of races run by a relay running team.

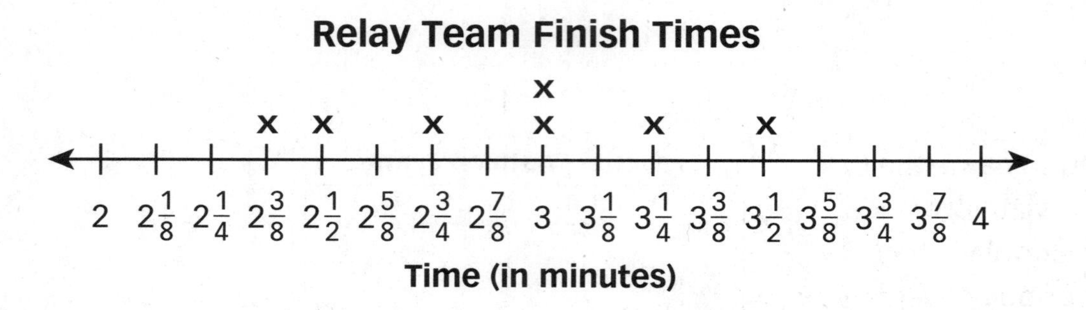

3 What is the most frequent time finished by the relay teams?

____

4 What is the difference in minutes between the fastest team and the slowest team?

Show your work.

Solution: _______ minutes

5 Mrs. Hall gave her students a math test. Of 15 students, 5 students earned an A, 6 students earned a B, and the same number of students earned a C as earned a D. Create a bar graph that represents this data.

Name: ____________________

Write Questions to Collect Data

Study the example showing how to identify a question that can be addressed with data. Then solve problems 1–7.

Example

Wyatt says he can collect data to answer each of the following questions about his favorite restaurant. Is Wyatt correct?

How many customers are served at the restaurant each day?
How many items are on the restaurant's menu?
How many customers can the restaurant seat?
What menu item is the favorite among customers?

Wyatt is not correct. The number of customers varies from day to day, so this question can be used to collect data. The favorite item on the menu will vary from person to person, so this question can also be used to collect data. However, the number of items on the menu and the number of people the restaurant can seat do not change. These questions have a single answer and cannot be used to collect data.

1 Describe the possible data that could be collected for the question, *How many customers are served at the restaurant each day?*

____

____

2 Describe the possible data that could be collected for the question, *What menu item is the favorite among customers?*

____

____

3 Write another question about the restaurant that could be answered by collecting data.

____

____

Solve.

4 *How many players are on the school volleyball team?* Can you use this question to collect data? Explain.

____

____

5 *How many times does the volleyball team spike the ball during each game?* Can you use this question to collect data? Explain.

____

____

6 Cross out each question that cannot be used to collect a set of data.

How fast can students in the class run the 100-meter dash?
What is the principal's favorite kind of juice?
What are the ages of students in the school choir?
What is the most popular book your class has read this year?
How many cars enter the school parking lot each hour?

7 Write a question that could be used to collect data on each of the following topics.

school lunch ____

____

textbooks ____

____

school teachers ____

____

Name: ______________________

Collect Data

Study the example showing how to determine if an observation, survey, or experiment should be used to collect a set of data. Then solve problems 1–5.

Example

Should an observation, survey, or experiment be used to collect data to answer the question, *How many people jog through the park each hour?*

The data that will be collected is any number greater than or equal to 0. Ask questions to determine the best method for collecting this data:

Observation: Can you watch people to find out how many jog through park in an hour?	✓ **Yes** You can observe people in the park during various hours of the day.
Survey: Can you ask people a question to find out how many people jog through the park in an hour?	✗ **No** You cannot survey people to find out this information.
Experiment: Can you repeat a procedure that will result in the number of people that jog through the park in an hour?	✗ **No** You cannot collect this data from an experiment.

1 Explain how to use an observation to collect the data for the question in the example above.

____

____

____

____

____

2 Henry asks children at the park to name their favorite area of the park: playground, walking trail, nature center, or bike path. Is Henry conducting an observation, survey, or experiment? Explain.

____

____

Vocabulary

observation: a method of collecting data by watching people or events in a natural setting.

survey: to gather information by asking questions.

experiment: a procedure that can be repeated to collect data.

Solve.

3 Francesca sits at an intersection for 30 minutes. She counts the number of convertibles, SUVs, and pickup trucks that pass through the intersection during this time. Is Francesca conducting an observation, survey, or experiment? Explain.

____

____

____

4 Rhett and his brother take turns rolling a number cube. They record the number of times the cube lands on the number 1 or 6. Are the boys conducting an observation, survey, or experiment? Explain.

____

____

5 Jordy wants to gather data about the distance a paper airplane can fly.

Part A

Should an observation, survey, or experiment be used to collect the data? Explain.

____

____

____

Part B

Using the method from Part A, gather data that can be used to answer the question you wrote. Record the data below.

____

____

____

Name: ______________________

Represent and Interpret Data

Study the example showing how to represent a set of data using a line plot. Then solve problems 1–3.

Example

Each day in January that it snows, Carrie measures the depth of the new snow to the nearest eighth of an inch. She collects the following data:

$2\frac{1}{8}$	$1\frac{7}{8}$	$1\frac{1}{4}$	$2\frac{5}{8}$	$1\frac{1}{2}$	$2\frac{3}{8}$	$1\frac{5}{8}$
$1\frac{5}{8}$	$2\frac{1}{8}$	3	$2\frac{1}{8}$	$1\frac{1}{4}$	2	$2\frac{5}{8}$

How can Carrie represent the data using a line plot?

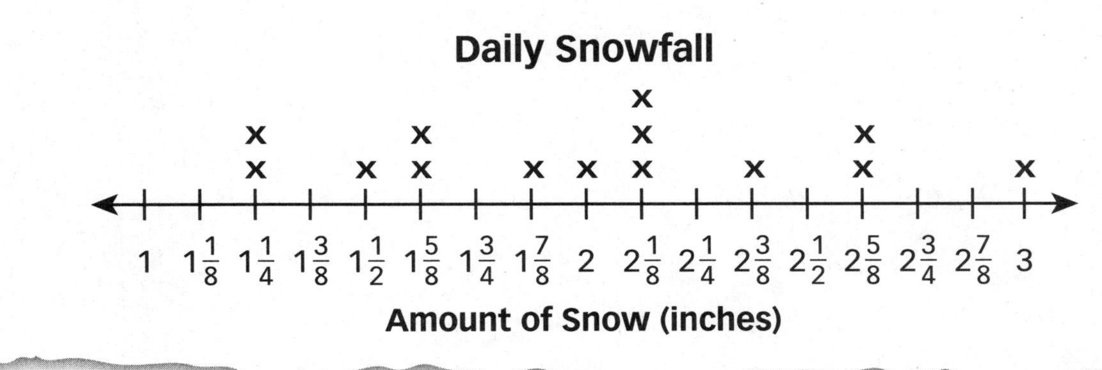

Use the line plot to interpret the data.

1 What is the greatest amount of snow that falls in one day? __________

2 Use the line plot to draw one conclusion about the data.

____

____

____

Vocabulary

frequency table a table that indicates how often something occurs in a set of data.

Solve.

3 Use a survey to collect and represent data from your teachers about their summer jobs.

Part A

Write a question that you can use to collect data from your teachers.

____

____

Part B

Survey your teachers to collect data. Organize your data in a frequency table.

Part C

Create a bar graph to represent the data.

Name: ______________________

Collecting and Representing Data

Solve the problems.

1 Which question about an animal rescue shelter will produce a variety of data?

A What was the first kind of animal ever adopted from the shelter?

B How many animals are adopted each month?

C How many people volunteer at the shelter?

D Does the shelter host adoption events?

2 Yolanda collects data about the digital devices people prefer to use. Out of 25 people, 13 people prefer a smartphone, 7 people prefer a tablet, and 5 people prefer a computer.

Part A

Represent this data using a frequency table.

Part B

Summarize the data.

____

____

Solve.

3 ***Part A***

Write a question that you can use to collect data from your classmates.

____

____

Part B

Describe the method you will use to collect the data.

____

____

____

____

Part C

Represent the data using a line plot or bar graph.

Part D

Write 2–3 sentences summarizing the data.

____

____

____

Dear Family,

This week your child is exploring angles.

Your child is learning that an angle is a kind of geometric shape.

angle a geometric shape made by two rays from a common endpoint, called a vertex.

Two pencils with erasers placed end to end can represent an angle.

A **right angle** looks like a square corner.

right angle

The pencils show a right angle.

An **acute angle** has a smaller opening than a right angle.

acute angle

The pencils show an acute angle.

An **obtuse angle** opens wider than a right angle.

obtuse angle

The pencils show an obtuse angle.

Invite your child to share what he or she knows about different kinds of angles by doing the following activity together.

NEXT

Identifying Angles Activity

Do an activity with your child to explore angles.

- Look around the house for objects that have different kinds of angles.

  Examples: Patches on a soccer ball have obtuse angles.
  A stair railing and a spindle form an acute angle.
  A corner of a window forms a right angle.

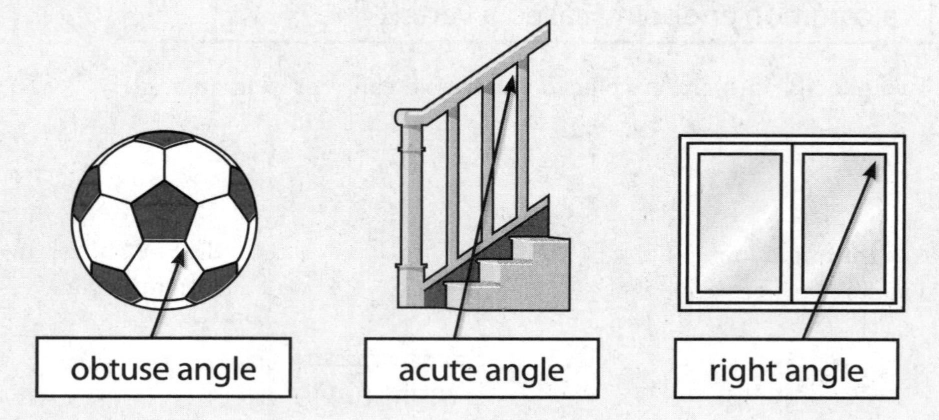

- Give points for each kind of angle you find: an acute angle is worth 3 points, an obtuse angle is worth 2 points, and a right angle is worth 1 point.
- Search for 10 minutes. Then count how many points each person has. The person with the most points wins.
- Challenge! Find an object that has all three kinds of angles.

Look for other real-life opportunities to identify different kinds of angles with your child.

Understand Angles

Name: ____________________

Prerequisite: **What does it mean to multiply with fractions?**

Study the example problem showing multiplication with a fraction. Then solve problems 1–6.

Example

4 friends shared a whole pizza. Each person ate an equal amount.

Draw lines on the circle at the right to show the fraction of the pizza that each person ate.

Use multiplication to show that the four parts together equal the whole.

$4 \times \frac{1}{4} = \frac{4}{1} \times \frac{1}{4} = \frac{4}{4} = 1$ whole

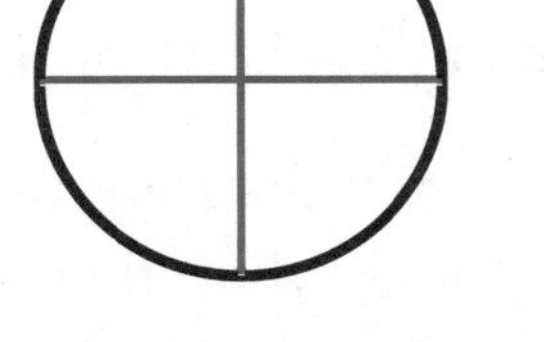

The pizza is divided into 4 parts. Each part is $\frac{1}{4}$ of the pizza.

1 8 friends shared a pizza. Each person ate an equal amount. Draw lines on the circle at the right to show the fraction of the pizza that each person ate.

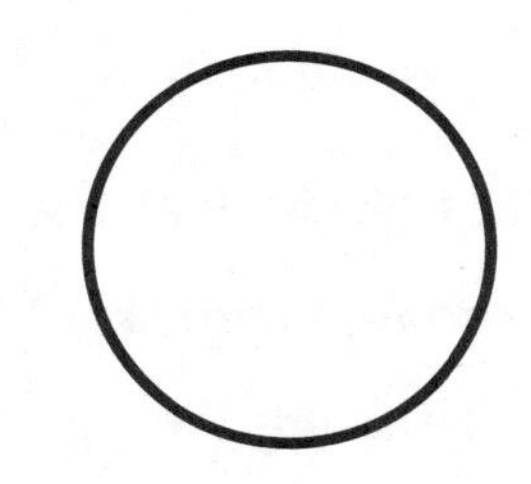

a. What fraction of the pizza did each person eat?

____

b. Use multiplication to show that all the parts are equal to the whole.

____

2 A pizza is cut into 8 equal slices.

a. What fraction of the pizza is each slice? ________

b. Mandy eats 2 slices. What fraction of the pizza did Mandy eat? ____________________

c. Use multiplication to explain how you found the answer to **b.** ____________________

Solve.

3 Look at the clock at the right. When the minute hand moves from the 12 to the 3, it moves over $\frac{1}{4}$ of a circle.

a. How many minutes are in 1 hour? _______

b. When the minute hand moves from the 12 to the 3, how many minutes have passed? Use fraction multiplication to show your answer.

$\frac{1}{4} \times$ _______ = _______ minutes

4 Look at the clock at the right.

a. When the minute hand moves from the 12 to the 6, what fraction of a circle does it move over?

_______ of a circle

b. How many minutes have passed? Use fraction multiplication to show your answer.

____

5 Look at the clock at the right. When the minute hand moves from the 12 to the 4, it moves over $\frac{1}{3}$ of a circle. How many minutes have passed? Use fraction multiplication to show your answer.

____

6 Look at the clock at the right. When the minute hand moves from the 12 to the 1, how many minutes have passed? Use fraction multiplication to show your answer.

____

Name: ______________________

Show Measures of Angles

Study the example showing the measure of an angle. Then solve problems 1–6.

Example

The drawing below shows an angle that turns through 9 one-degree angles.

1°

How many degrees does the angle measure?

The angle measures 9° because it turns through 9 one-degree angles.

The measure of any angle is equal to the number of one-degree angles it turns through.

1 An angle turns through 60 one-degree angles. What is the measure of the angle? _______ degrees

2 An angle turns through 160 one-degree angles. What is the measure of the angle? _______ degrees

3 The circle at the right has 4 equal parts. The angle shown in the circle is a right angle.

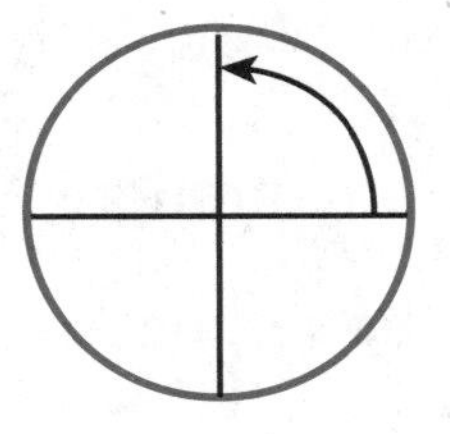

a. What fraction of the circle does the right angle turn through? _______ of the circle

b. Complete the sentence.

A circle has 360°. A right angle turns through

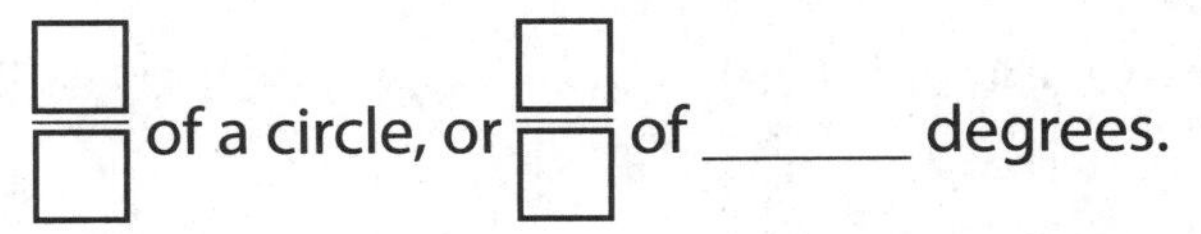

$\frac{\square}{\square}$ of a circle, or $\frac{\square}{\square}$ of _______ degrees.

c. Use fraction multiplication to show how you can find the measure of a right angle.

____

Vocabulary

angle a geometric shape made by two rays that meet at a common endpoint, called a vertex.

right angle an angle that looks like a square corner and measures 90°.

Solve.

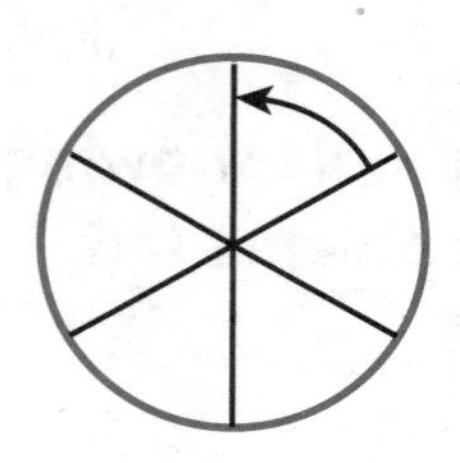

4 The circle at the right has 6 equal parts. The angle shown in the circle is an acute angle.

a. What fraction of the circle does the acute angle turn through? ______ of the circle

b. Complete the sentence.
A circle has 360°. The acute angle turns through $\frac{\square}{\square}$ of the circle, or $\frac{\square}{\square}$ of ______ degrees.

c. Use fraction multiplication to show how you can find the measure of the acute angle.

____

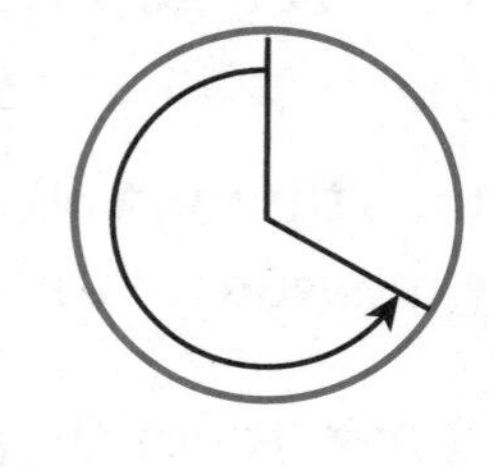

5 The larger part of the circle at the right is twice as big as the smaller part.

a. What fraction of the circle is the smaller part? $\frac{\square}{3}$

b. What fraction of the circle is the larger part? $\frac{\square}{3}$

c. What fraction of the circle does the angle shown by the arrow turn through? $\frac{\square}{3}$ of the circle

d. Complete the sentence.

A circle has 360°. The angle shown by the arrow turns through $\frac{\square}{\square}$ of the circle, or $\frac{\square}{\square}$ of ______ degrees.

e. Use fraction multiplication to show how you can find the measure of the angle shown by the arrow.

____

6 What is the measure of an angle that turns through $\frac{1}{12}$ of a circle?

____

Vocabulary

acute angle an angle that has fewer degrees than a right angle.

Name: ______________________

Reason and Write

Study the example. Underline two parts that you think make it a particularly good answer and a helpful example.

Example

Describe and compare the angles shown by the hands on the clocks below. What kinds of angle are shown? Which angle has a greater measure?

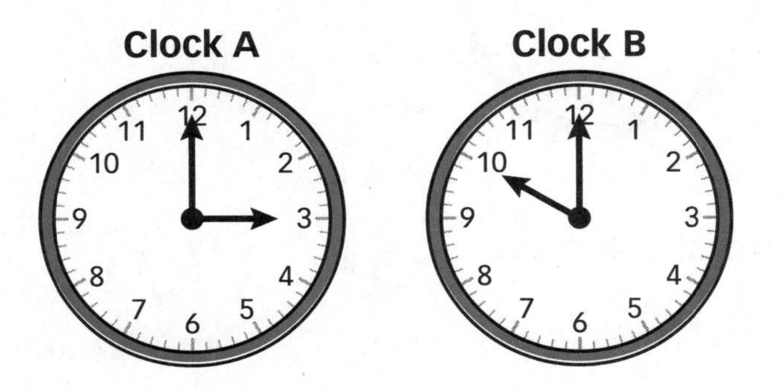

Show your work. Use numbers and words to explain your answer.

The angle formed by the hands of Clock A turns through 15 minutes out of 60 minutes on the clock.

This is $\frac{15}{60}$, or $\frac{1}{4}$, of the circle on the clock.

$\frac{1}{4}$ of 360 degrees in a circle is the measure of the angle.

$$\frac{1}{4} \times 360 = 90$$

The angle measures 90 degrees, so it is a right angle.

The angle formed by the hands of Clock B turns through 10 minutes out of 60 minutes.

This is $\frac{10}{60}$, or $\frac{1}{6}$, of the circle.

$\frac{1}{6}$ of 360 degrees in a circle is the measure of the angle.

$$\frac{1}{6} \times 360 = 60$$

The angle measures 60 degrees, so it is an acute angle.

The angle in Clock A has a greater measure than the angle in Clock B because 90 degrees > 60 degrees.

Where does the example . . .

- describe each angle?
- compare the measures of the angles?
- use numbers to explain?
- use words to explain?

Solve the problem. Use what you learned from the model.

Describe and compare the angles shown by the hands on the clocks below. What kinds of angle are shown? Which angle has a greater measure?

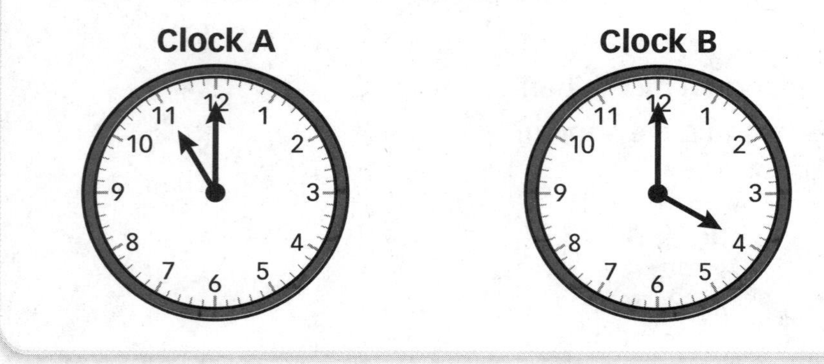

Show your work. Use numbers and words to explain your answer.

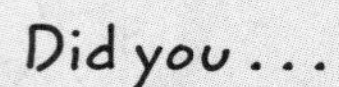

- describe each angle?
- compare the measures of the angles?
- use numbers to explain?
- use words to explain?

Dear Family,

This week your child is learning to measure and draw angles.

Your child is learning how to estimate the measure of an angle, as well as how to find an angle's exact measure.

Estimate the measure of an angle by using benchmarks, such as a right angle and a straight angle. For example, to estimate the measure of the purple angle below, compare it to a right angle and to a straight angle.

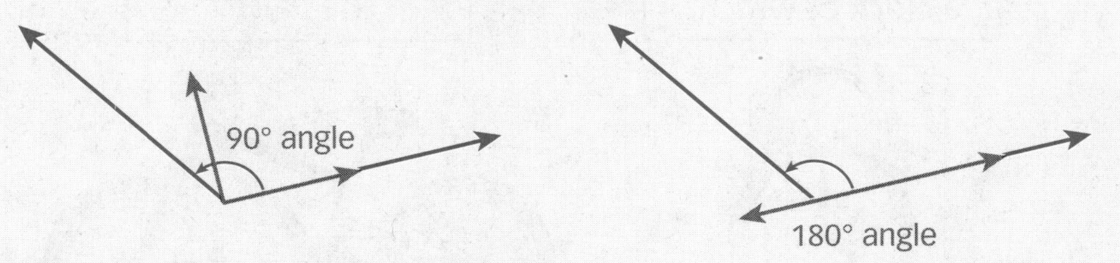

A right angle has a measure of 90 degrees. A straight angle has a measure of 180 degrees. The measure of the purple angle is between 90 degrees and 180 degrees.

To find the exact measure of the angle, your child is learning to use a tool called a protractor.

- Line up the center point of the protractor with the vertex of the angle.
- Then line up one ray with the 0° mark.
- Read the mark on the protractor that the other ray passes through.

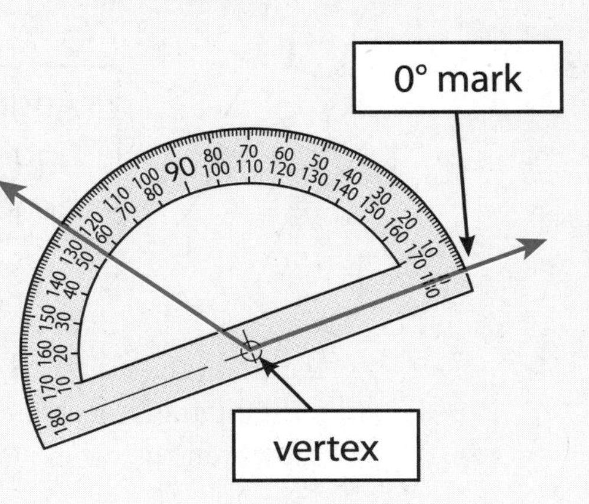

The angle measures 125°. (The ray also passes through the 55° mark, but since the angle is bigger than a 90° angle, the measure is not 55°.)

Invite your child to share what he or she knows about measuring and drawing angles by doing the following activity together.

Measuring Angles Activity

Do an activity with your child to estimate the measure of angles.

- Identify angles in and around the house or outside in the yard or neighborhood. You can also look through magazines or newspapers for pictures that show angles.

  Examples of angles you might find (or make) are:

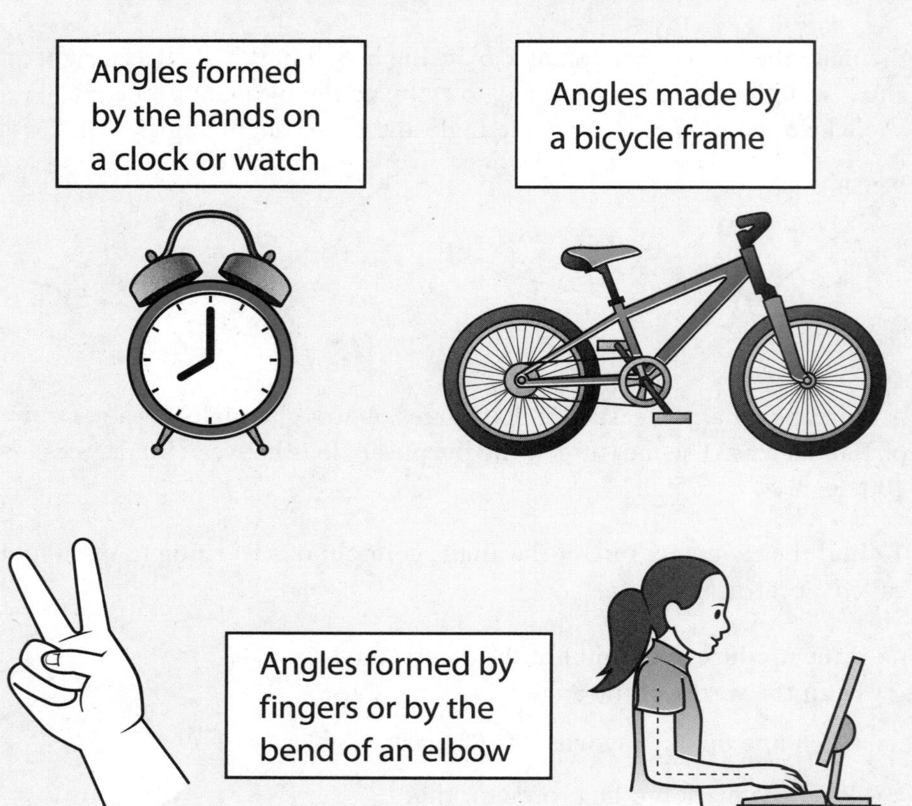

- Estimate the measure of each angle by using right angles and straight angles as benchmarks. You can use the benchmark angles shown on the other side of this page.

Look for other real-life opportunities to estimate angle measures with your child.

Name: ______________________

Use a Protractor to Measure Angles

Study the example showing how to use a protractor to measure an angle. Then solve problems 1–5.

Example

Omar drew the angle at the right. What is the measure of the angle?

Line up the 0° or the 180° mark on a protractor with one ray of the angle.

Line up the center point of the protractor with the vertex of the angle.

Look at the other ray. Read the number of degrees on the protractor. Read the number that is less than 90, since the angle is less than 90°.

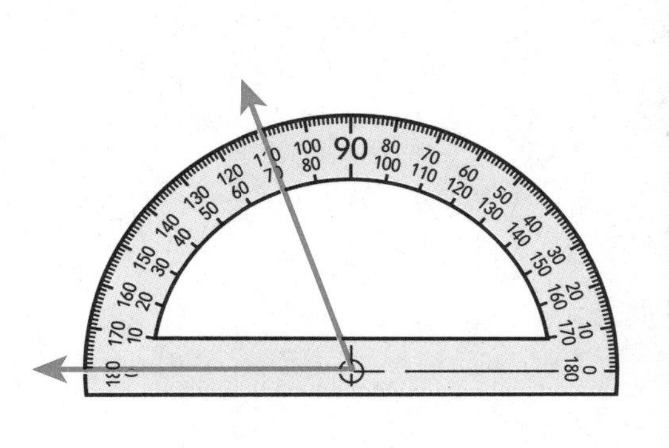

The angle measures 70°.

1 Read the number of degrees on the protractor to find the measure of the angle.

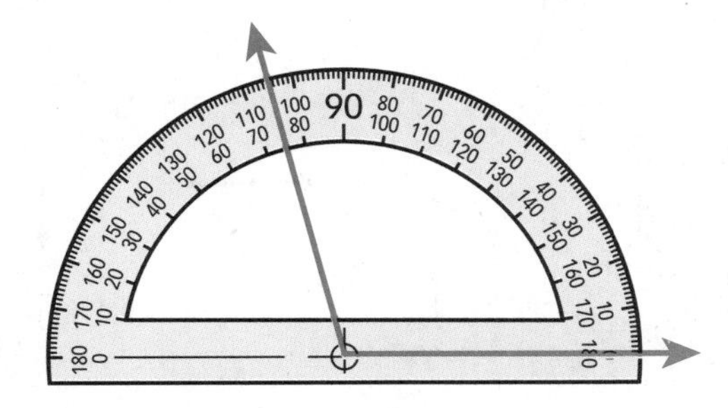

The angle measures _______ degrees.

2 Use a protractor to measure the angle below.

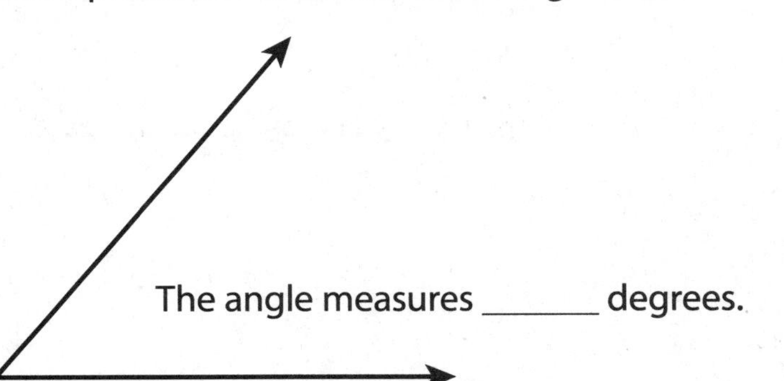

The angle measures _______ degrees.

Vocabulary

ray a straight row of points that starts at one point and goes on forever in one direction.

vertex the point where two rays or lines meet to form an angle.

protractor a tool used to measure angles.

Solve.

For problems 3–5, use a protractor to measure the angles. Write each measure.

3 The beam from the flashlight forms an angle.

The angle measures _______ degrees.

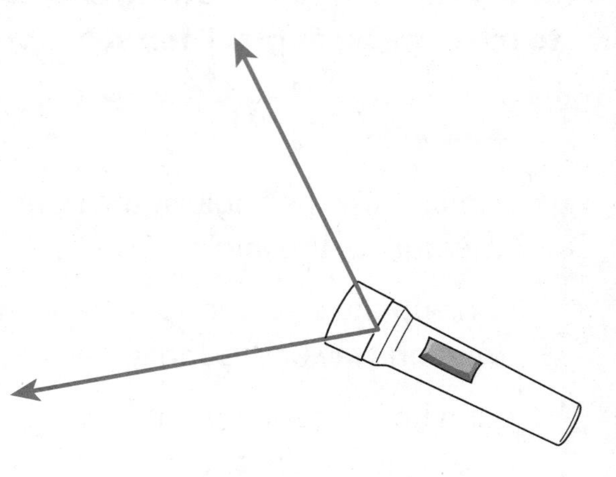

4 Measure one angle of the polygon at the right.

The angle measures _______ degrees.

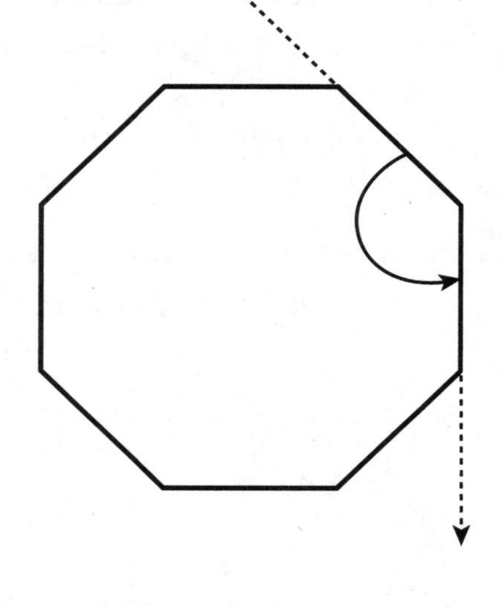

5 Measure the angles of the triangle at the right.

Angle *A* measures _______ degrees.

Angle *B* measures _______ degrees.

Angle *C* measures _______ degrees.

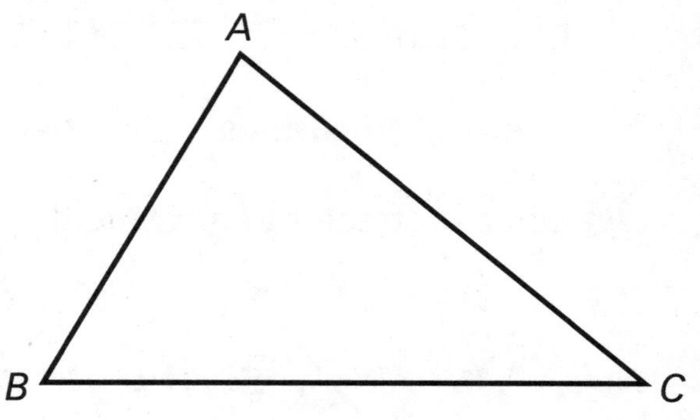

Name: ___________________________

Draw Angles

Study the example showing how to draw an angle. Then solve problems 1–6.

Example

Stephanie wants to draw a 60° angle. She drew a ray and positioned the endpoint of the ray on a protractor's center point. Then she drew a point at 0° on the ray. How does she draw the other ray to form a 60° angle?

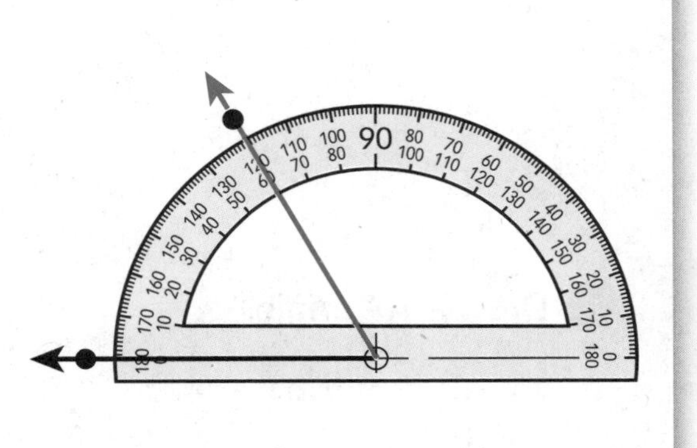

Find 60° on the protractor.

Draw a point at the 60°-degree mark.

Draw a ray from the vertex through this point.

1 Draw a ray to show a 70° angle.

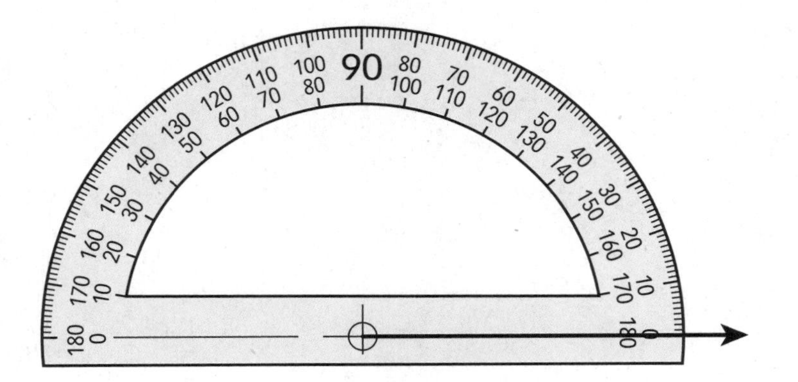

2 Draw a ray to show a 100° angle.

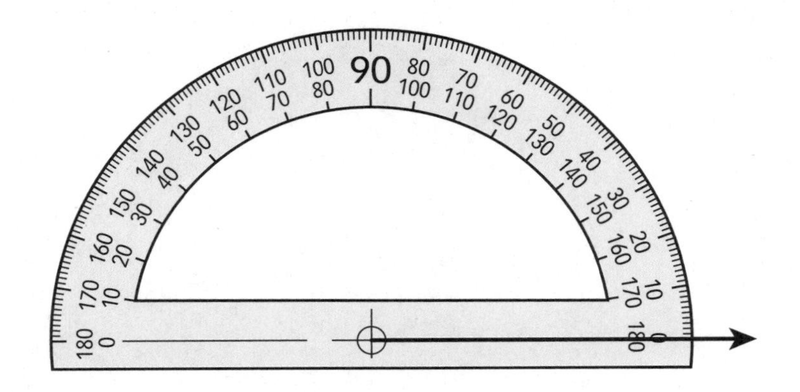

Vocabulary

ray a straight row of points that starts at one point and goes on forever in one direction.

vertex the point where two rays or lines meet to form an angle.

protractor a tool used to measure angles.

Solve.

3 Draw a 160° angle.

4 Draw a 20° angle.

5 Draw a 45° angle.

6 Draw a 135° angle.

Name: ______________________

Measure and Draw Angles

Solve the problems.

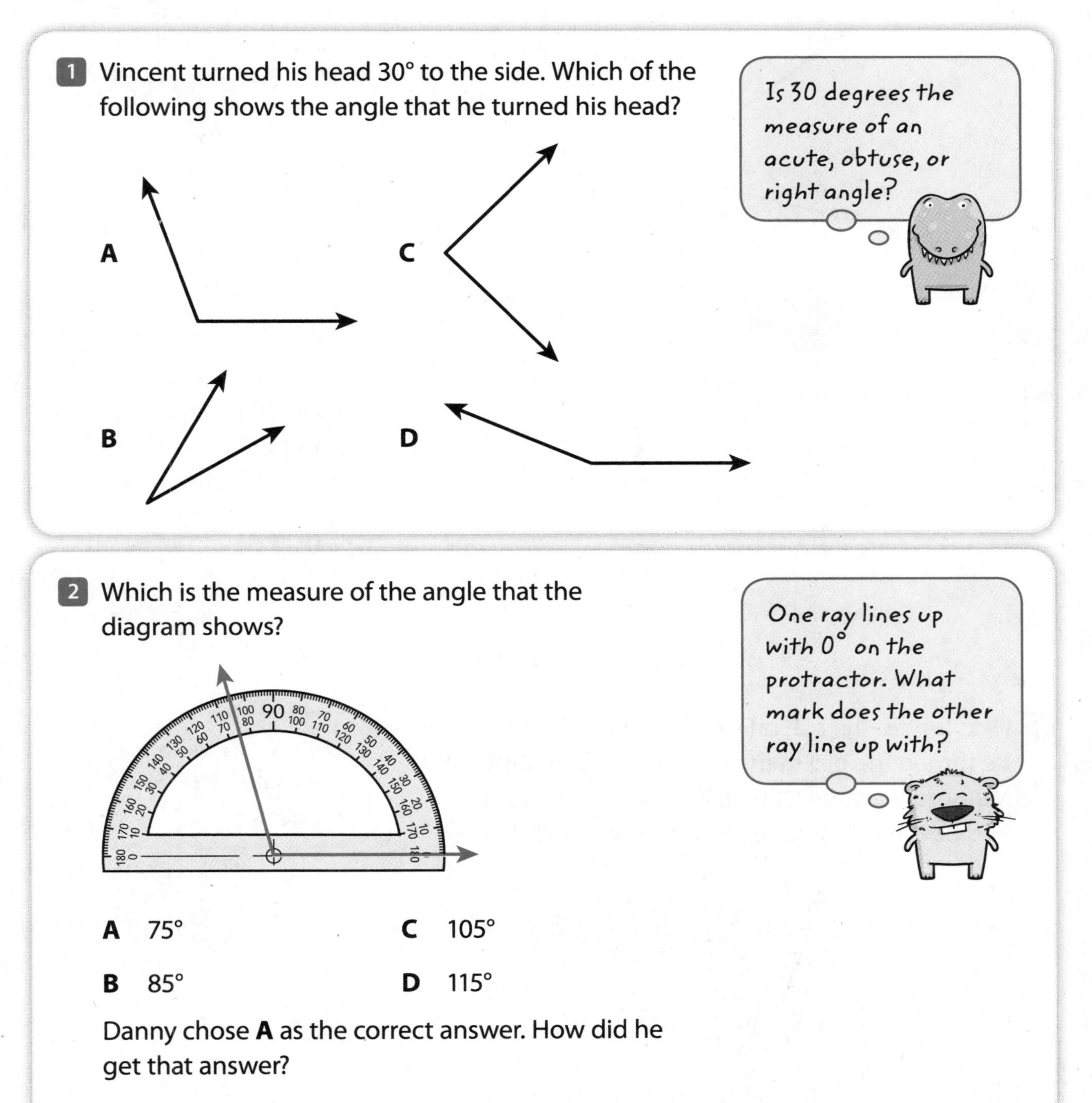

1 Vincent turned his head 30° to the side. Which of the following shows the angle that he turned his head?

A

B

C

D

2 Which is the measure of the angle that the diagram shows?

A 75°

B 85°

C 105°

D 115°

Danny chose **A** as the correct answer. How did he get that answer?

____

____

____

Solve.

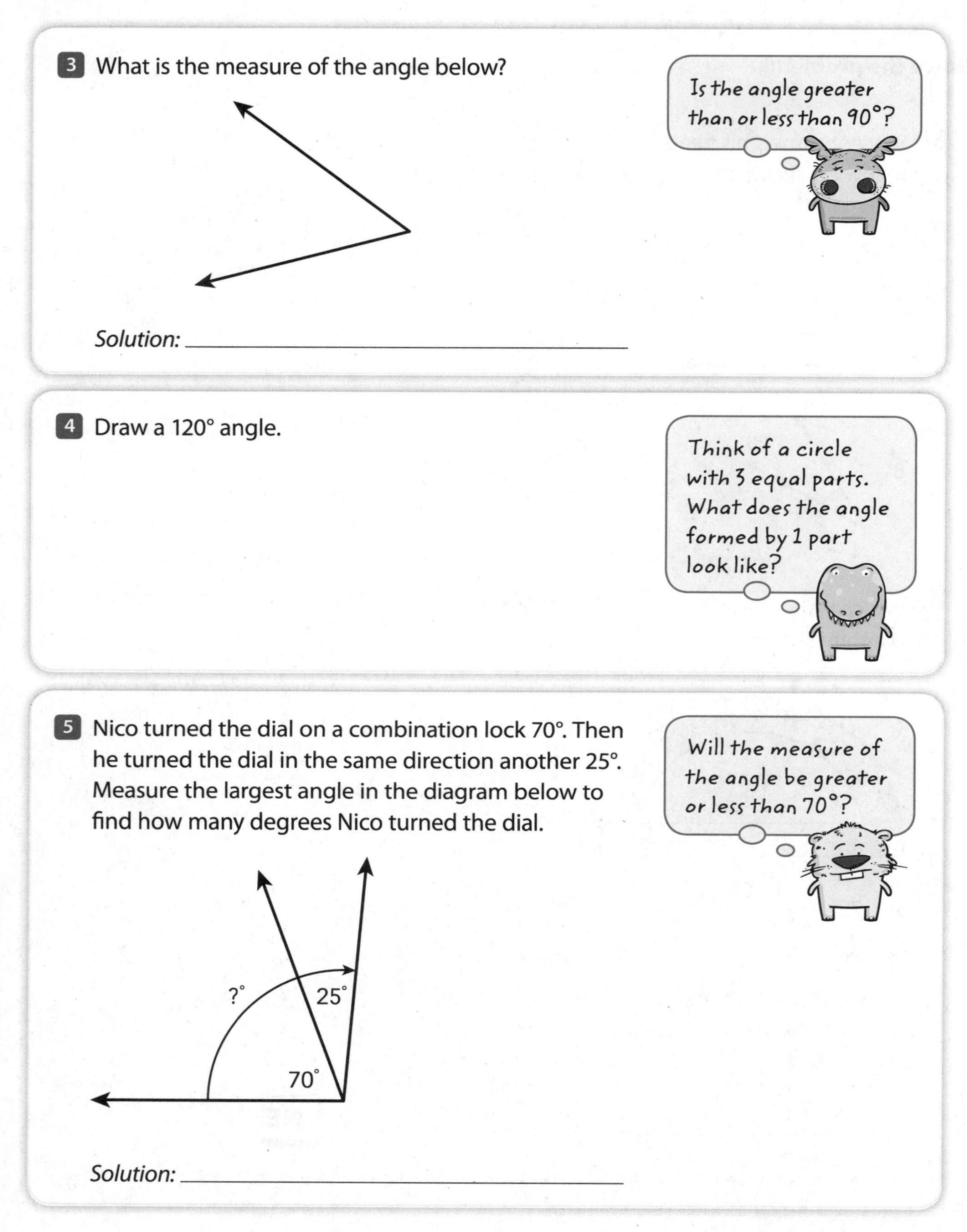

3 What is the measure of the angle below?

Solution: ______________________

4 Draw a 120° angle.

5 Nico turned the dial on a combination lock 70°. Then he turned the dial in the same direction another 25°. Measure the largest angle in the diagram below to find how many degrees Nico turned the dial.

Solution: ______________________

Dear Family,

This week your child is learning to add and subtract with angles.

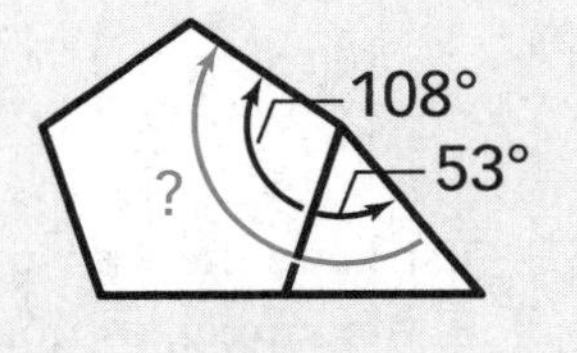

The two shapes at the right are placed together as shown. Two angle measures are given: 108° and 53°.

Since there are no gaps and no overlaps between the shapes, you can add the two angle measures together to find the measure of the larger angle formed by the two angles in the shapes.

108° + 53° = 161°

The larger combined angle measures 161°.

Your child is also learning to use subtraction to find angle measures. In the example above, if the measure of the larger angle was given and the measure of one of the other angles was unmarked, your child could subtract to find the measure of the unmarked angle.

For example, 161° − 108° = 53°.

Invite your child to share what he or she knows about adding and subtracting angles by doing the following activity together.

Add and Subtract with Angles Activity

Do an activity with your child to practice adding angle measures.

Materials: sheet of paper, scissors

- Cut out a piece from a rectangular sheet of paper. Cut at an angle.

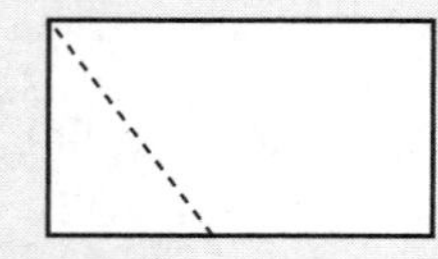

- Estimate the measure of the angle at the bottom of the piece you cut. For example, estimate that the angle measures about 50 degrees.

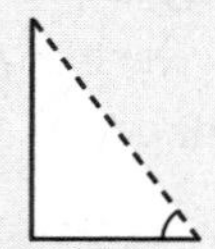

- Then estimate the measure of the angle at the bottom corner where you cut the sheet of paper. For example, estimate that the angle measures about 130 degrees.

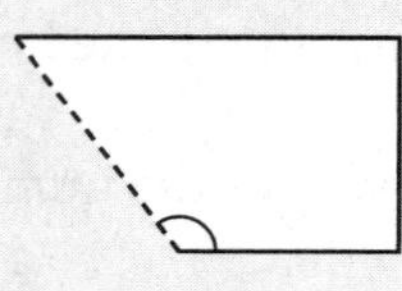

- Now put the two pieces of paper back together. Add the estimates of the angle measures in order to find the measure of the angle formed by combining both angles. For example, $50° + 130° = 180°$.

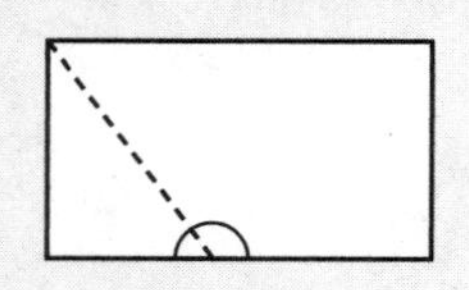

- Ask your child to explain how you know the measure of the combined angle is 180 degrees. (Both angles combine to form a straight angle, which has a measure of 180°.)

Add and Subtract with Angles

Name: ______________________

Prerequisite: Measure and Draw Angles

Study the example explaining how to use a protractor to measure angles to solve a word problem. Then solve problems 1–5.

Example

Charlie is designing a roof for a new building. He draws the angles below to show two roof designs. What is the measure of the angle at the top of each roof in the drawings?

Use a protractor to measure each angle.

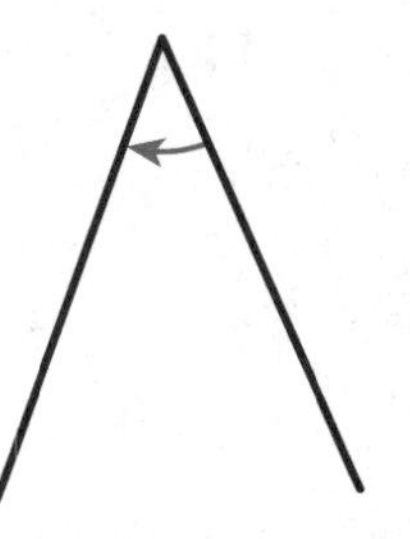

This angle measures ______.

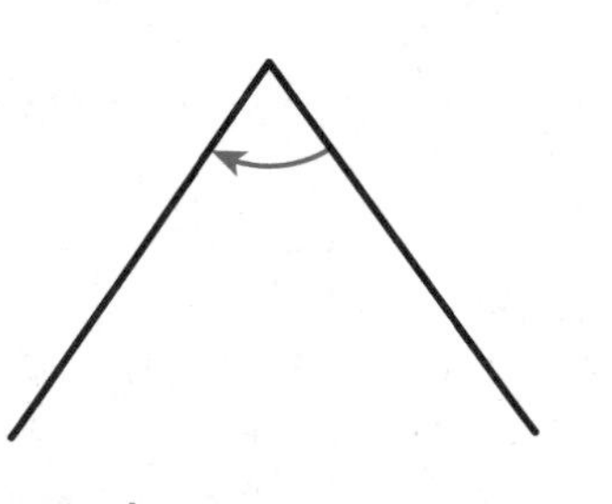

This angle measures ______.

1 Draw a roof design that has an angle measure between 42° and 68°.

This angle measures ______.

2 Draw a roof design that has an obtuse angle. What does the angle measure?

This angle measures ______.

Solve.

3 Madison drew three rays and realized she had drawn an acute and an obtuse angle.

a. Label the angles *acute* and *obtuse*.

b. Use a protractor to measure each angle. Write the angle measure.

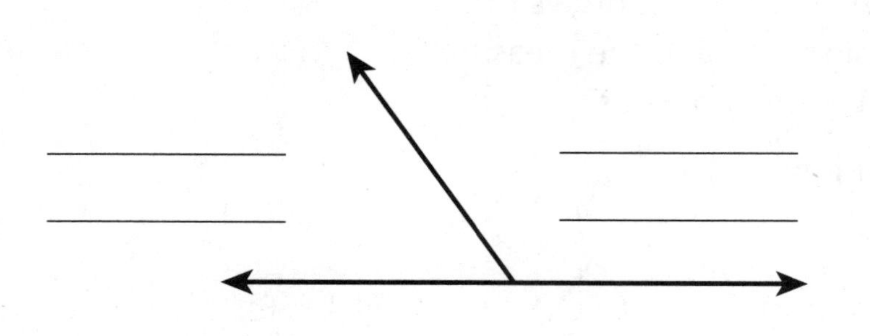

4 Draw a 152° angle.

5 Measure each angle in the quadrilateral below. Write each angle measure.

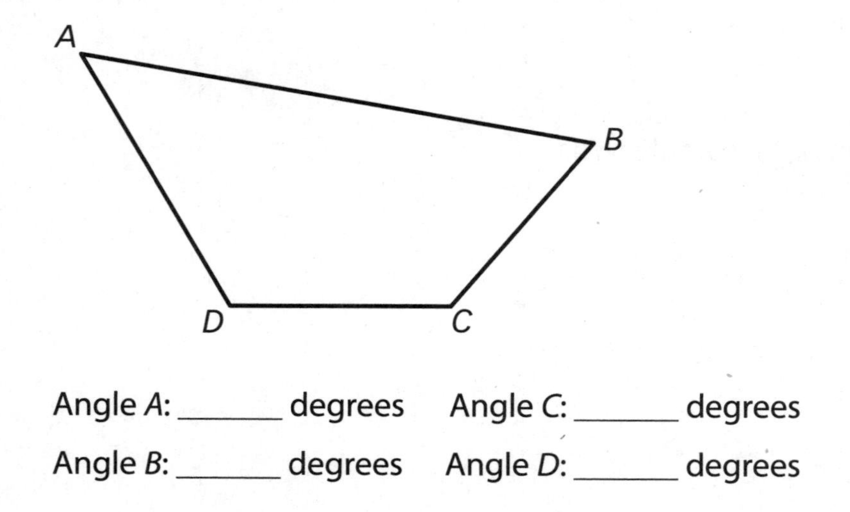

Angle *A*: _______ degrees   Angle *C*: _______ degrees

Angle *B*: _______ degrees   Angle *D*: _______ degrees

Name: ____________________

Combine Angles

Study the example problem showing how to combine smaller angles to form a larger angle. Then solve problems 1–5.

Example

A spotlight in a theater casts a beam that has an angle measure of 24°.

If four spotlights are placed so that they have a common endpoint, what is the measure of the greater angle formed by the beams of all four spotlights?

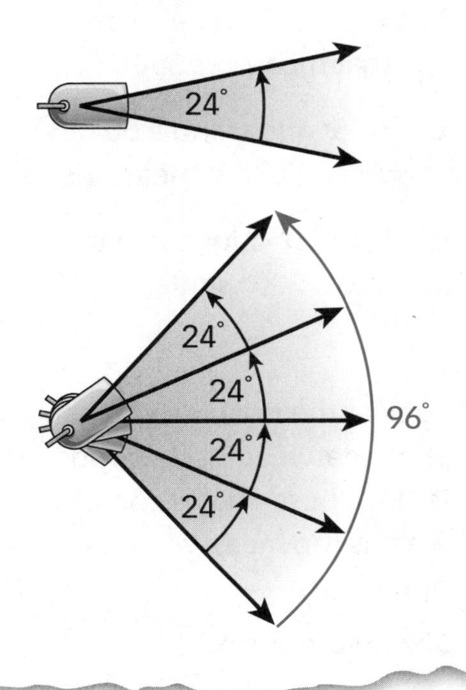

Four 24° angles compose the greater angle. Use addition to combine the angles.

$24° + 24° + 24° + 24° = 96°$

The measure of the greater angle is 96°.

1 Look at the example above. Suppose three spotlights are placed to have a common endpoint. What is the measure of the greater angle formed by the beams of the three spotlights? Write an addition equation to find the measure of this angle.

____

2 Another way to compose a 96° angle is to combine two angles: a 90° angle and a 6° angle. Write an addition equation to show why this is true.

____

Vocabulary

compose to combine parts.

Solve.

3 Tell whether each statement is *True* or *False*.

a. A 20° angle and a 70° angle can be composed into a 90° angle. ☐ True ☐ False

b. Three 50° angles compose an angle that measures 350°. ☐ True ☐ False

c. A 15° angle and a 60° angle compose an angle that measures 75°. ☐ True ☐ False

d. Four 50° angles can be composed into a 200° angle. ☐ True ☐ False

4 Look at the drawing of a hand fan at the right. The angle between each wooden stick on the fan is 12°. If 11 of these angles combine to form the open fan, what is the measure of the purple angle on the open fan?

Show your work.

Solution: ______________________________

5 Sam lifts the front of his skateboard at a 15° angle to the ground as he gets ready to jump. He lifts his skateboard another 27° when he jumps. What is the measure of the angle that Sam lifts his skateboard from the ground?

Show your work.

Solution: ______________________________

Name: ______________________

Use Addition and Subtraction to Find Unknown Angles

Study the example problem showing how to use subtraction to find an unknown angle measure. Then solve problems 1–6.

Example

Emma turned the knob on a combination lock 117°. How many more degrees does she need to turn the knob to make one full turn?

Write and solve an equation to find the measure of the unknown angle.

$$360° - 117° = x$$
$$243° = x$$

Emma needs to turn the knob another 243°.

A full turn is 360°.

1 Alice is pushing her brother in a swing. The swing is hanging straight down. She pulls the swing back 35° and lets go. The swing moves forward 65°. How many degrees forward from the original straight down position of the swing did the swing move?

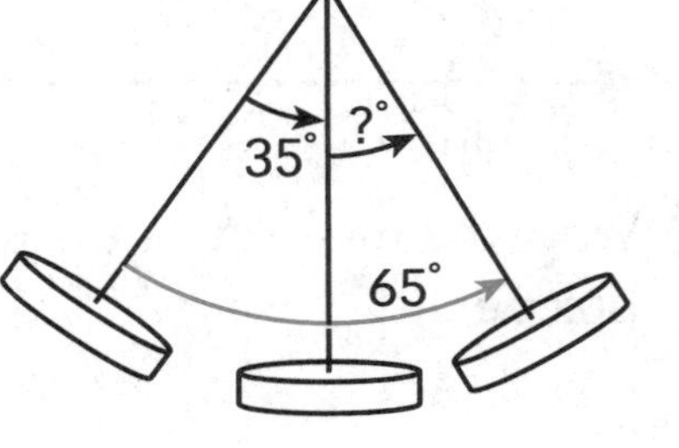

Show your work.

Solution: ______________________

2 A sprinkler in a backyard turns through 180°. The sprinkler has turned 96° so far. How many more degrees will the sprinkler turn through to reach 180°?

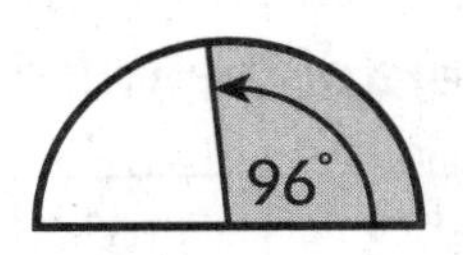

Solution: ______________________

Solve.

3 A sprinkler turns through 180° every 5 seconds. It turns through 36° every second. Fill in the table below.

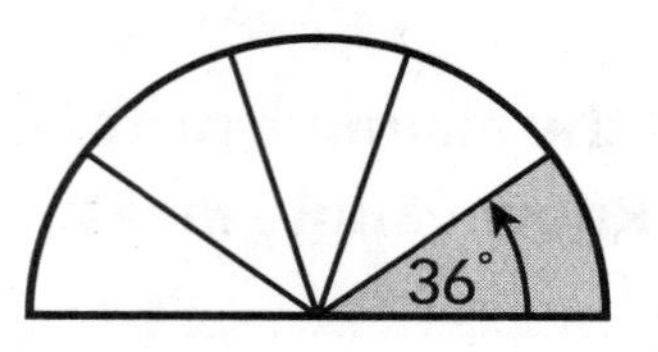

Time (seconds)	Degrees
1	
2	
3	
4	
5	

4 Write the measure of the unknown angle in the box below.

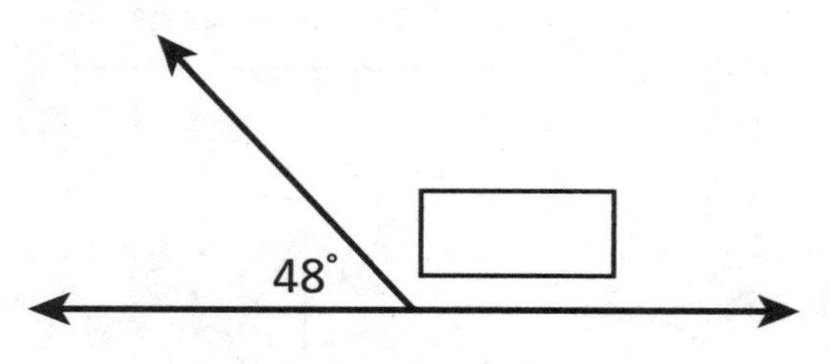

5 Write the measure of the unknown angle in the box below.

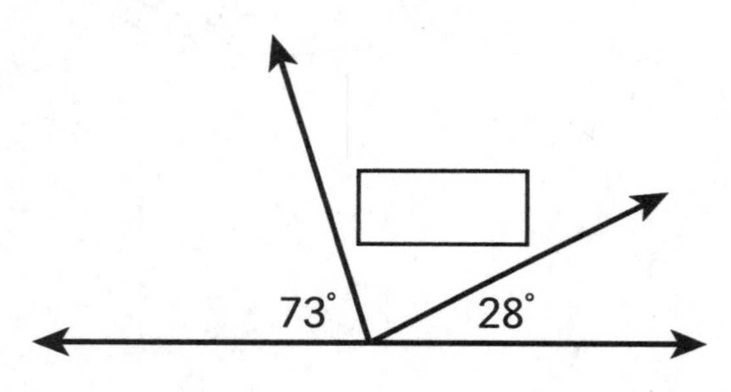

6 Use the angle measures below to fill in the boxes in the diagram with the correct angle measures.

45°	110°	115°	135°

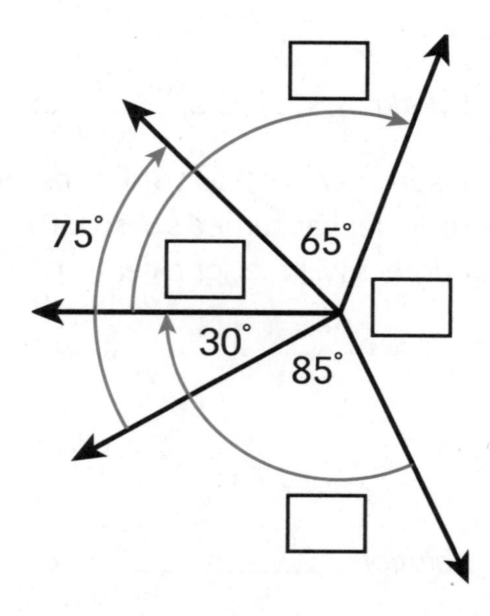

Name: ______________________________

Add and Subtract with Angles

Solve the problems.

1 Alex blew on a pinwheel. The pinwheel turned 240°. How many degrees more does the pinwheel need to turn to make one full turn?

A 60°

B 120°

C 180°

D 360°

2 Vicky turned the knob on her combination lock one full turn and then another 144°. How many degrees did she turn the knob?

A 144°

B 216°

C 360°

D 504°

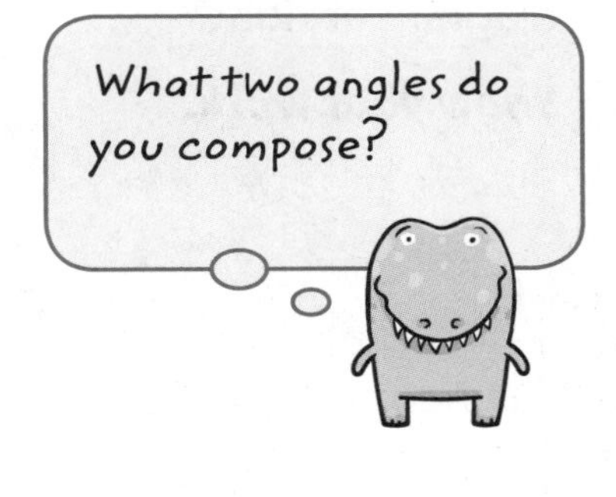

Jen chose **A** as the correct answer. How did she get that answer?

____

____

____

____

Solve.

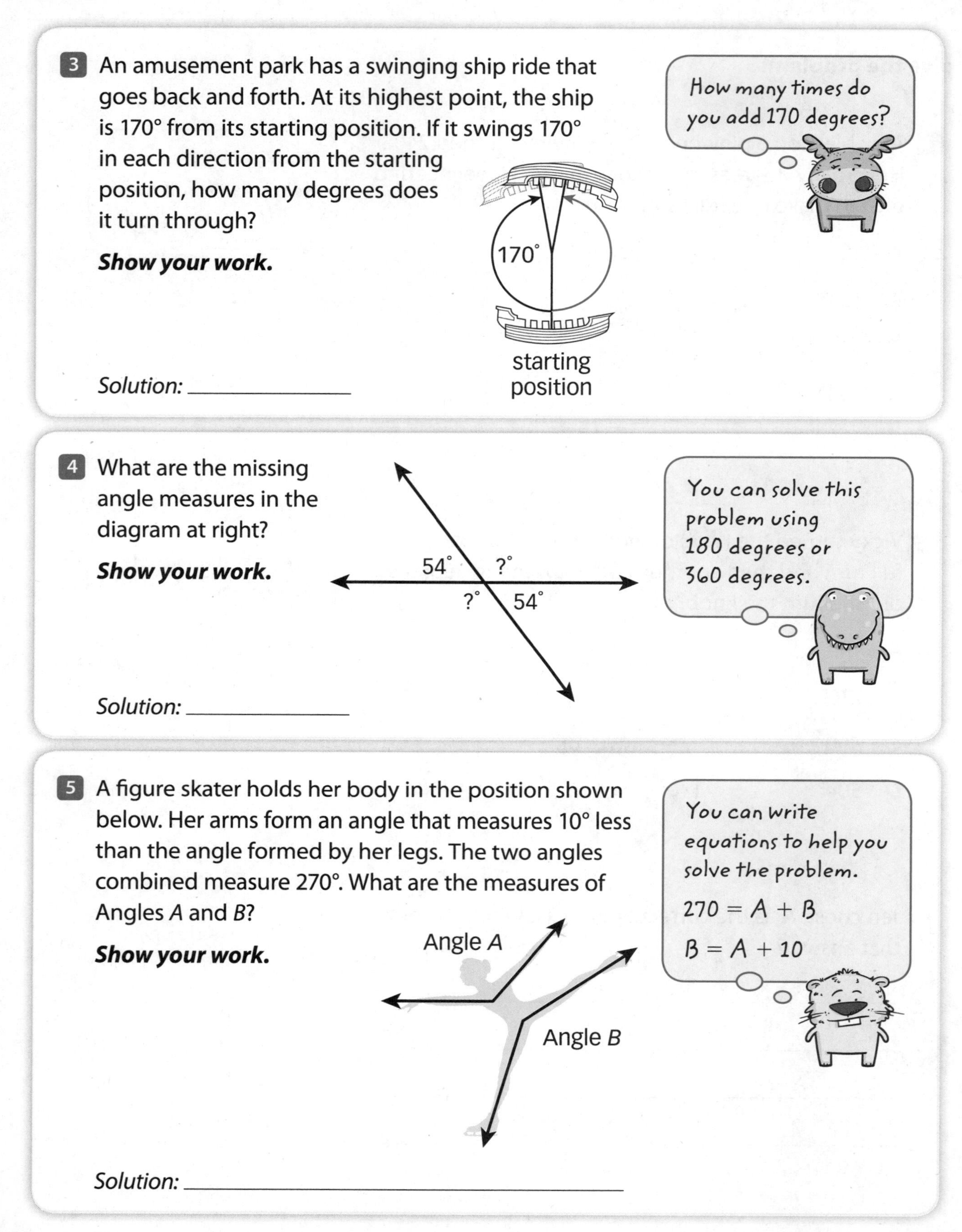

3 An amusement park has a swinging ship ride that goes back and forth. At its highest point, the ship is 170° from its starting position. If it swings 170° in each direction from the starting position, how many degrees does it turn through?

Show your work.

Solution: ________________

4 What are the missing angle measures in the diagram at right?

Show your work.

Solution: ________________

5 A figure skater holds her body in the position shown below. Her arms form an angle that measures 10° less than the angle formed by her legs. The two angles combined measure 270°. What are the measures of Angles *A* and *B*?

Show your work.

Solution: ________________________________

Unit 5 Game

Name: ______________________

Angle Sums

What you need: Recording Sheet, 2 sets of Angle Sums Game Cards, 1 protractor for each player

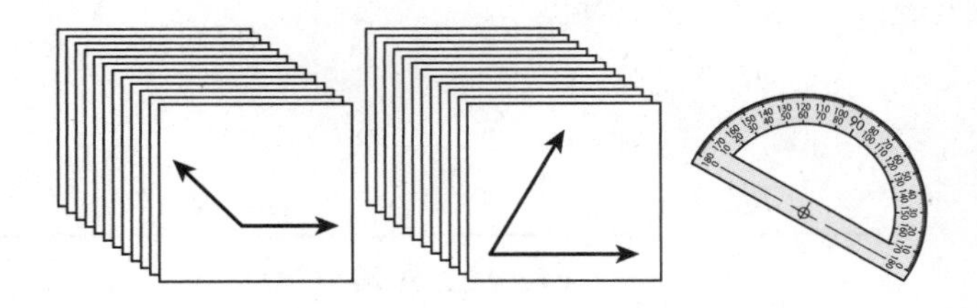

Directions

- Mix both sets of Game Cards. Stack the cards and lay out 6 cards face up.
- Each player will choose a total of 2 cards. Take turns picking each card. Return the 2 unused cards to the stack. Your goal is to choose two angles that will have the greatest angle measure when they are combined.

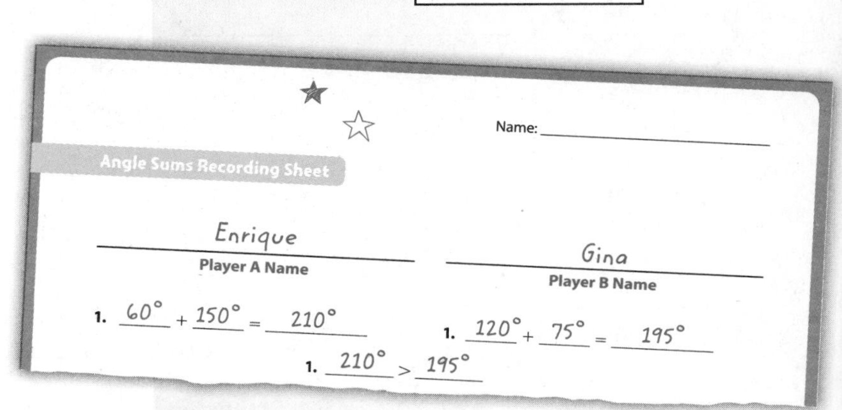

- Both players use a protractor to measure their angles. Players add their angle measures and write their addition equations on the Recording Sheet. Remember to write the degree symbol (°)!
- Players compare the combined angle measures. The player with the greater combined angle measure wins the round.
- Set aside the cards you used. In each round, choose 2 new cards. The loser of the round picks the first card in the next round. The player with more wins after 5 rounds wins the game.

Name: ____________________

Angle Sums Recording Sheet

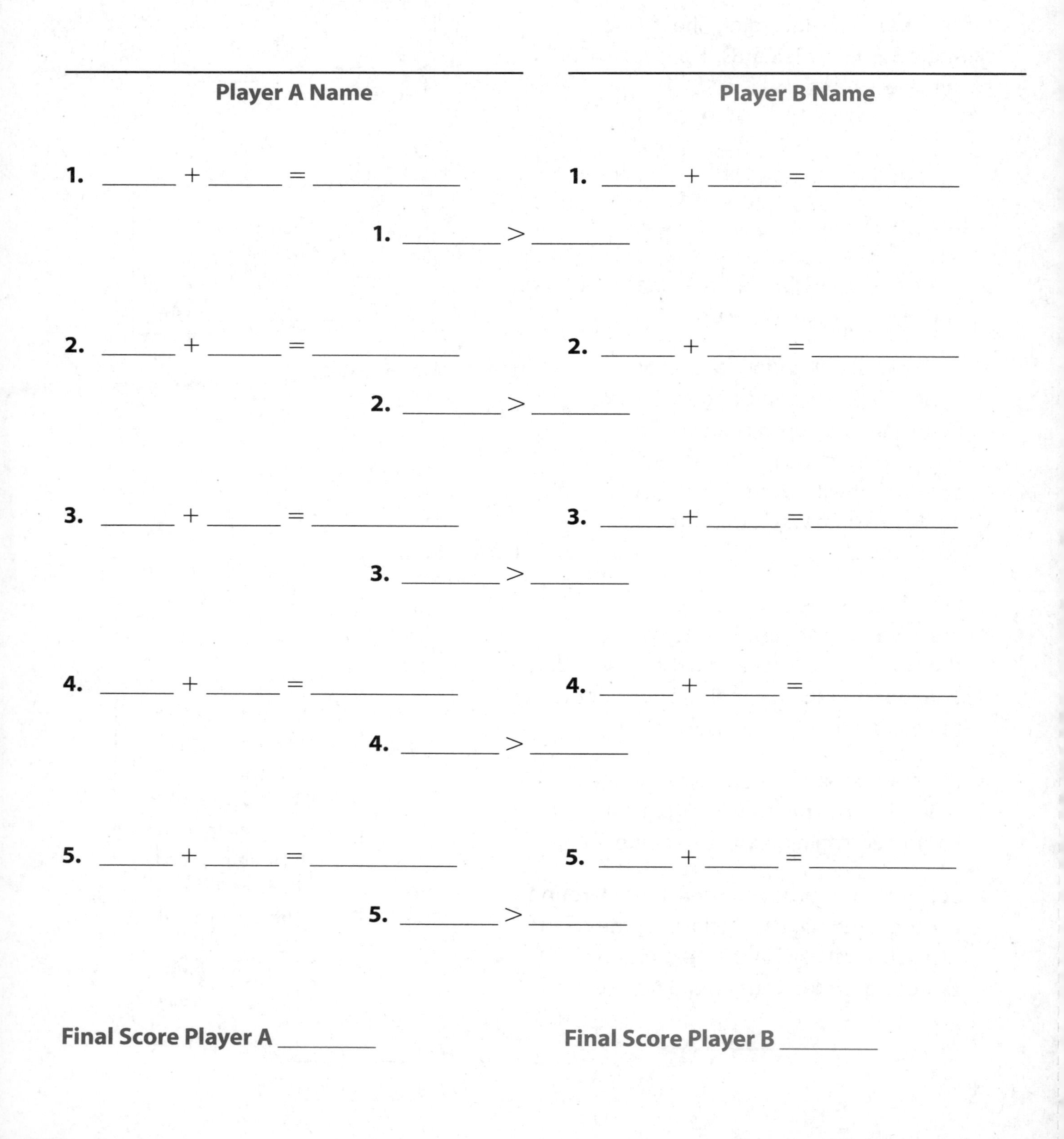

____________________	____________________
Player A Name	**Player B Name**

1. ______ + ______ = __________ **1.** ______ + ______ = __________

1. ________ > ________

2. ______ + ______ = __________ **2.** ______ + ______ = __________

2. ________ > ________

3. ______ + ______ = __________ **3.** ______ + ______ = __________

3. ________ > ________

4. ______ + ______ = __________ **4.** ______ + ______ = __________

4. ________ > ________

5. ______ + ______ = __________ **5.** ______ + ______ = __________

5. ________ > ________

Final Score Player A ________ **Final Score Player B** ________

Angle Sums Game Cards

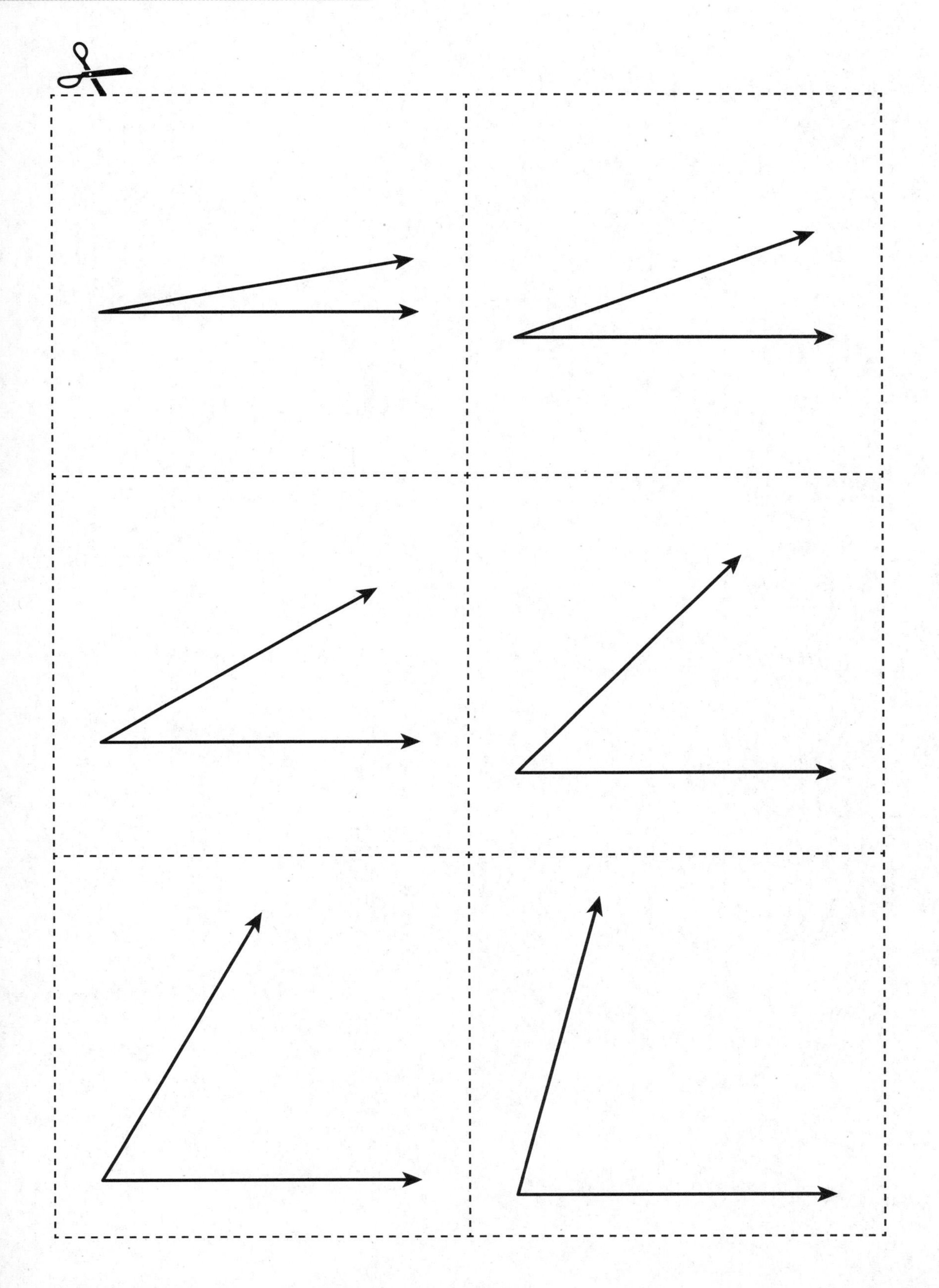

Angle Sums Game Cards (continued)

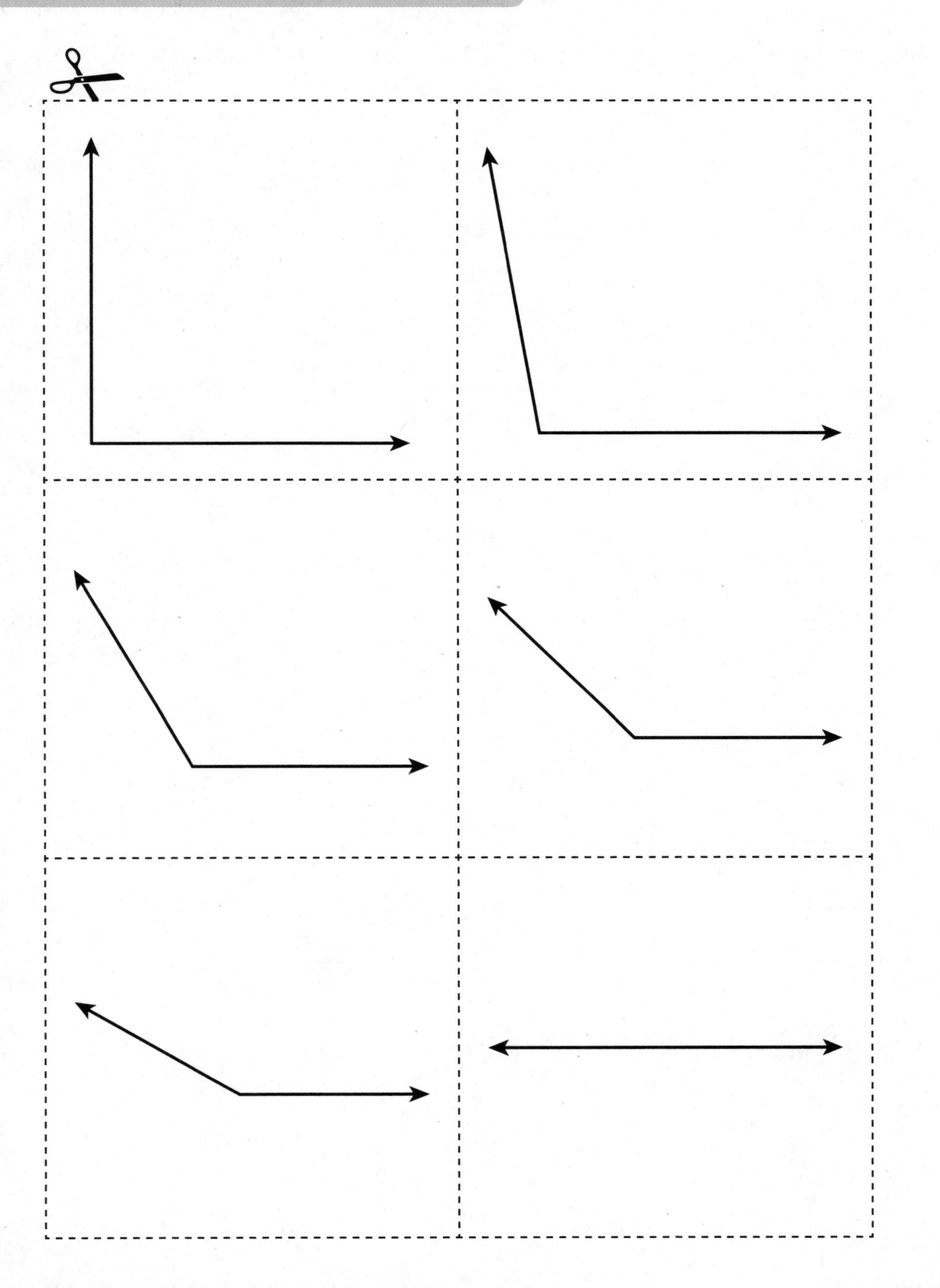

Angle Sums Game Cards

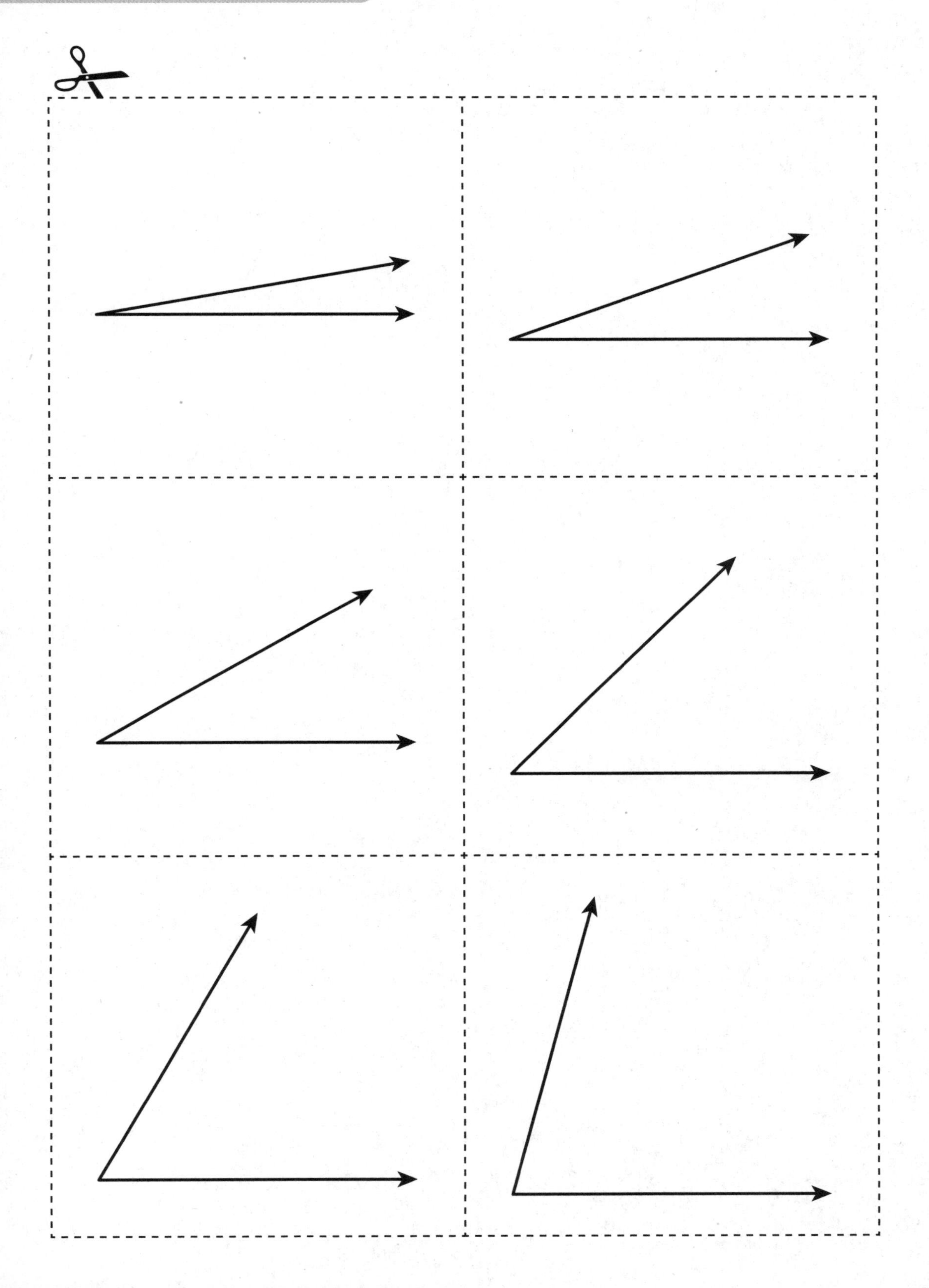

Name: ______________________

Angle Sums Game Cards (continued)

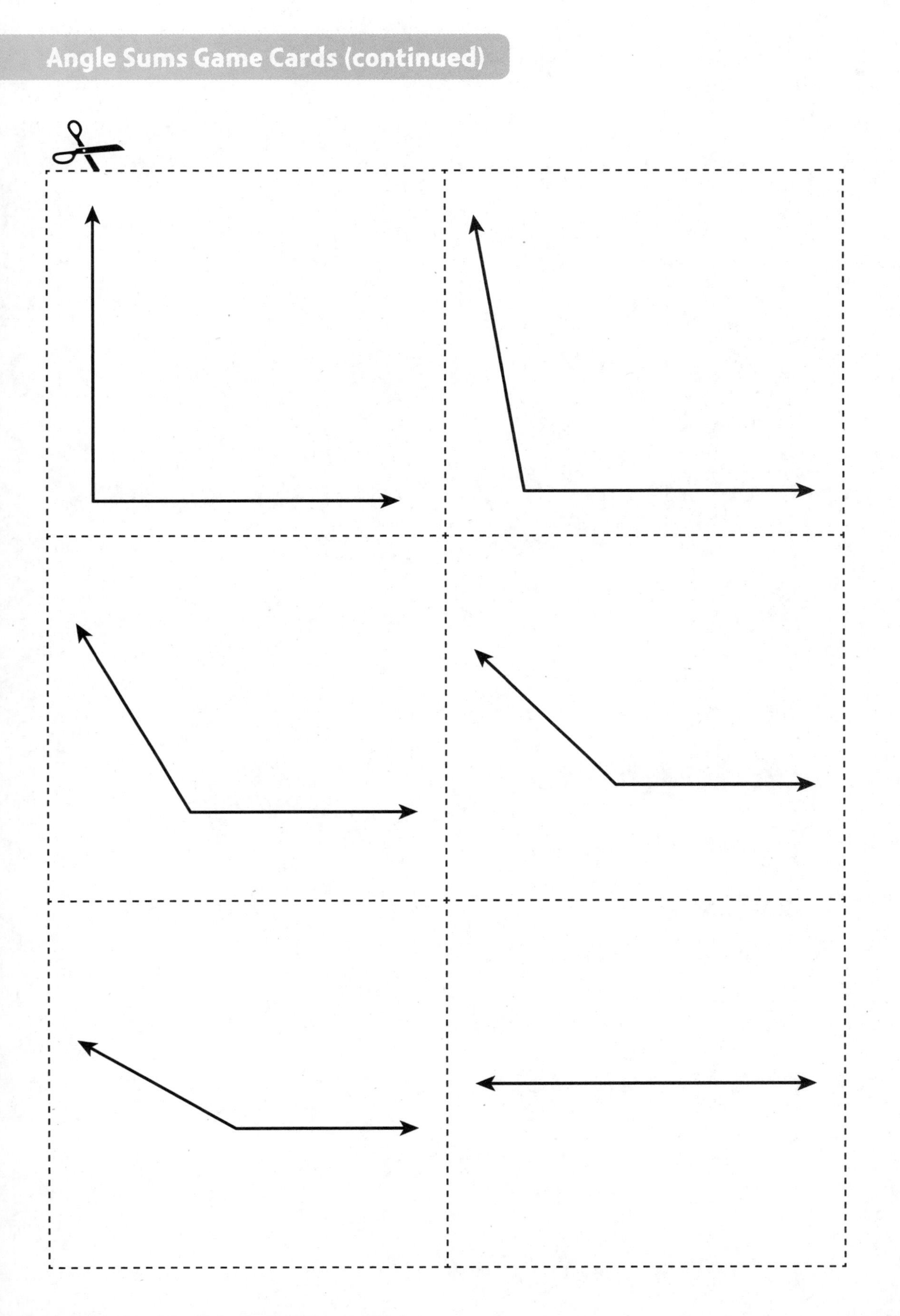

Unit 5 Practice

Name: ______________________

Measurement and Data Analysis

In this unit you learned to:	Lesson
convert units of length, weight, volume, and time, for example: 5 feet $=$ 60 inches.	23, 24, 25
solve word problems about time, money, distances, volumes, and masses, for example: 4 L of juice $+$ 300 mL of juice $=$ 4,300 mL of juice.	24, 25, 27A
use the area formula for rectangles, for example: $A = 3 \times 9$ for a rectangle with a length of 9 and a width of 3.	26
use the perimeter formula for rectangles, for example: $P = (2 \times 12) + (2 \times 5)$ for a rectangle with a length of 12 and a width of 5.	26
interpret circle graphs, and collect and represent data.	27B, 27C
measure angles using a protractor, for example: an angle on a stop sign is 135°.	28, 29
solve addition and subtraction problems with angles, for example: $165° - 23° = 142°$.	30

Use these skills to solve problems 1–5.

1 Tell whether each statement is *True* or *False*.

a. 12 yards $=$ 4 feet

☐ True ☐ False

b. 2 kilograms $=$ 2,000 grams

☐ True ☐ False

c. 1 hour $=$ 360 seconds

☐ True ☐ False

d. 4,000 kilometers $=$ 4 meters

☐ True ☐ False

e. 3 pounds $=$ 48 ounces

☐ True ☐ False

2 The school library is holding a summer reading challenge. Students who meet a goal of reading 16 hours or more receive a prize. There are 10 weeks of summer break. If a student reads 4 days a week, how many minutes does a student need to read each day to meet the goal?

Show your work.

Solution: ______________

Solve.

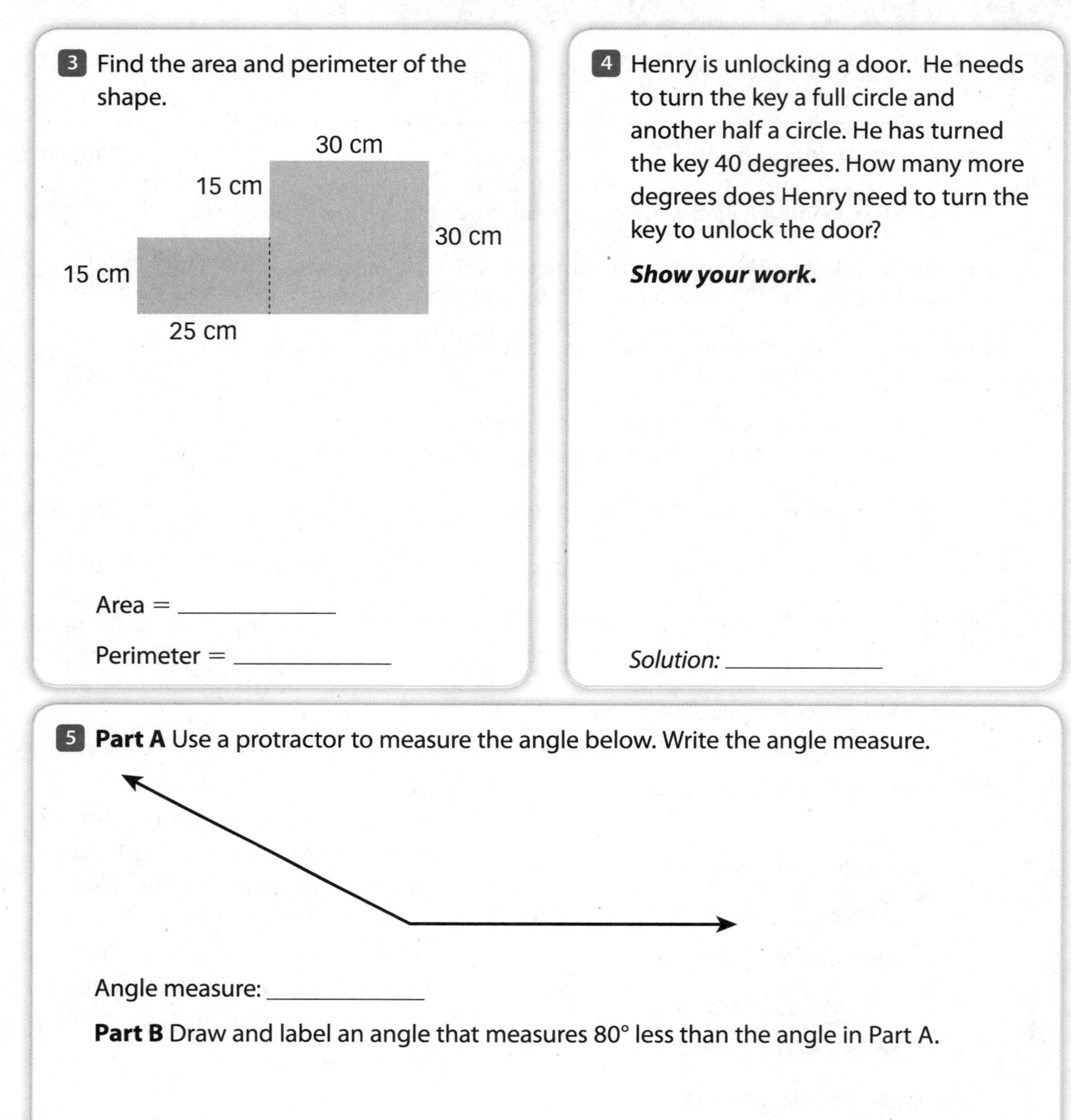

3 Find the area and perimeter of the shape.

Area = ____________

Perimeter = ____________

4 Henry is unlocking a door. He needs to turn the key a full circle and another half a circle. He has turned the key 40 degrees. How many more degrees does Henry need to turn the key to unlock the door?

Show your work.

Solution: ____________

5 **Part A** Use a protractor to measure the angle below. Write the angle measure.

Angle measure: ____________

Part B Draw and label an angle that measures 80° less than the angle in Part A.

Unit 5 Performance Task

Name: ______________________

Answer the questions and show all your work on separate paper.

Joey does yard and garden work for his neighbors on the weekend. He can mow a yard with 100 square meters of lawn in 10 minutes. He can weed a 5-meter long flower garden that borders a yard in 10 minutes.

The chart below shows the sizes of the yards and flower borders for four neighbors.

	Smith	Jackson	Ruiz	Hall
Length of Yard	40 meters	30 meters	20 meters	20 meters
Width of Yard	10 meters	20 meters	25 meters	35 meters
Size of Flower Border	Half of the width of the yard	Half of the width of the yard	Entire width of the yard	Half of the length of the yard

Joey wants to work on some of the yards and flower borders this weekend. He plans to start work at 9 o'clock Saturday morning. He wants to finish by noon so that he can go to soccer practice.

Which yards and flower borders should Joey plan to work on Saturday? What time will he be finished with the work? Explain your reasoning.

Checklist

Did you . . .

- ☐ organize the information?
- ☐ use a formula to find area?
- ☐ check that the results make sense?

Reflect on the Process Standards

After you complete the task, choose one of the following questions to answer.

1. **Reason Mathematically** How did you decide which yards and flower borders Joey should work on?

2. **Be Precise** How did you determine what time Joey would finish the work?

Performance Task Tips

Word Bank Here are some words that you might use in your answer.

length	equal	minutes
width	sum	hours
area	meters	square meters

Models Here are some models that you might use to find the solution.

Neighbor	Length of Yard	Width of Yard	Area of Yard	Minutes to Mow the Yard

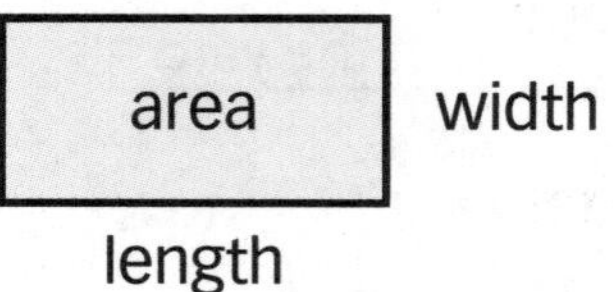

Sentence Starters Here are some sentence starters that might help you write an explanation.

The area of ______________________________

It will take ____________ minutes to ____________

The total time ______________________________

If Joey does ________________, then ___________

Unit 5 Vocabulary

Name: ______________________

My Examples

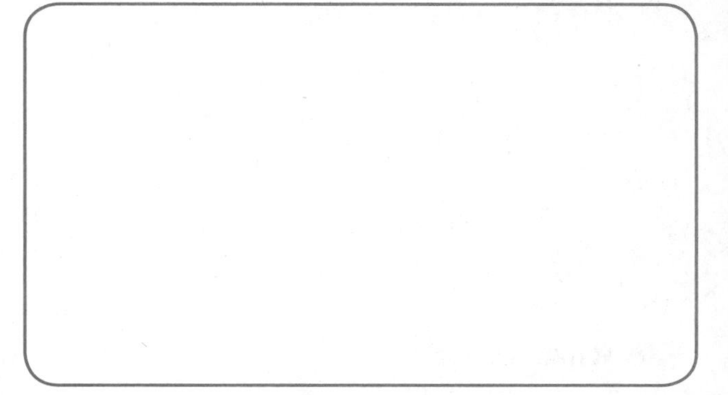

convert

to change from one unit to another unit

line plot

a graph using marks along a number line to show how many objects are in a set

angle

a geometric shape made by two rays that meet at a common endpoint, called a vertex

right angle

an angle that looks like a square corner and measures 90°

My Examples

acute angle

an angle that has fewer degrees than a right angle

obtuse angle

an angle that has more degrees than a right angle

protractor

a tool used to measure angles

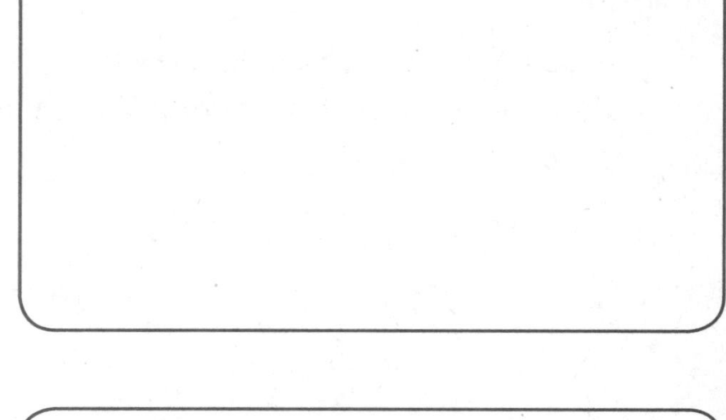

vertex

the point where two rays or lines meet to form an angle

My Examples

ray

a straight row of points that starts at one point and goes on forever in one direction

decompose

to split up into parts

compose

to combine parts

My Words

My Words	My Examples

Points, Lines, Rays, and Angles

Name: ____________________

Prerequisite: Describe the Properties of Shapes

Study the example showing how to describe the sides and angles in shapes. Then solve problems 1–6.

Example

Compare the triangles below. What is the same and different about the shapes?

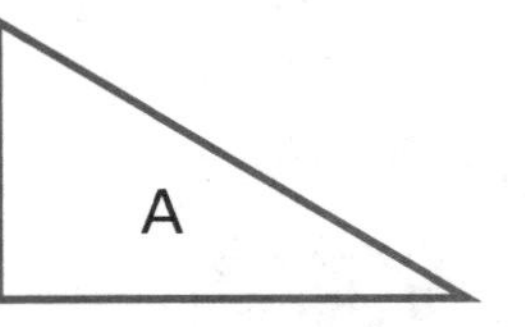

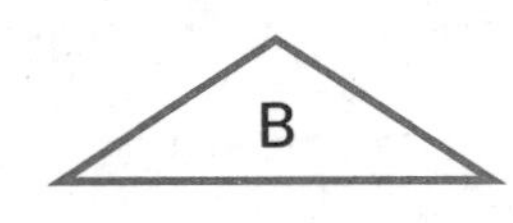

Same

Both triangles have 3 sides.
Both triangles have 3 angles.

Different

Triangle A has 1 square corner and Triangle B has no square corners.
Triangle A has 0 sides the same length and Triangle B has 2 sides the same length.

1 Look at the shapes below. Read the descriptions in the table. Draw each shape in the column that describes it.

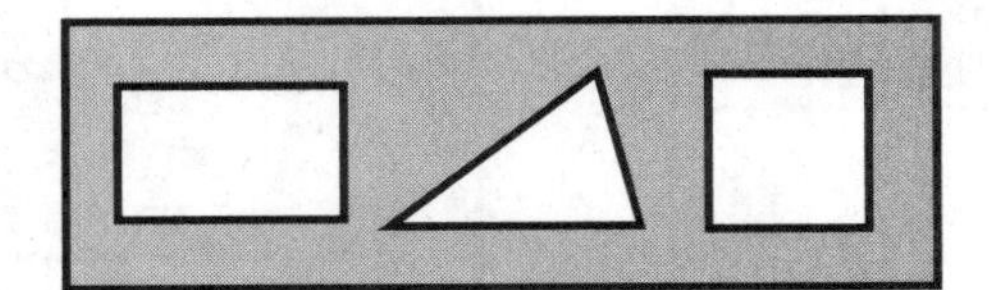

All square corners *and* all sides the same length	Square corners *and* some sides the same length	No square corners *and* no sides the same length

2 Describe the sides and angles of the pentagon at the right.

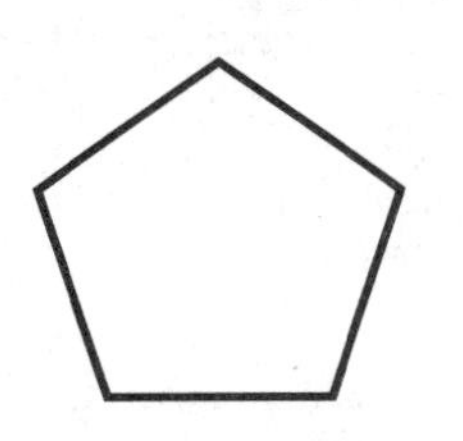

____

____

Solve.

3 Describe how the two shapes shown are alike.

____

____

____

For problems 4–6, use the shapes at the right.

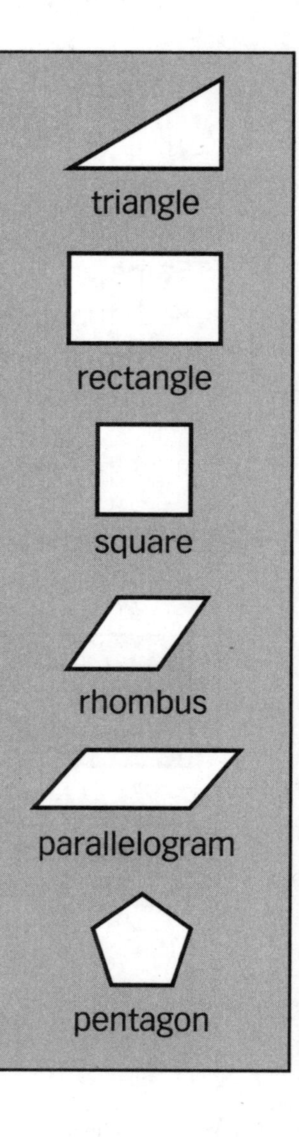

4 Fill in the table. Write each shape in the column that describes the number of sides and angles it has.

Fewer than 4 sides and 4 angles	4 sides and 4 angles	More than 4 sides and 4 angles

5 Fill in the table. Write each shape in the column that describes the length of its sides.

All sides the same length	Some sides the same length	No sides the same length

6 Fill in the table below. Write each shape in the column that describes whether it has square corners or has no square corners.

Has a square corner	Has no square corners

Name: ______________________

Identify Points, Lines, Line Segments, and Rays

Study the example that shows a drawing with points, lines, line segments, and rays. Then solve problems 1–9.

Example

Amy made a drawing of a letter "A" in her math notebook. Use geometry words to describe the drawing.

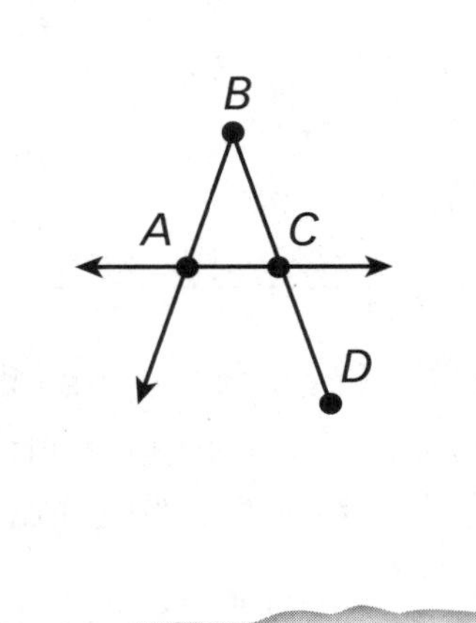

There are 4 points on the drawing:
point A, point B, point C, and point D.

There is a line segment from point B to point D. $\overline{BD}$

There is a line through points A and C. $\overleftrightarrow{AC}$

There is a ray from point B through point A. $\overrightarrow{BA}$

Use the drawing below to answer questions 1–4.

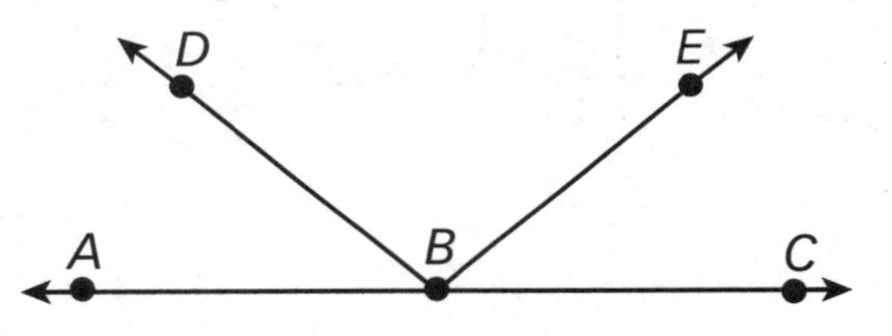

1 How many lines are in the drawing? ______

2 How many rays are in the drawing? ______

3 Write the name of the line in the drawing.

____

4 Write the names of the rays in the drawing.

____

5 Look at the shape at the right. How many line segments are in the shape? ______

Vocabulary

point a single location in space.

B

line segment a straight row of points that starts at one point and ends at another point.

line a straight row of points that goes on forever in both directions.

ray a straight row of points that starts on one point and goes on forever in one direction.

B A

Solve.

6 Label each sign below. Write *line*, *line segment*, or *ray*.

_______________ _______________ _______________ _______________ _______________

7 Look at the drawing below. Choose *Yes* or *No* to tell whether each line, line segment, ray, or angle is shown in the drawing.

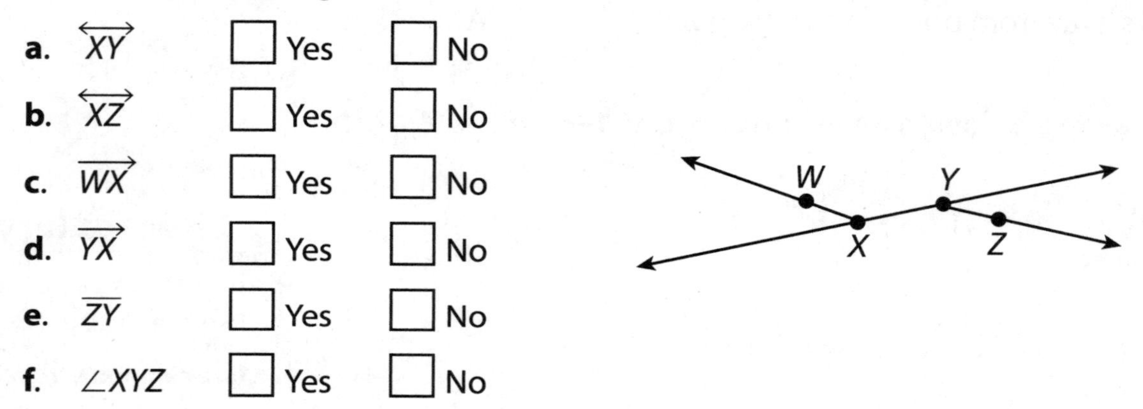

a. $\overleftrightarrow{XY}$ ☐ Yes ☐ No

b. $\overleftrightarrow{XZ}$ ☐ Yes ☐ No

c. $\overrightarrow{WX}$ ☐ Yes ☐ No

d. $\overrightarrow{YX}$ ☐ Yes ☐ No

e. $\overline{ZY}$ ☐ Yes ☐ No

f. $\angle XYZ$ ☐ Yes ☐ No

8 Use geometry words and symbols to describe the rhombus shown.

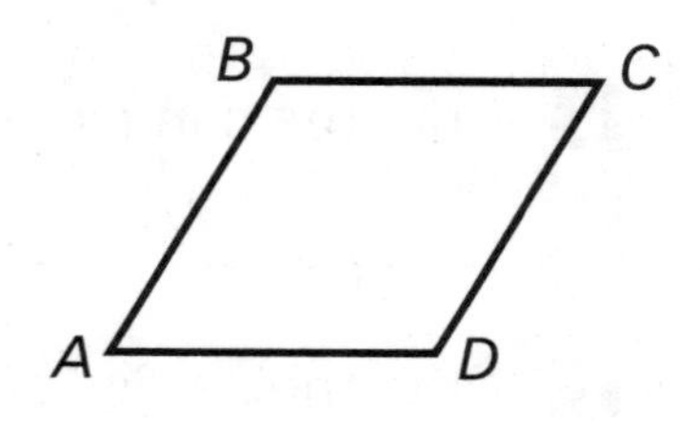

____

____

____

9 Read the description of a shape below. Then draw the shape at the right.

> It has 3 line segments, $\overline{RS}$, $\overline{ST}$, $\overline{TR}$.
>
> Line segments $\overline{RS}$ and $\overline{TR}$ are the same length.
>
> It has 1 square corner, $\angle R$.

Name: ______________________

Identify Angles

Study the example identifying angles in a shape. Then solve problems 1–10.

Example

Name and describe the angles in the shape below.

∠*A* is a right angle. It has a shape like a square corner.

∠*B* is also a right angle.

∠*C* is an obtuse angle. It has a wider opening than a right angle.

∠*D* is an acute angle. It has a smaller opening than a right angle.

The shape has 2 right angles, 1 acute angle, and 1 obtuse angle.

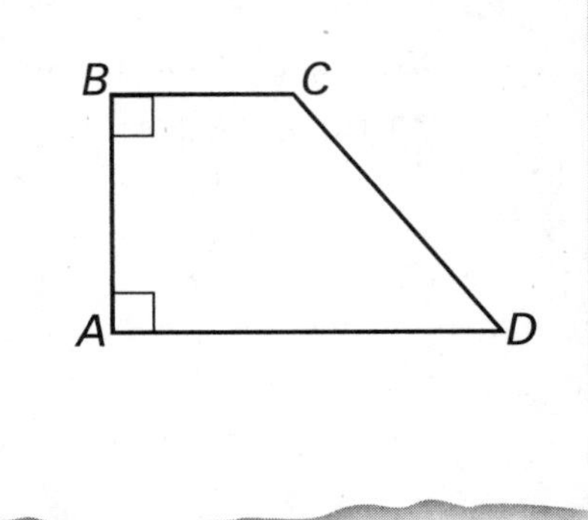

Use the shape at the right to answer questions 1–5.

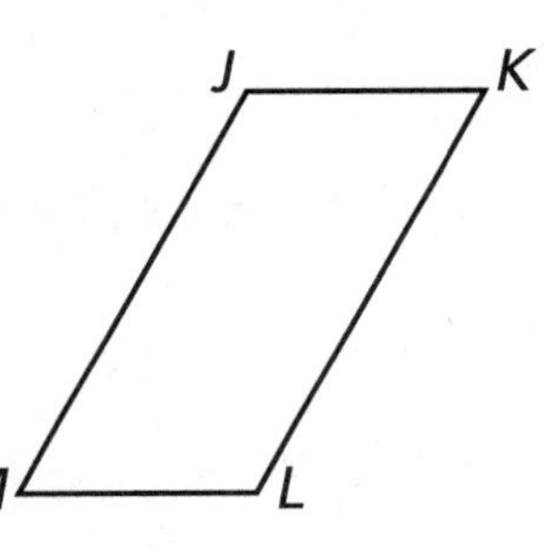

1. How many right angles are in this shape? _______

2. How many acute angles are in this shape? _______

3. How many obtuse angles are in this shape? _______

4. Name the acute angles in the shape.

____

5. Name the obtuse angles in the shape.

____

6. Look at the shape at the right. Describe the number and kind of angles it has.

____

____

Solve.

Jasmine drew this pentagon. She says that all pentagons have 5 sides of equal length and 5 obtuse angles.

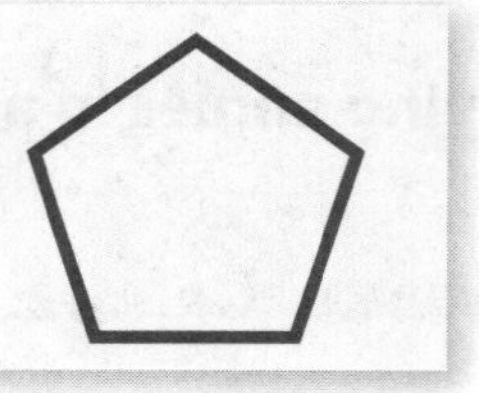

7 Draw a pentagon that is different from the one Jasmine drew. Describe the lines and angles of your pentagon.

____

____

____

8 In what way is Jasmine's thinking correct?

____

____

9 In what way is Jasmine's thinking incorrect?

____

____

10 Which of the following statements describes the shape at the right? Circle all that apply.

A The shape has acute angles.

B The shape has right angles.

C The shapes has obtuse angles.

D The shape has 6 angles.

Dear Family,

This week your child is learning to classify two-dimensional shapes.

Shapes can be sorted into groups based on the kinds of sides they have and the kind of angles they have. Some shapes your child is classifying are triangles, quadrilaterals such as squares, rhombuses, trapezoids, and parallelograms, and hexagons.

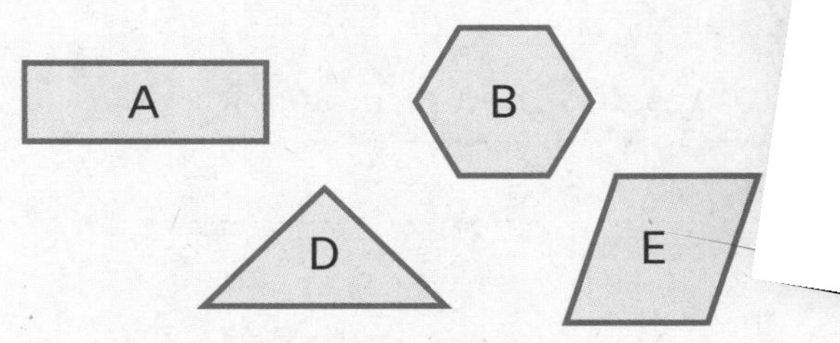

One way to classify shapes is by the kinds of sides they have.

- Shapes A and C both have pairs of parallel sides and pairs of perpendicular sides.
- Shapes B and E have pairs of parallel sides only.

Another way to classify shapes is by the kinds of angles they have.

- Shapes A, C, and D all have at least one right angle.
- Shapes D and E each have some acute angles.
- Shape B has all obtuse angles and shape E has some obtuse angles.

Triangles can be classified by their angles and sides.

- Triangle C is a right triangle. It has a right angle.
- Triangle D is an equilateral triangle. All its sides are the same length.

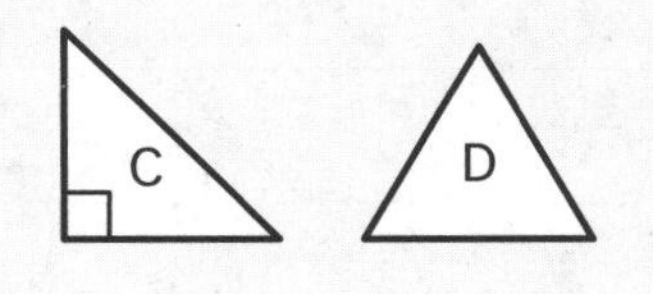

Invite your child to share what he or she knows about classifying two-dimensional figures by doing the following activity together.

Describe Two-Dimensional Shapes Activity

Do an activity with your child to describe sides and angles of shapes.

- Use the grid of dots below or make a dot grid on another sheet of paper.
- One person draws a shape. The shape could be a triangle, a quadrilateral, or another kind of shape.
- The other person describes the shape. Be sure to talk about any [illegible] d perpendicular sides that the shape has. [illegible] gles of the shape, too!
- [illegible] e turns drawing a shape and describing it.

Classify Two-Dimensional Figures

Name: ______________________

Prerequisite: Classify Quadrilaterals

Study the example showing how to classify and compare quadrilaterals. Then solve problems 1–7.

Example

Is every square also a rectangle and a rhombus?
Use a table to compare quadrilaterals.

Quadrilateral	4 sides 4 angles	4 square corners	2 pairs of parallel sides	2 pairs of sides that are the same length	4 sides that are the same length
square	✔	✔	✔	✔	✔
rectangle	✔	✔	✔	✔	sometimes
rhombus	✔	sometimes	✔	✔	✔

Yes. Every square can be named as a rectangle and a rhombus.

1 A parallelogram is a quadrilateral with 2 pairs of parallel sides and 2 pairs of sides that are the same length. Circle the quadrilaterals below that are parallelograms.

2 Look at problem 1. Is quadrilateral B a parallelogram? Explain.

____

____

3 A rectangle is a quadrilateral. Describe a rectangle by telling about its sides and its corners.

____

____

Solve.

4 Use the words in the box. Name each shape below. Use as many words from the box as apply. Describe the sides and corners of each shape.

quadrilateral
parallelogram
rectangle
rhombus
square

a. **b.**

a. Names: ______________________________

Description: ______________________________

____

____

b. Names: ______________________________

Description: ______________________________

____

____

5 Draw a quadrilateral that has at least 1 pair of parallel sides, but no square corners.

6 Draw a quadrilateral that has at least 1 square corner, but is not a rectangle.

7 Draw a quadrilateral that does not have pairs of parallel sides or sides of the same length.

belong in this group.

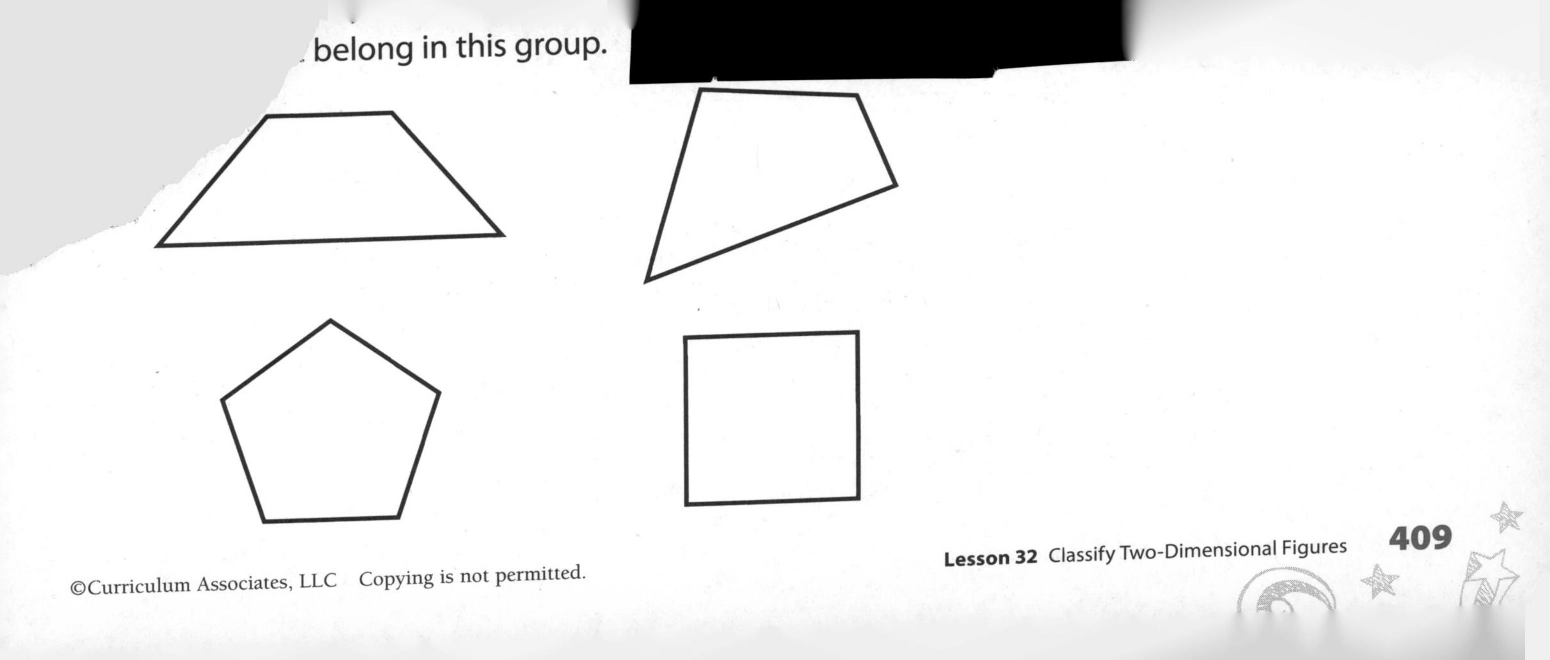

Speed limit sign

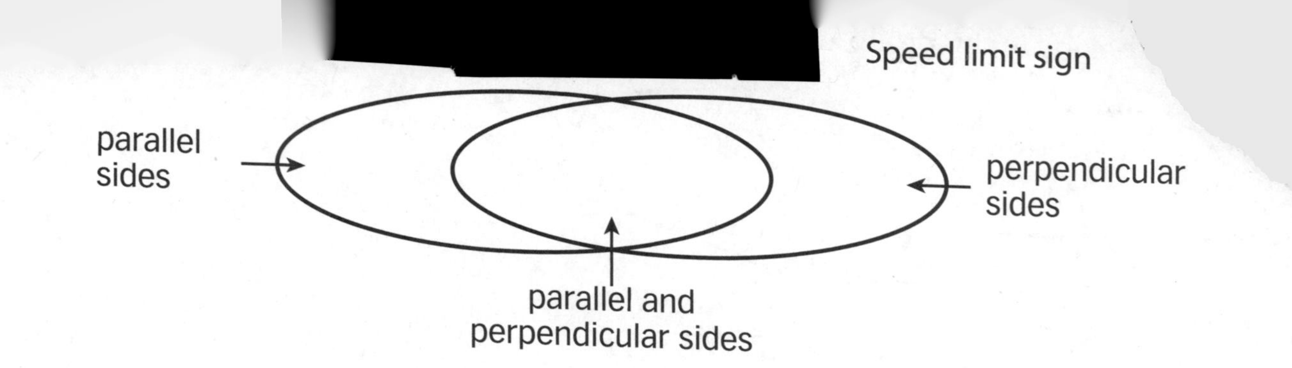

Name: ____________________

Sort Shapes Based on Angles

Study the example showing how to sort shapes into groups based on angles. Then solve problems 1–5.

Example

Label each angle in the shapes below with "a" for acute, "r" for right, and "o" for obtuse. Then draw an arrow from each shape to the group it belongs to.

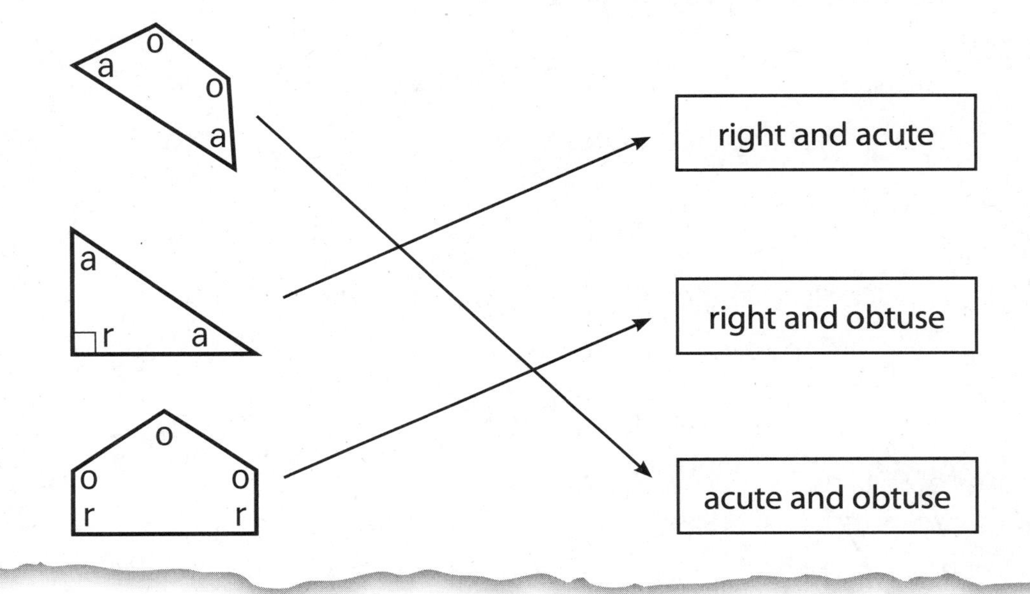

1 Write the number of acute, right, and obtuse angles for each pentagon shown in the table below.

	Acute	**Right**	**Obtuse**
X			
Y			

2 Explain how these pentagons are different based on their angles.

____

____

Solve.

3 Choose *Yes* or *No* to tell whether each shape belongs in the group described.

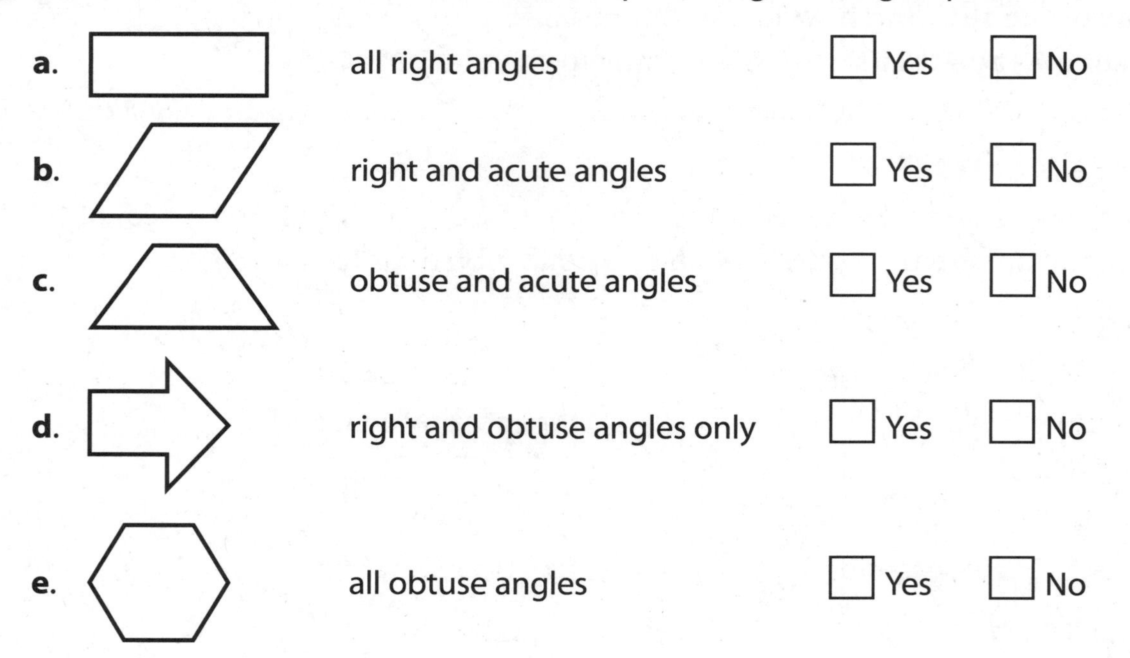

a. all right angles ☐ Yes ☐ No

b. right and acute angles ☐ Yes ☐ No

c. obtuse and acute angles ☐ Yes ☐ No

d. right and obtuse angles only ☐ Yes ☐ No

e. all obtuse angles ☐ Yes ☐ No

4 Describe a group that the two shapes below belong in, based on the kind of angles the shapes have.

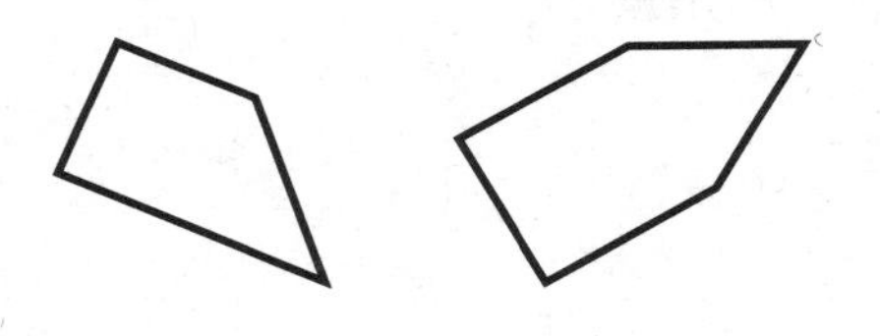

____

5 Look at the shapes in problem 4. Where do they belong in the Venn diagram below? Mark the place with an X.

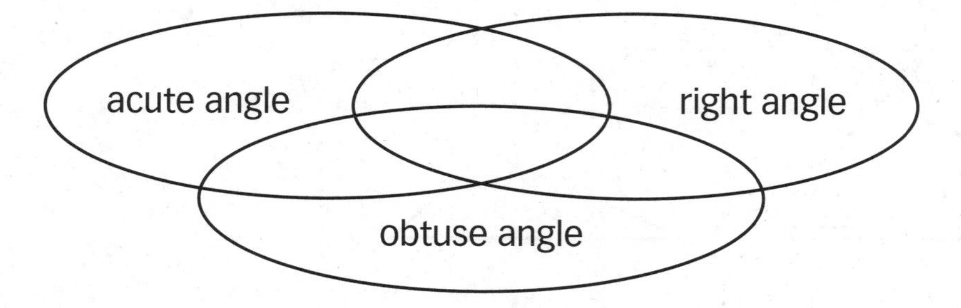

Name: ____________________

Sort Triangles Based on Sides and Angles

Study the example showing how to sort triangles into groups based on kinds of angles and lengths of sides. Then solve problems 1–4.

Example

What is the same about the two triangles shown at the right? What is different?

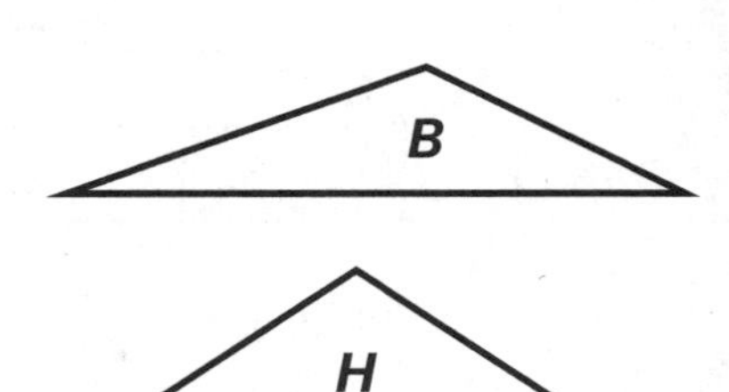

You can sort triangles into groups based on the kinds of angles they have: acute, right, or obtuse.

You can also sort triangles based on the lengths of their sides.

equilateral: 3 equal sides
isosceles: 2 equal sides
scalene: 0 equal sides

Triangles *B* and *H* are the same because they are both obtuse triangles. They each have 1 obtuse angle.

Triangles *B* and *H* are different because triangle *B* is a scalene triangle and triangle *H* is an isosceles triangle.

1 Look at the table. Name each triangle below based on the kinds of angles it has and the lengths of its sides.

Name	Description of Angles
acute	3 acute angles
right	1 right angle
obtuse	1 obtuse angle

Name	Description of Sides
equilateral	3 equal sides
isosceles	2 equal sides
scalene	0 equal sides

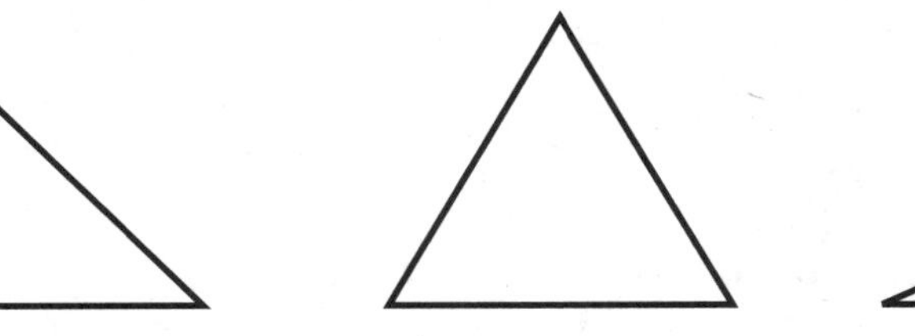

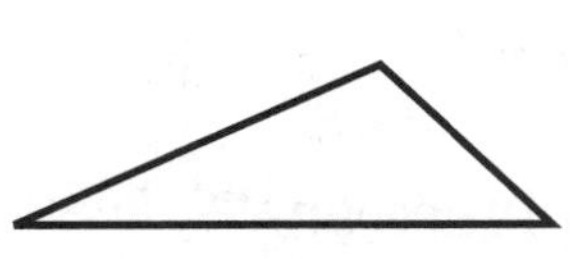

______________ ______________ ______________

Solve.

2 Look at the name of each triangle below. Then use the numbers in the boxes to write the missing length for one side of each triangle.

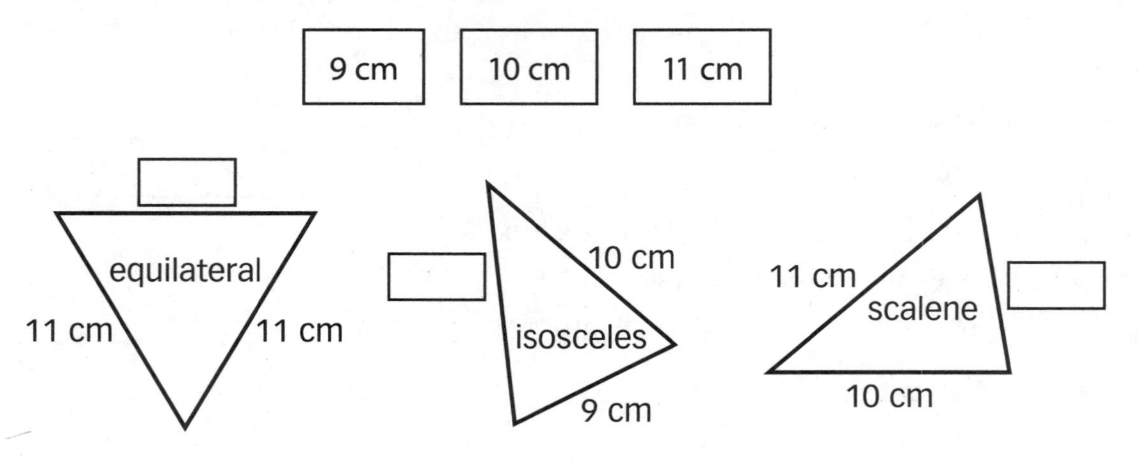

3 Norma drew the lines shown below on a piece of paper. Write labels inside each triangle formed by the lines: "a" for acute, "r" for right, "o" for obtuse, "e" for equilateral, "i" for isosceles, "s" for scalene.

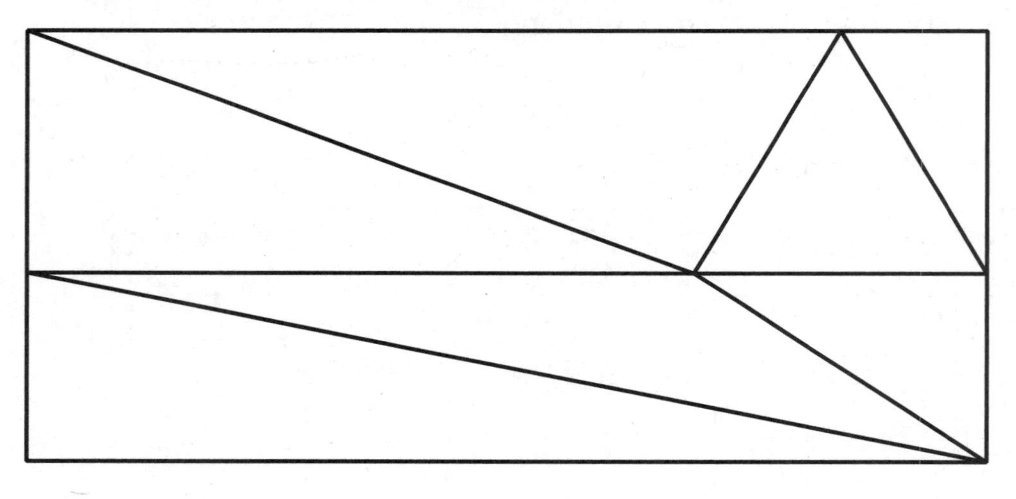

4 Circle the letter of each true statement below.

a. An obtuse triangle does not have acute angles.

b. A scalene triangle can be isosceles.

c. Equilateral triangles are always acute.

d. Isosceles triangles may also be equilateral.

e. Right triangles are scalene or isosceles.

Name: ______________________

Classify Two-Dimensional Figures

Solve the problems.

1 Which is the best name for the group of triangles below?

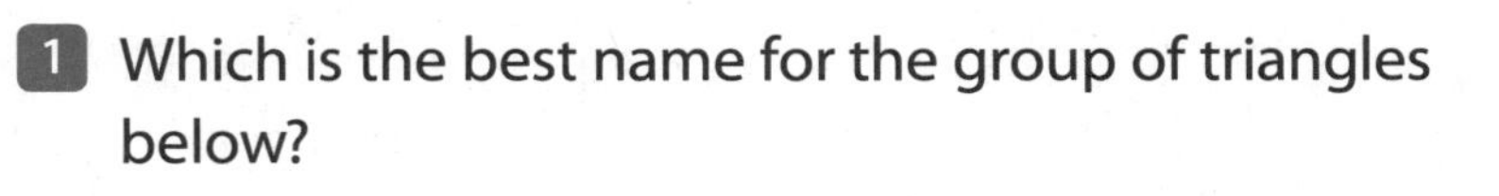

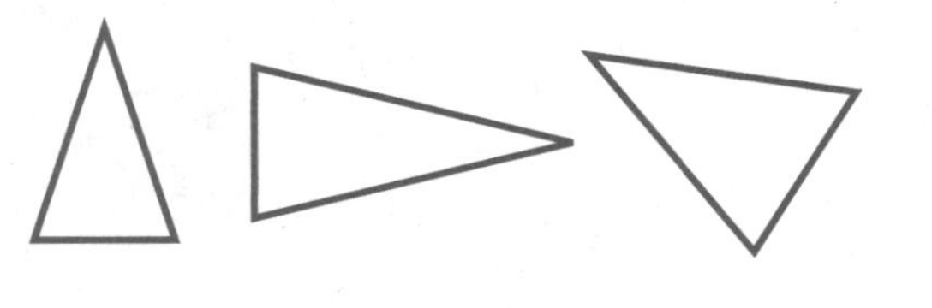

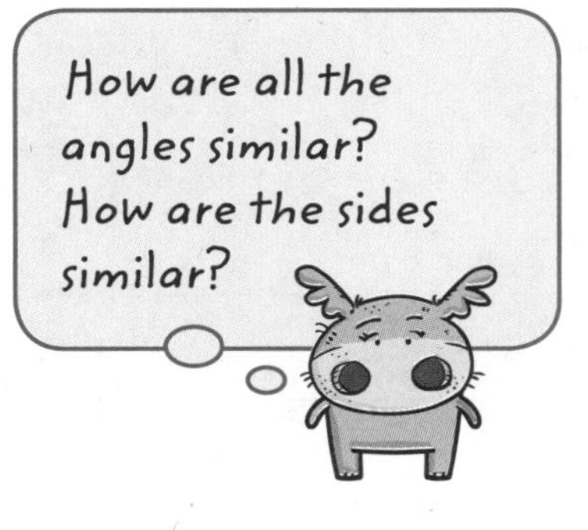

A acute, scalene

B acute, isosceles

C obtuse, scalene

D obtuse, isosceles

2 Which choice best describes the group this shape belongs in, based on the kinds of sides and angles it has?

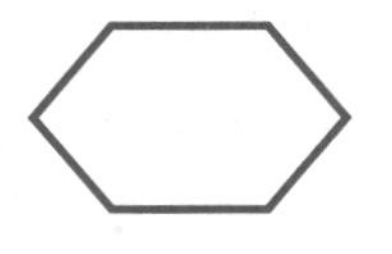

Are the sides parallel or perpendicular? Are the angles acute, obtuse, or right?

A parallel sides, acute angles

B perpendicular sides, acute angles

C parallel sides, obtuse angles

D perpendicular sides, obtuse angles

Angela chose **A** as the correct answer. How did she get that answer?

____

____

____

____

Solve.

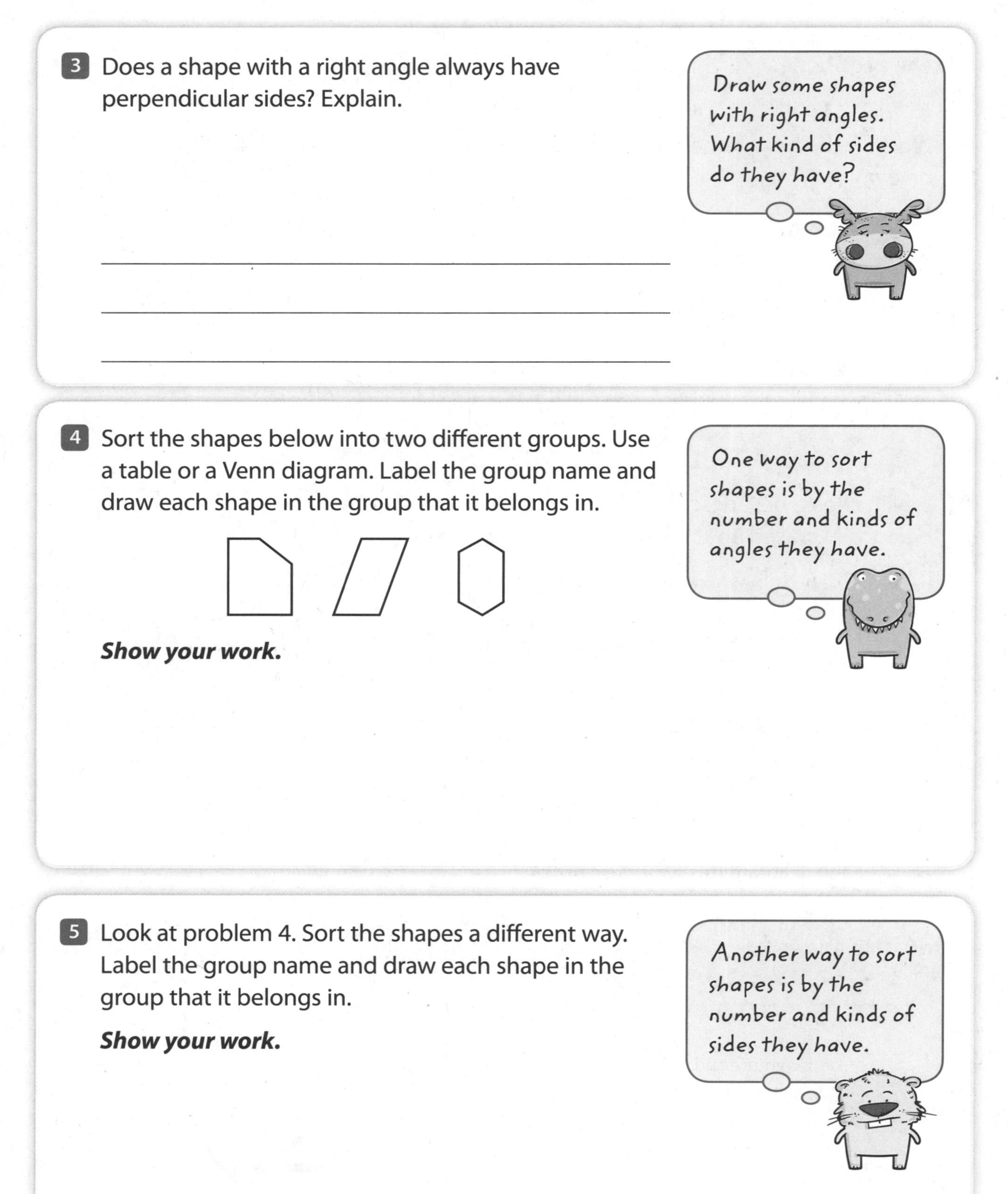

3 Does a shape with a right angle always have perpendicular sides? Explain.

____

____

____

4 Sort the shapes below into two different groups. Use a table or a Venn diagram. Label the group name and draw each shape in the group that it belongs in.

Show your work.

5 Look at problem 4. Sort the shapes a different way. Label the group name and draw each shape in the group that it belongs in.

Show your work.

Lesson 33

Symmetry

Name: ______________________

Prerequisite: Divide Shapes into Equal Parts

Study the example showing how to divide a shape into equal parts. Then solve problems 1–5.

Example

Show two different ways to divide a square into 4 equal parts.

Each part is $\frac{1}{4}$ of the square.

Each equal part is the same shape.

The 4 equal parts are rectangles.

The 4 equal parts are squares.

1 Show another way to divide a square into 4 equal parts. Then complete the sentence.

Each part is _______ of the square.

2 Divide the rectangle below into 2 equal parts. Then complete the sentence.

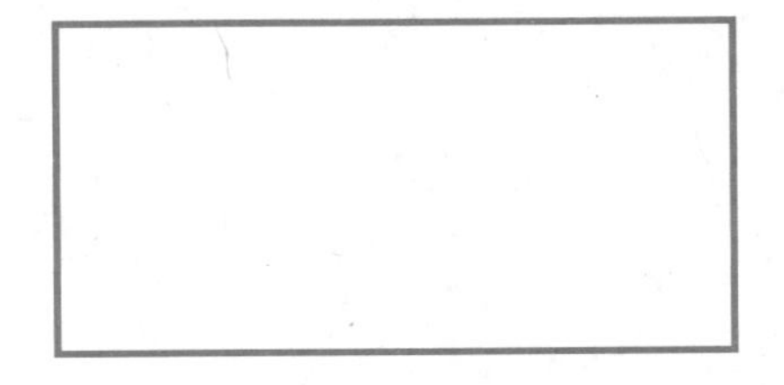

Each part is _______ of the rectangle.

Solve.

3 The rectangle below at the left is divided into 8 equal parts.

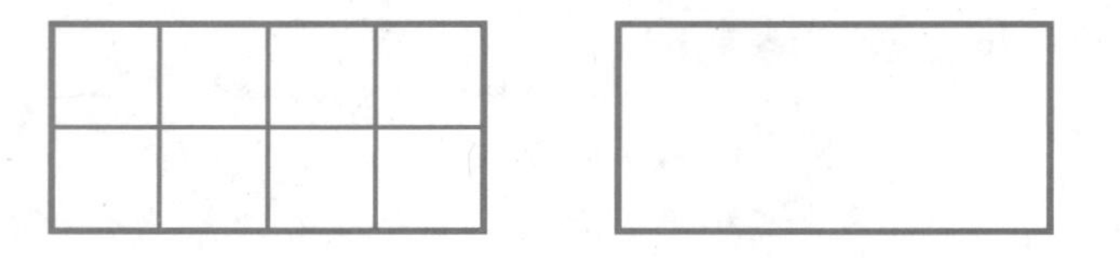

a. Draw lines on the rectangle at the right to show a different way to divide the rectangle into 8 equal parts.

b. What fraction of the rectangle is each part? _______

4 Draw a rectangle and divide it into 4 equal parts. What fraction of the rectangle is each part?

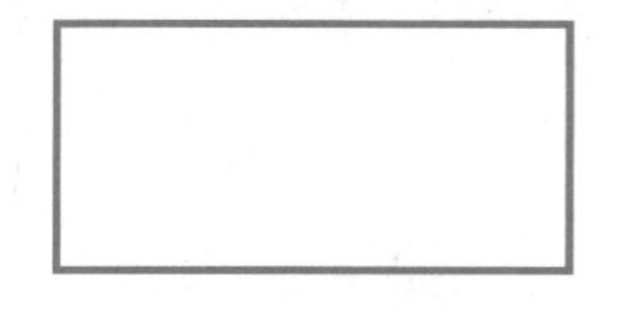

Each part is _______ of the rectangle.

5 Liam is making a game board. He wants the game board to have 20 equal sections. Show one way that he could divide the board into 20 equal sections. How many rows are there and how many equal parts in each row?

Show your work.

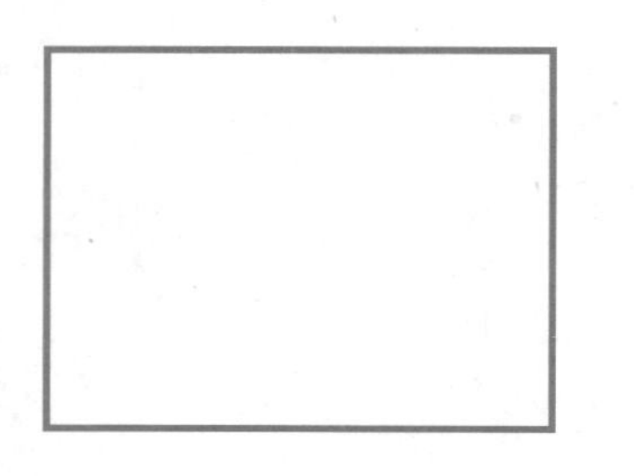

Solution: ____

____

Name: ______________________

Find a Line of Symmetry

Study the example showing how to find a line of symmetry. Then solve problems 1–5.

Example

Which shape has more lines of symmetry—
a rectangle, an equilateral triangle, or a square?

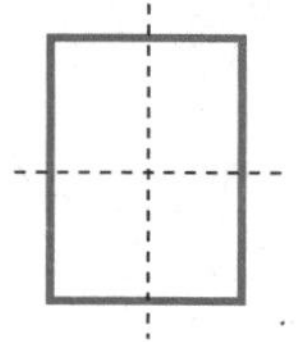

A rectangle has 2 lines of symmetry.

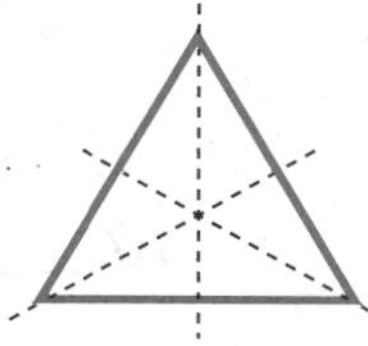

An equilateral triangle has 3 lines of symmetry.

A square has 4 lines of symmetry.

A square has more lines of symmetry than a rectangle and an equilateral triangle.

1 Circle the shapes below that have at least one line of symmetry.

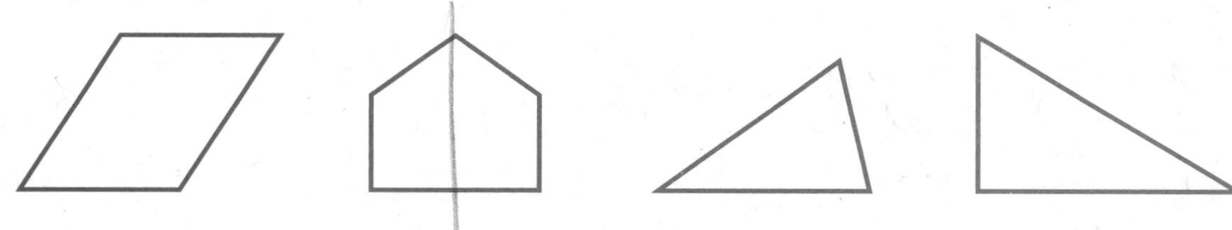

2 Circle the shape below that has a greater number of lines of symmetry.

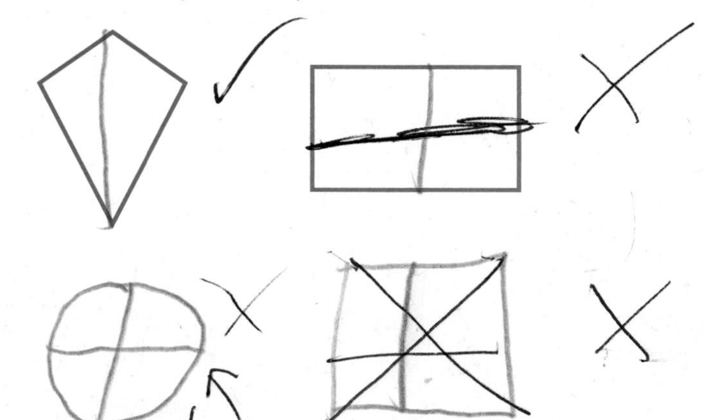

Vocabulary

line of symmetry a line dividing a shape into two matching parts.

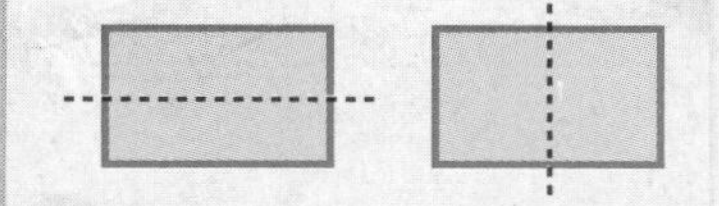

Solve.

3 Circle the shapes below that have exactly 4 lines of symmetry.

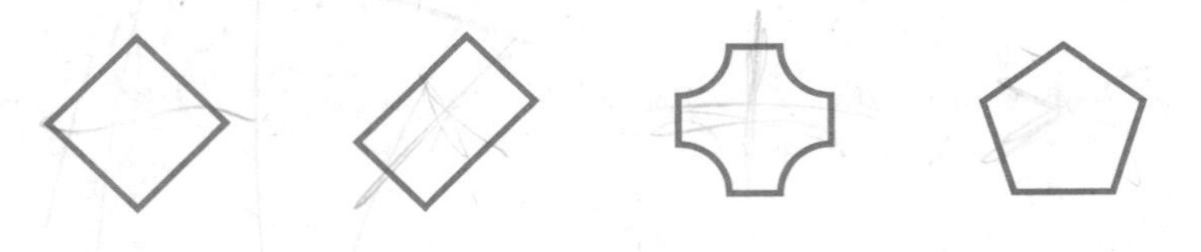

4 Look at the rectangle in problem 3. How many lines of symmetry does it have? Explain.

____

____

____

____

5 Choose *Yes* or *No* to tell whether the line drawn on each block letter is a line of symmetry.

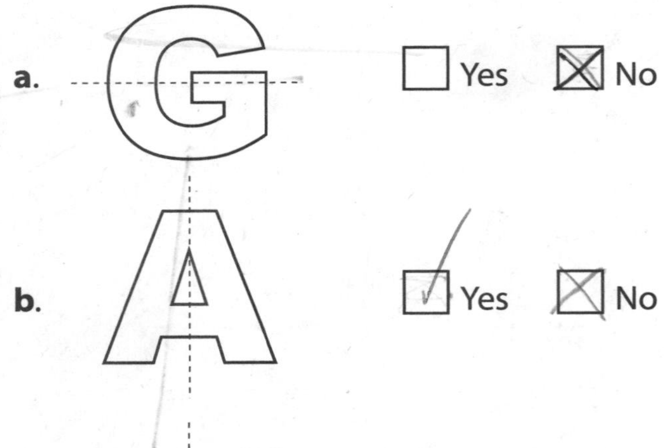

a. ☐ Yes ☒ No

b. ☐ Yes ☐ No

c. 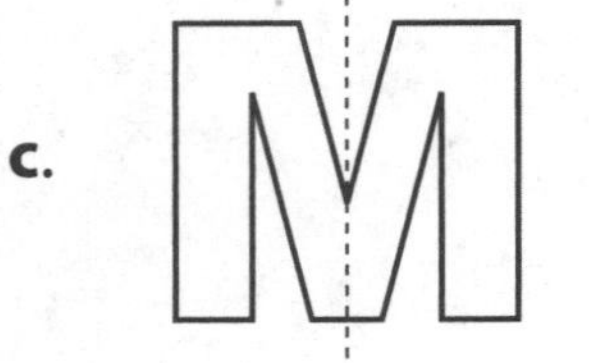  Yes ☐ No

d. 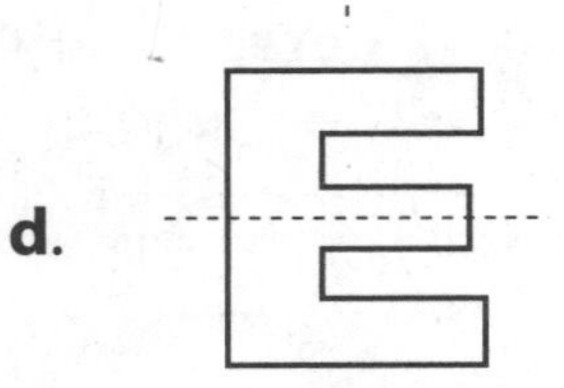 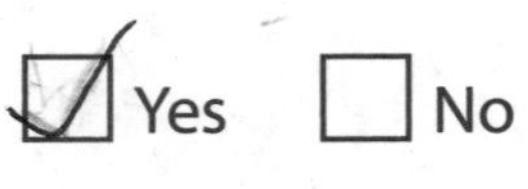 Yes ☐ No

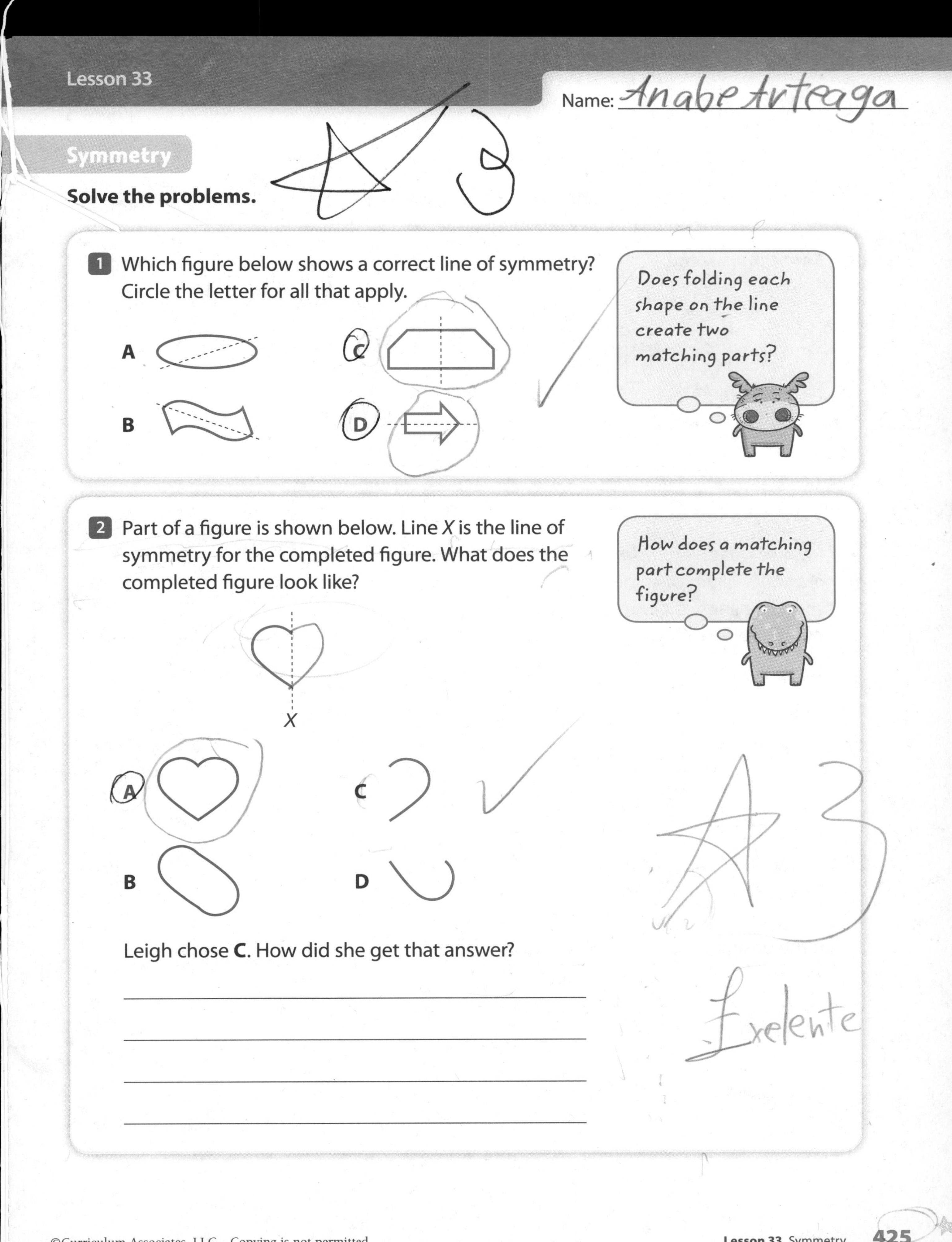

Name: Anabe Arteaga

Symmetry

Solve the problems.

1 Which figure below shows a correct line of symmetry? Circle the letter for all that apply.

A

B

C

D

Does folding each shape on the line create two matching parts?

2 Part of a figure is shown below. Line X is the line of symmetry for the completed figure. What does the completed figure look like?

X

A

B

C

D

How does a matching part complete the figure?

Leigh chose **C**. How did she get that answer?

____

____

____

____

Solve.

3 Draw all the lines of symmetry on the figure below. How many lines of symmetry are there?

Show your work.

Can you fold the figure in more than one way to show matching parts?

Solution:

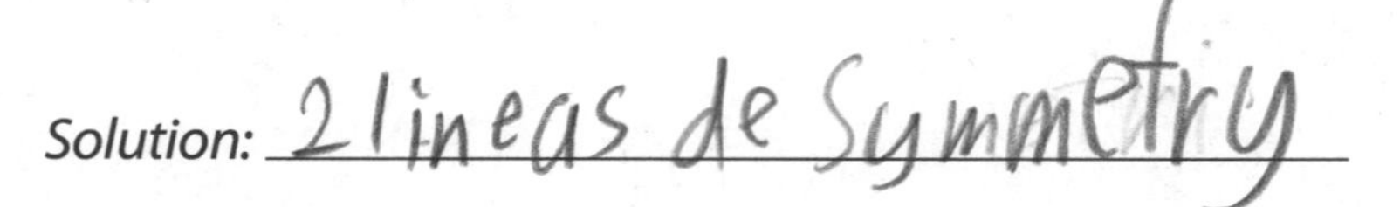

4 Name a quadrilateral that always has the same number of lines of symmetry. Draw the shape and show the lines of symmetry. Explain why the number of lines of symmetry is always the same.

Show your work.

What are the different kinds of quadrilaterals? How many lines of symmetry do they have?

Solution: Square

Unit 6 Game

Name: ______________________

Shape Round-Up

What you need: Recording Sheet, Game Board, Game Cards, 32 counters

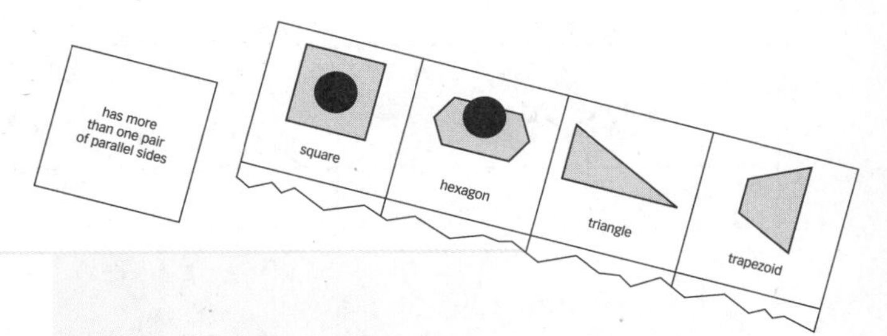

Directions

- Mix the Game Cards. Place them facedown in a stack.
- When it's your turn, draw a card and place counters on all of the shapes on your Game Board that match the description on the card.
- On your Recording Sheet, write the description from the Game Card and draw the shapes you covered on your Game Board. Then place the Game Card in a discard pile.
- Players take turns. Place only one counter on each space on the Game Board. If you use all the Game Cards, remix and reuse the cards in the discard pile.
- The winner is the first player to cover all the shapes on their Game Board.

Name: Javi

Shape Round-Up Recording Sheet

Description on Game Card	Shapes Covered on Game Board
has more than one pair of parallel sides	

My Game Card reads "has more than one pair of parallel sides." I put counters on my Game Board over all the shapes with more than one pair of parallel sides.

Name: ____________________

Shape Round-Up Recording Sheet

Description on Game Card	Shapes Covered on Game Board

Name: ______________________

Shape Round-Up Game Board

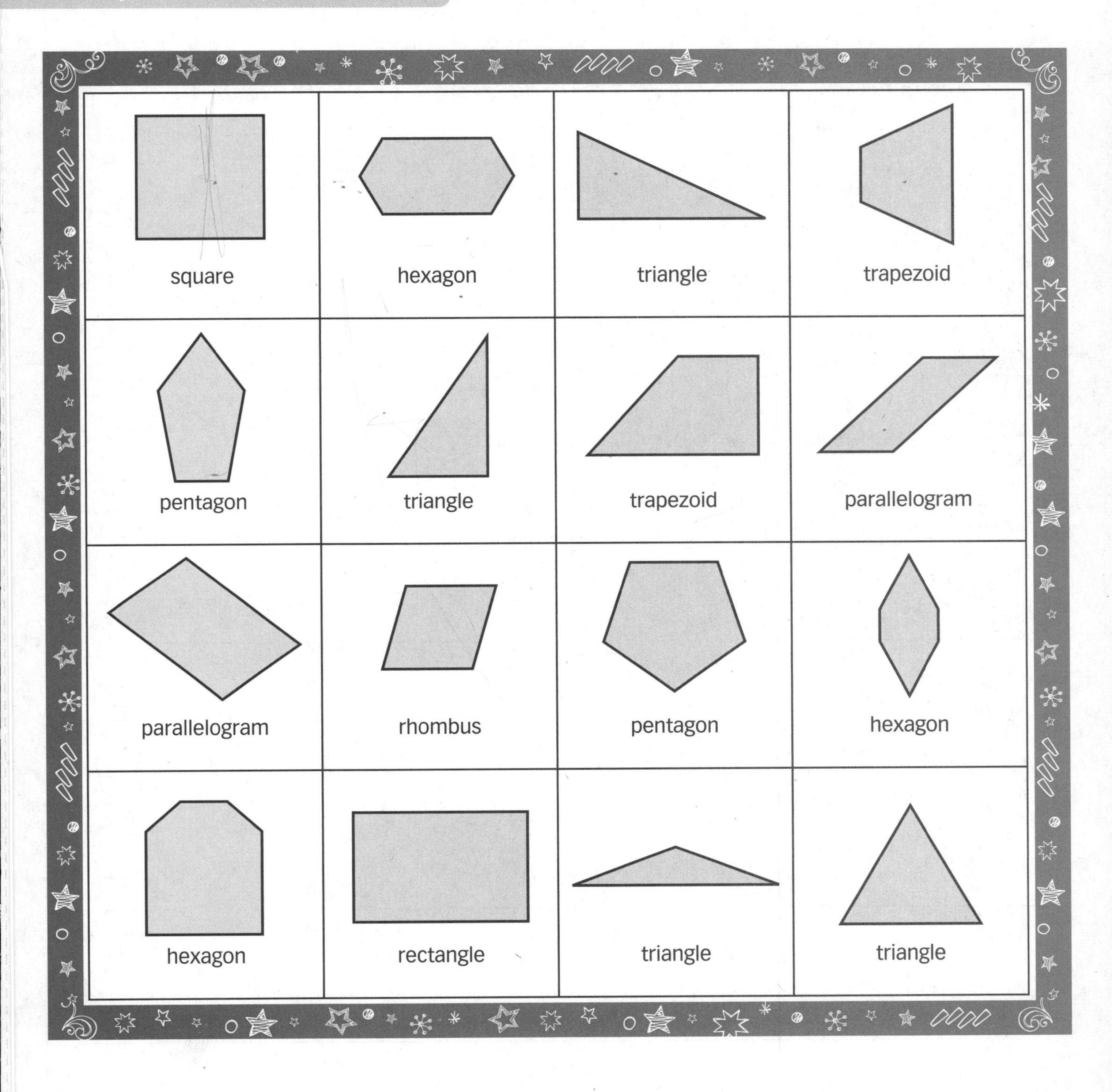

Shape Round-Up Game Cards

has acute angle(s)	has obtuse angle(s)	has right angle(s)	has more than one pair of parallel sides
has more than one pair of perpendicular sides	has acute angles and obtuse angles	has acute angles and right angles	has exactly one pair of parallel sides
has exactly one pair of perpendicular sides	acute triangle	obtuse triangle	right triangle
has more than 4 obtuse angles	has right angles and obtuse angles	has no sides that are parallel	has no sides that are perpendicular

Unit 6 Practice

Name: ______________________

Geometry

In this unit you learned to:	Lesson
draw and identify points, lines, line segments, rays, and perpendicular and parallel lines, for example: a plus sign has perpendicular lines.	31
draw and identify angles (right, acute, obtuse), for example: a square has 4 right angles.	31
classify two-dimensional figures based on sides and angles, for example: regular pentagons and hexagons have all obtuse angles.	32
draw and identify lines of symmetry, for example: a square has 4 lines of symmetry.	33

Use these skills to solve problems 1–4.

1 Tell whether each sentence is *True* or *False*.

a. An acute angle has a larger opening than a right angle. ☐ True ☐ False

b. Any shape with more than 4 sides has only obtuse angles. ☐ True ☐ False

c. A triangle can have 1 right angle or 1 obtuse angle, but not both. ☐ True ☐ False

d. An angle is formed by 2 rays. ☐ True ☐ False

2 Name each triangle below based on the kinds of angles it has and the length of its sides.

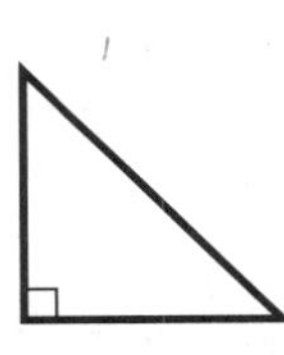

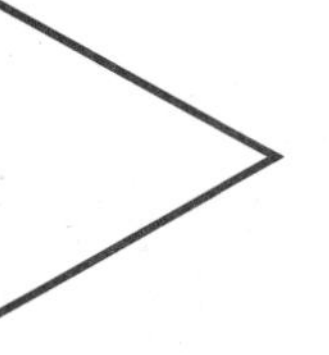

______________ ______________ ______________

Solve.

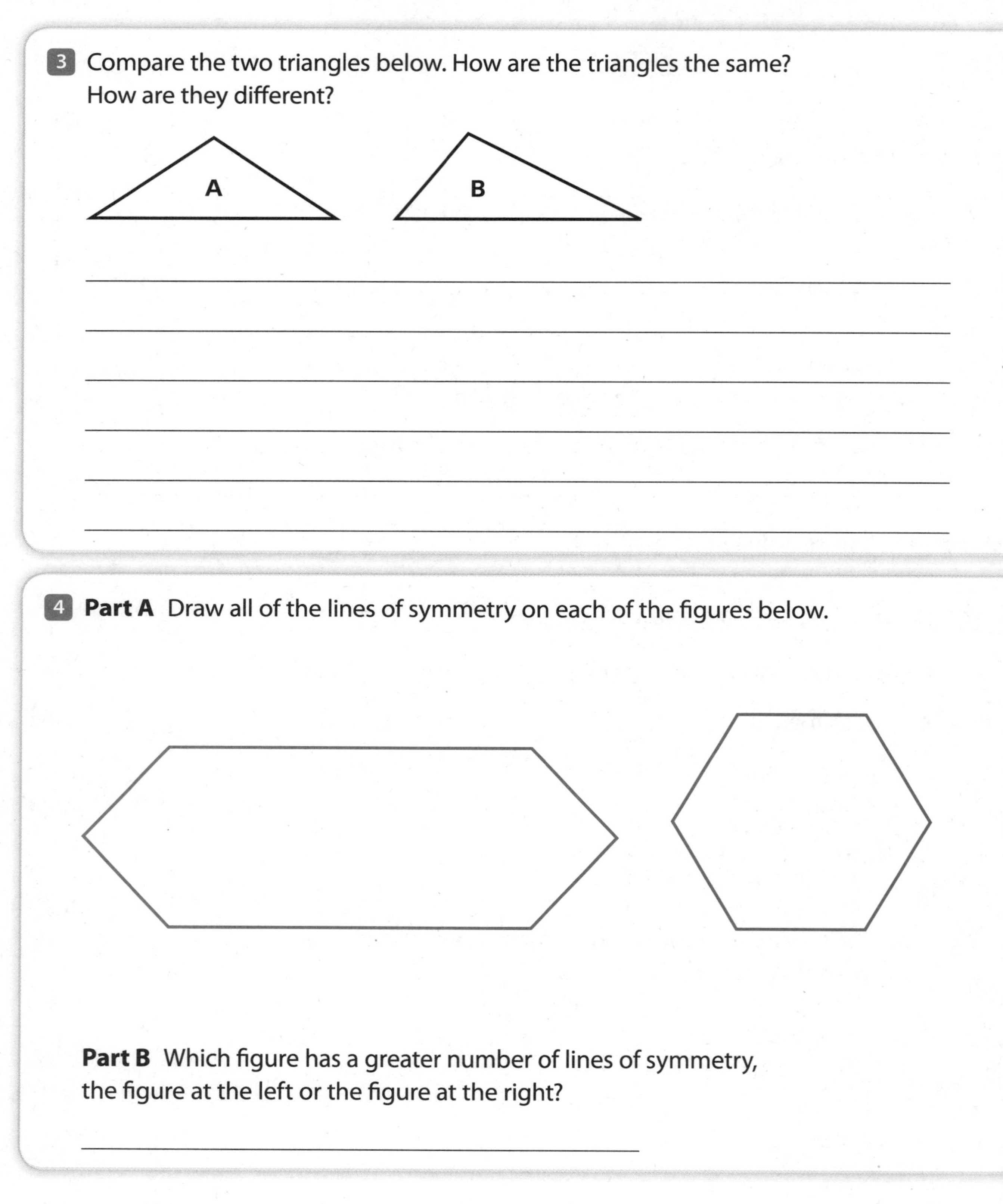

3 Compare the two triangles below. How are the triangles the same? How are they different?

4 **Part A** Draw all of the lines of symmetry on each of the figures below.

Part B Which figure has a greater number of lines of symmetry, the figure at the left or the figure at the right?

Unit 6 Performance Task

Name: ____________________

Answer the questions and show all your work on separate paper.

Your math teacher has asked you to design a flower. The flower must be formed only from geometric shapes. Here is the example the teacher gives.

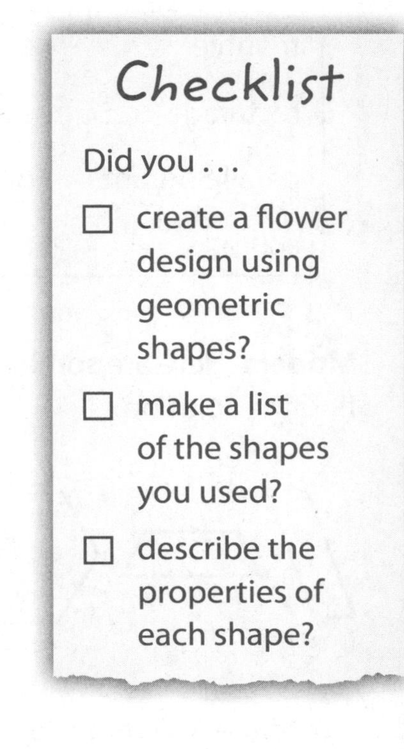

Create a design for a flower. You can use the shapes shown on the back of this page. You can also use other geometric shapes. Draw a picture of your flower. On a separate sheet of paper, list the names of all the different shapes you used. Also describe the properties of each shape.

Reflect on the Process Standards

After you complete the task, choose one of the following questions to answer.

1 **Reason Mathematically** How did you decide which shapes to use to create your flower design?

2 **Be Precise** How does your description of the properties of the shapes help someone understand what your flower design looks like?

Performance Task Tips

Word Bank Here are some words that you might use in your answer.

triangle	angle	parallel
rectangle	equilateral	right
parallelogram	obtuse	side
acute	trapezoid	perpendicular

Models Here are some models that you might use to find the solution.

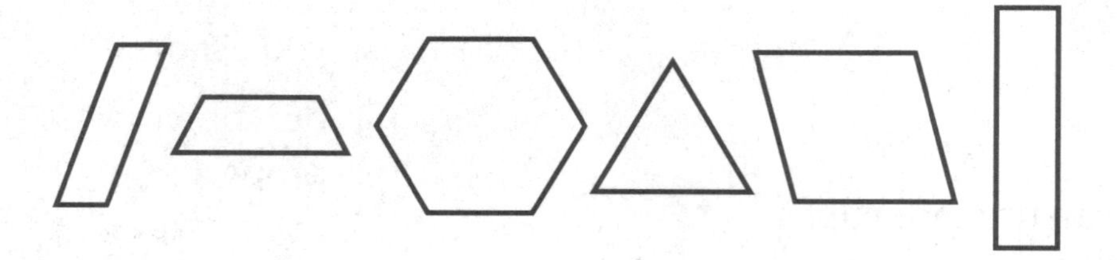

Sentence Starters Here are some sentence starters that might help explain your work.

I used ______________ to make ________________

The sides of the shape are ______________________

The angles are ______________________________

The shape is _______________________________

Unit 6 Vocabulary

Name: ____________________

My Examples

point

a single location in space

line segment

a straight row of points that starts at one point and ends at another point

line

a straight row of points that goes on forever in both directions

ray

a straight row of points that starts at one point and goes on forever in one direction

My Examples

angle

a geometric shape formed by two rays (or lines or line segments) that meet at a common endpoint, called a vertex

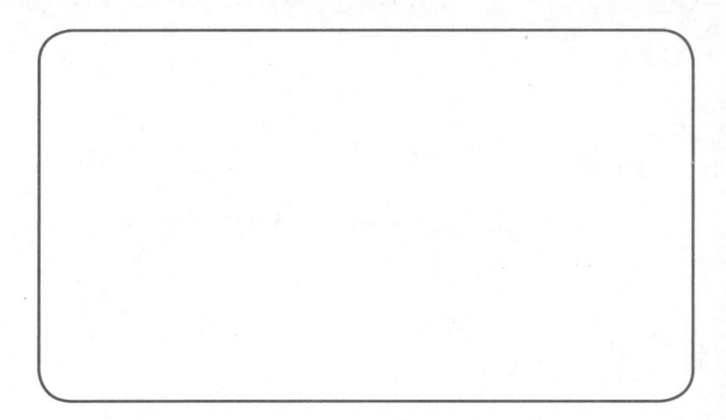

parallel lines

two lines that are always the same distance apart and will never cross

perpendicular lines

two lines that cross at a 90° angle

equilateral triangle

a triangle that has all three sides with the same length

My Examples

isosceles triangle

a triangle that has two sides with the same length

scalene triangle

a triangle that has no sides with the same length

acute triangle

a triangle that has three acute angles

right triangle

a triangle that has one right angle

My Examples

obtuse triangle

a triangle that has one obtuse angle

line of symmetry

a line dividing a shape into two matching parts

My Words

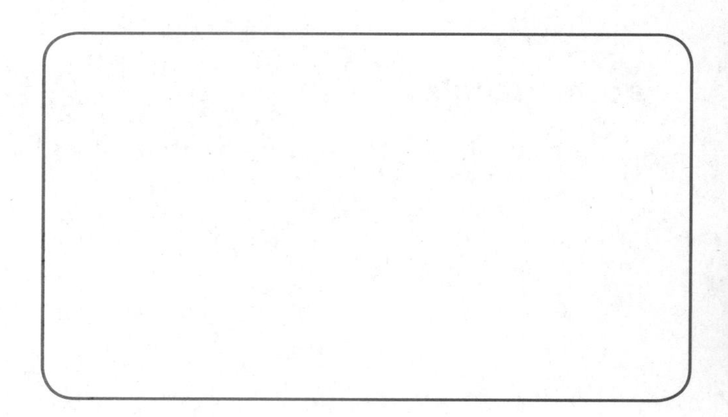

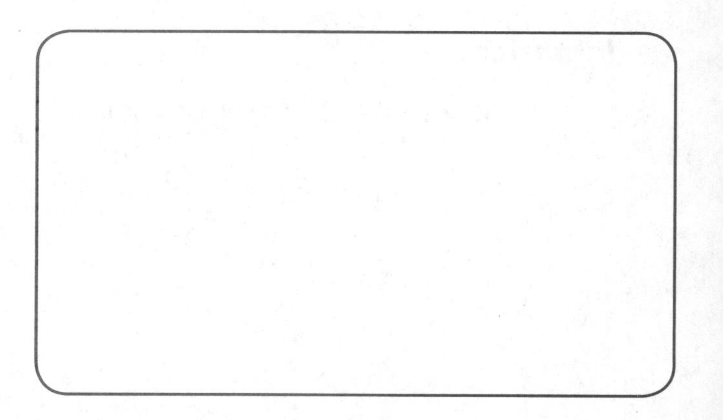

Fluency Table of Contents

Multi-Digit Addition—Skills Practice

Name: ____________________

Add within 10,000. **Form A**

1. 2,145 + 653

2. 5,260 + 417

3. 1,083 + 2,513

4. 2,864 + 7,135

5. 1,248 + 532

6. 3,709 + 152

7. 4,561 + 1,054

8. 5,726 + 3,742

9. 3,750 + 456

10. 2,538 + 167

11. 1,659 + 3,291

12. 4,806 + 3,255

13. 6,725 + 385

14. 5,218 + 938

15. 6,002 + 2,999

16. 8,375 + 1,625

17. 4,278 + 3,956

18. 9,407 + 396

19. 3,098 + 2,574

20. 2,710 + 5,690

Multi-Digit Addition—Skills Practice

Name: ____________________

Add within 10,000. **Form B**

1 1,247 + 532	**2** 3,415 + 243	**3** 1,068 + 1,510	**4** 4,037 + 5,062
5 2,653 + 412	**6** 1,087 + 637	**7** 1,960 + 3,204	**8** 6,723 + 1,238
9 4,058 + 852	**10** 2,718 + 534	**11** 3,605 + 2,795	**12** 2,806 + 6,294
13 6,725 + 385	**14** 5,218 + 938	**15** 7,538 + 2,462	**16** 3,999 + 4,006
17 7,092 + 1,865	**18** 8,444 + 565	**19** 5,146 + 3,175	**20** 8,470 + 1,525

Multi-Digit Addition—Skills Practice

Name: ____________________

Add within 100,000.

Form A

1 10,352 + 1,430	**2** 16,164 + 1,325	**3** 20,753 + 10,104	**4** 50,618 + 24,350
5 15,200 + 999	**6** 32,145 + 4,625	**7** 64,102 + 17,254	**8** 24,390 + 56,180
9 93,752 + 598	**10** 46,250 + 23,805	**11** 12,643 + 52,794	**12** 54,622 + 34,588
13 23,856 + 15,246	**14** 47,423 + 19,836	**15** 49,999 + 3,999	**16** 90,187 + 9,783
17 84,678 + 6,395	**18** 27,329 + 15,896	**19** 52,098 + 28,107	**20** 48,365 + 51,635

Multi-Digit Addition—Skills Practice

Name: ______________________

Add within 100,000.

Form B

1 10,943 + 2,035

2 17,342 + 1,340

3 12,453 + 20,143

4 61,238 + 24,501

5 34,210 + 1,399

6 72,643 + 8,142

7 15,920 + 63,254

8 45,806 + 54,159

9 94,627 + 987

10 68,254 + 2,438

11 26,513 + 25,974

12 21,942 + 38,657

13 23,658 + 8,467

14 47,652 + 27,836

15 29,999 + 3,999

16 84,316 + 15,684

17 74,895 + 16,395

18 57,918 + 25,896

19 42,968 + 20,947

20 45,163 + 27,989

Multi-Digit Addition—Repeated Reasoning

Name: ____________________

Find place value patterns in the tens.

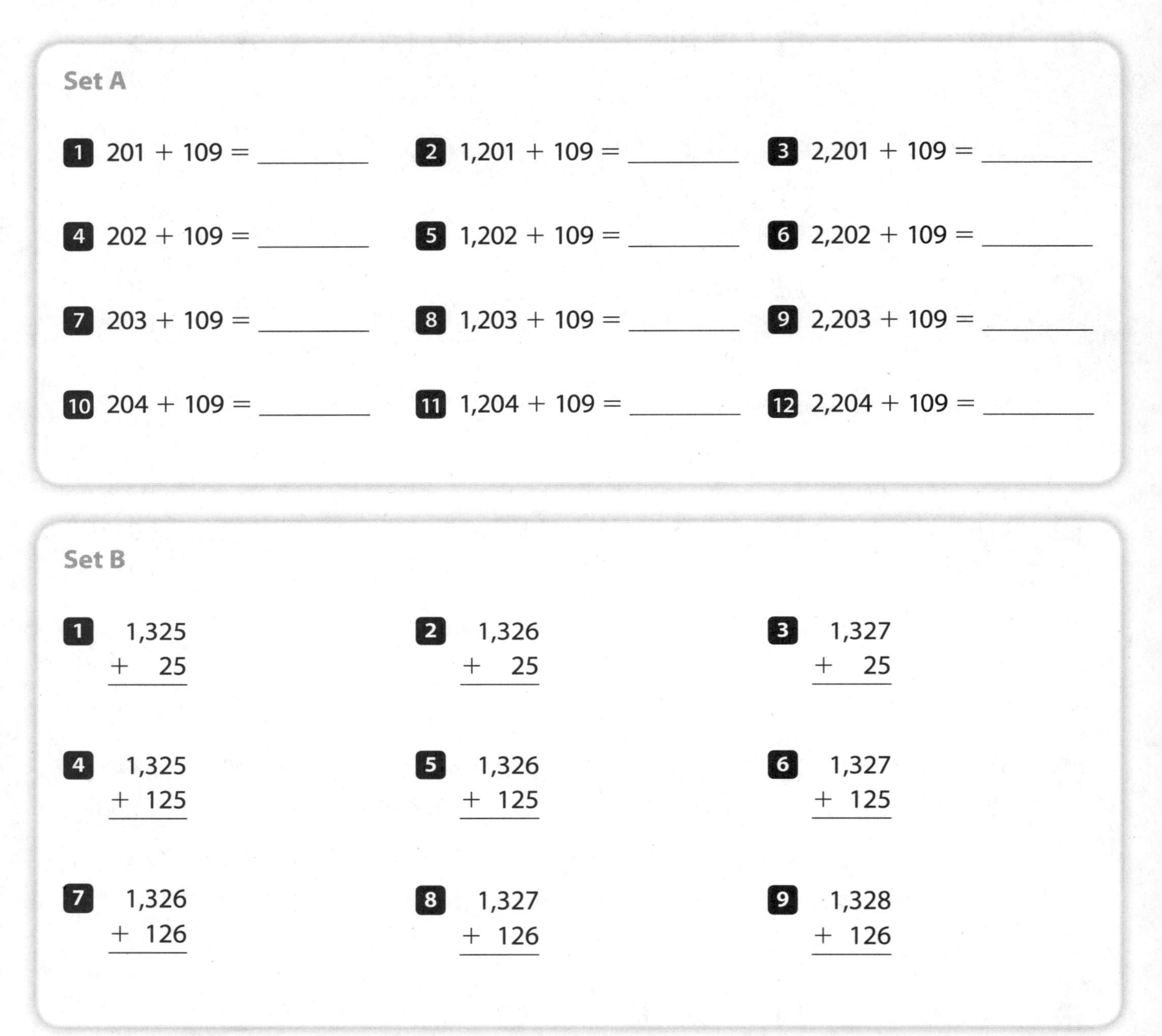

Set A

1. 201 + 109 = ________
2. 1,201 + 109 = ________
3. 2,201 + 109 = ________
4. 202 + 109 = ________
5. 1,202 + 109 = ________
6. 2,202 + 109 = ________
7. 203 + 109 = ________
8. 1,203 + 109 = ________
9. 2,203 + 109 = ________
10. 204 + 109 = ________
11. 1,204 + 109 = ________
12. 2,204 + 109 = ________

Set B

1. $\begin{array}{r} 1,325 \\ +\ \ 25 \\ \hline \end{array}$
2. $\begin{array}{r} 1,326 \\ +\ \ 25 \\ \hline \end{array}$
3. $\begin{array}{r} 1,327 \\ +\ \ 25 \\ \hline \end{array}$
4. $\begin{array}{r} 1,325 \\ +\ 125 \\ \hline \end{array}$
5. $\begin{array}{r} 1,326 \\ +\ 125 \\ \hline \end{array}$
6. $\begin{array}{r} 1,327 \\ +\ 125 \\ \hline \end{array}$
7. $\begin{array}{r} 1,326 \\ +\ 126 \\ \hline \end{array}$
8. $\begin{array}{r} 1,327 \\ +\ 126 \\ \hline \end{array}$
9. $\begin{array}{r} 1,328 \\ +\ 126 \\ \hline \end{array}$

Describe a pattern you see in one of the sets of problems above.

____

____

____

 Name: ____________

Find place value patterns in the hundreds.

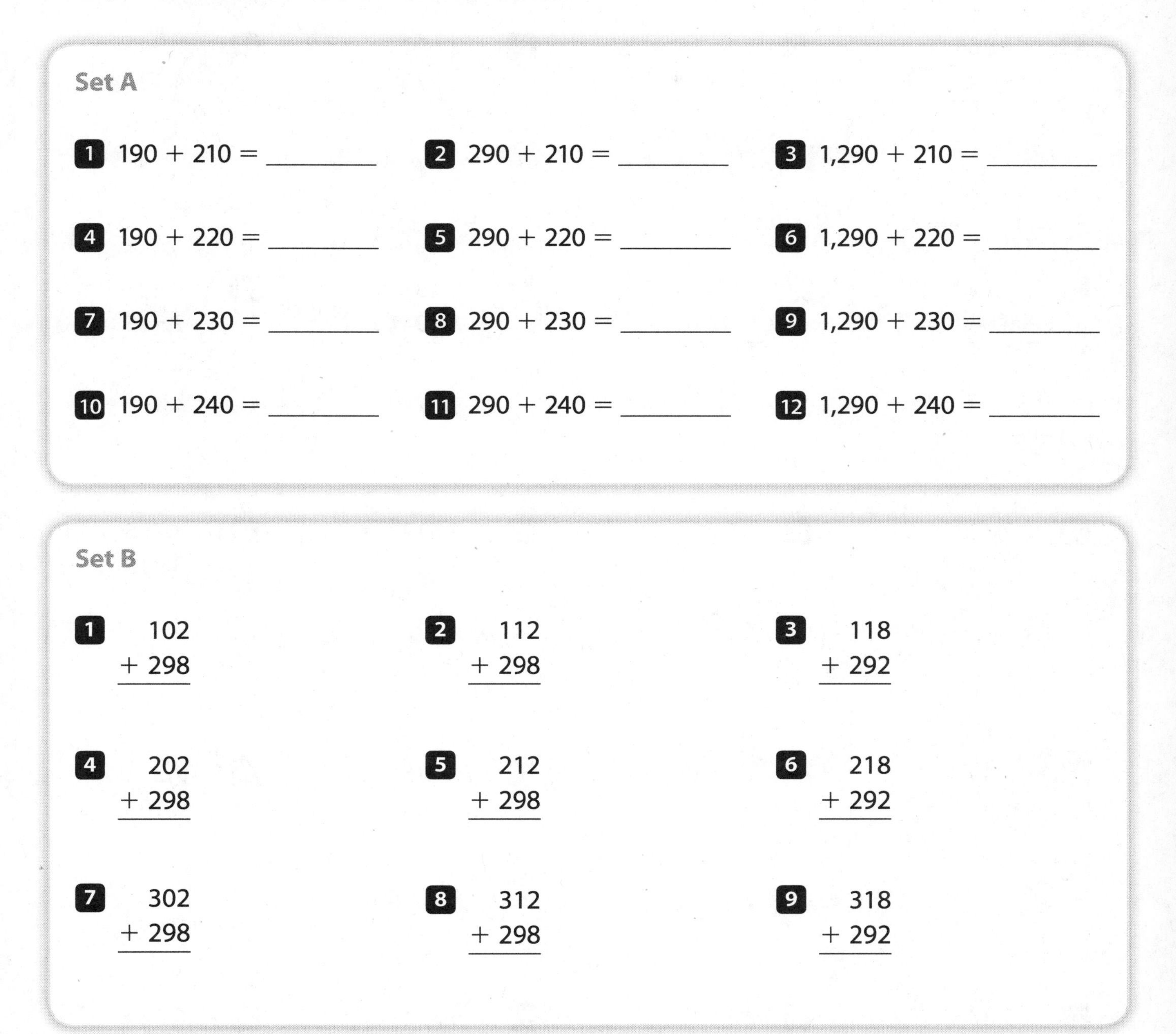

Set A

1. 190 + 210 = ______
2. 290 + 210 = ______
3. 1,290 + 210 = ______
4. 190 + 220 = ______
5. 290 + 220 = ______
6. 1,290 + 220 = ______
7. 190 + 230 = ______
8. 290 + 230 = ______
9. 1,290 + 230 = ______
10. 190 + 240 = ______
11. 290 + 240 = ______
12. 1,290 + 240 = ______

Set B

1. 102 + 298 = ______
2. 112 + 298 = ______
3. 118 + 292 = ______
4. 202 + 298 = ______
5. 212 + 298 = ______
6. 218 + 292 = ______
7. 302 + 298 = ______
8. 312 + 298 = ______
9. 318 + 292 = ______

Describe a pattern you see in one of the sets of problems above.

____

____

____

Multi-Digit Subtraction—Skills Practice

Name: ______________________

Subtract within 10,000. **Form A**

1 4,865 − 2,341	**2** 1,788 − 1,263	**3** 2,592 − 1,271	**4** 7,342 − 4,132
5 8,790 − 6,688	**6** 3,743 − 626	**7** 9,487 − 1,394	**8** 6,427 − 2,515
9 2,637 − 2,419	**10** 3,780 − 671	**11** 8,618 − 3,425	**12** 4,756 − 3,813
13 8,403 − 6,520	**14** 1,438 − 839	**15** 4,725 − 1,439	**16** 7,275 − 4,188
17 5,274 − 2,778	**18** 2,923 − 1,976	**19** 5,824 − 2,948	**20** 6,743 − 2,878

Multi-Digit Subtraction—Skills Practice

Name: ____________________

Subtract within 10,000. **Form B**

1. 5,647 − 3,210 =
2. 2,748 − 312 =
3. 5,429 − 4,003 =
4. 6,918 − 4,105 =
5. 8,263 − 1,453 =
6. 1,397 − 1,239 =
7. 4,131 − 2,051 =
8. 7,382 − 2,581 =
9. 2,732 − 1,108 =
10. 4,803 − 615 =
11. 8,652 − 3,481 =
12. 3,607 − 2,801 =
13. 8,275 − 2,391 =
14. 3,120 − 1,052 =
15. 9,253 − 198 =
16. 6,732 − 5,587 =
17. 4,366 − 1,568 =
18. 1,812 − 945 =
19. 7,493 − 2,594 =
20. 7,423 − 2,846 =

Multi-Digit Subtraction—Skills Practice

Name: ______________________

Subtract within 100,000. **Form A**

1 47,863 − 251	**2** 19,038 − 11,018	**3** 28,682 − 3,270	**4** 76,429 − 20,306
5 81,235 − 20,017	**6** 36,725 − 1,582	**7** 94,130 − 20,125	**8** 64,728 − 3,914
9 28,236 − 8,915	**10** 58,623 − 26,374	**11** 72,160 − 2,087	**12** 38,412 − 25,651
13 34,210 − 8,105	**14** 10,714 − 9,456	**15** 63,258 − 21,399	**16** 40,805 − 15,912
17 53,126 − 45,928	**18** 80,052 − 71,963	**19** 24,350 − 9,582	**20** 100,000 − 86,932

Multi-Digit Subtraction—Skills Practice

Name: ____________________

Subtract within 100,000.

Form B

1 53,641 − 1,320	**2** 85,472 − 82,302	**3** 93,245 − 32,025	**4** 43,619 − 20,301
5 30,582 − 156	**6** 12,987 − 2,793	**7** 82,056 − 50,330	**8** 73,542 − 25,402
9 27,810 − 15,675	**10** 94,321 − 4,255	**11** 65,852 − 23,890	**12** 18,376 − 8,953
13 15,008 − 2,409	**14** 20,530 − 19,790	**15** 99,325 − 38,547	**16** 50,364 − 37,148
17 36,825 − 28,967	**18** 38,972 − 19,999	**19** 45,000 − 37,955	**20** 100,000 − 23,871

Multi-Digit Subtraction—Repeated Reasoning

Name: ______________________

Find patterns in subtracting small numbers.

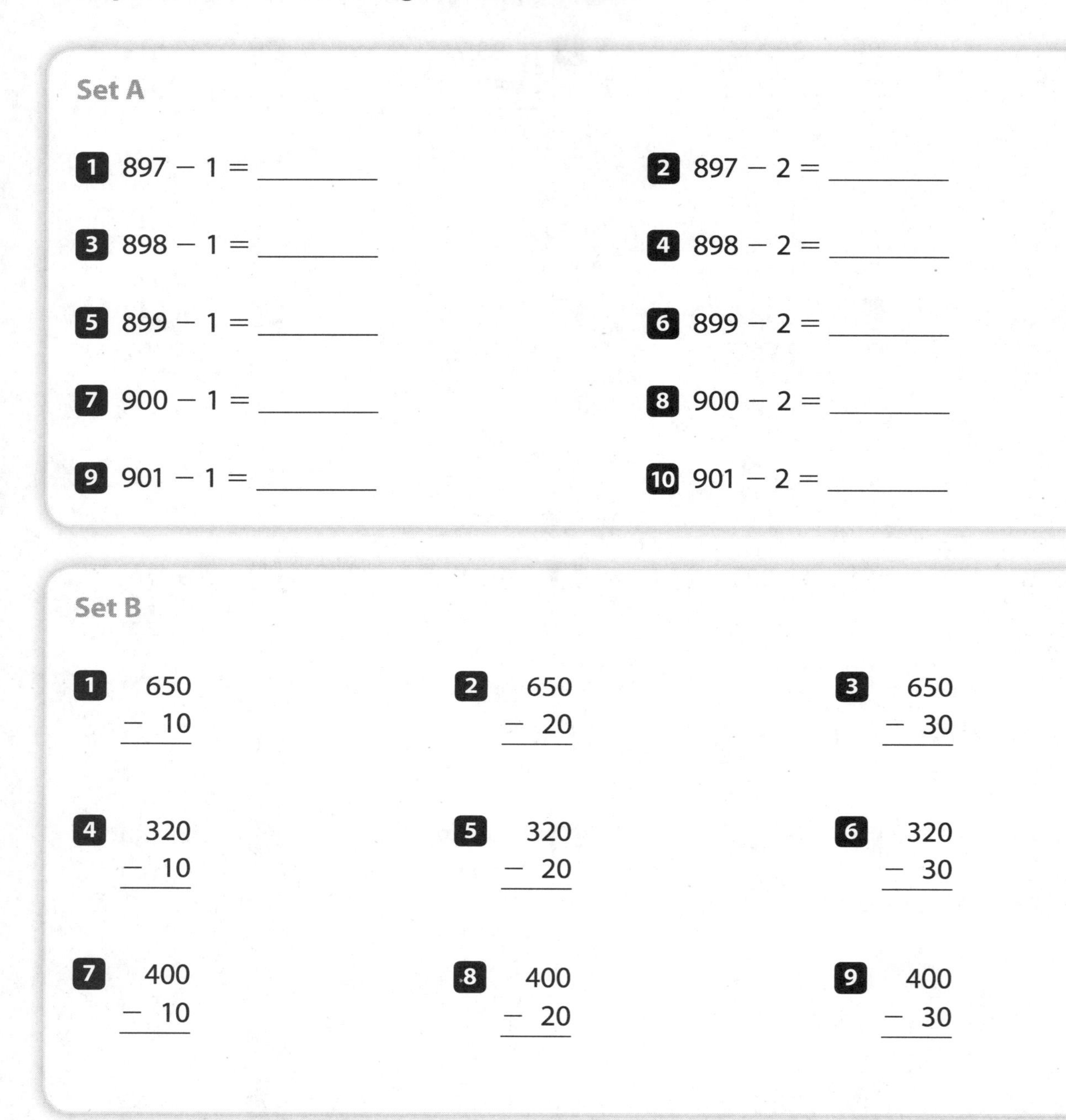

Set A

1 897 − 1 = ________

2 897 − 2 = ________

3 898 − 1 = ________

4 898 − 2 = ________

5 899 − 1 = ________

6 899 − 2 = ________

7 900 − 1 = ________

8 900 − 2 = ________

9 901 − 1 = ________

10 901 − 2 = ________

Set B

1 $650 - 10$

2 $650 - 20$

3 $650 - 30$

4 $320 - 10$

5 $320 - 20$

6 $320 - 30$

7 $400 - 10$

8 $400 - 20$

9 $400 - 30$

Describe a pattern you see in one of the sets of problems above.

____

____

____

Multi-Digit Subtraction—Repeated Reasoning

Name: ____________________

Find place value patterns in subtracting hundreds.

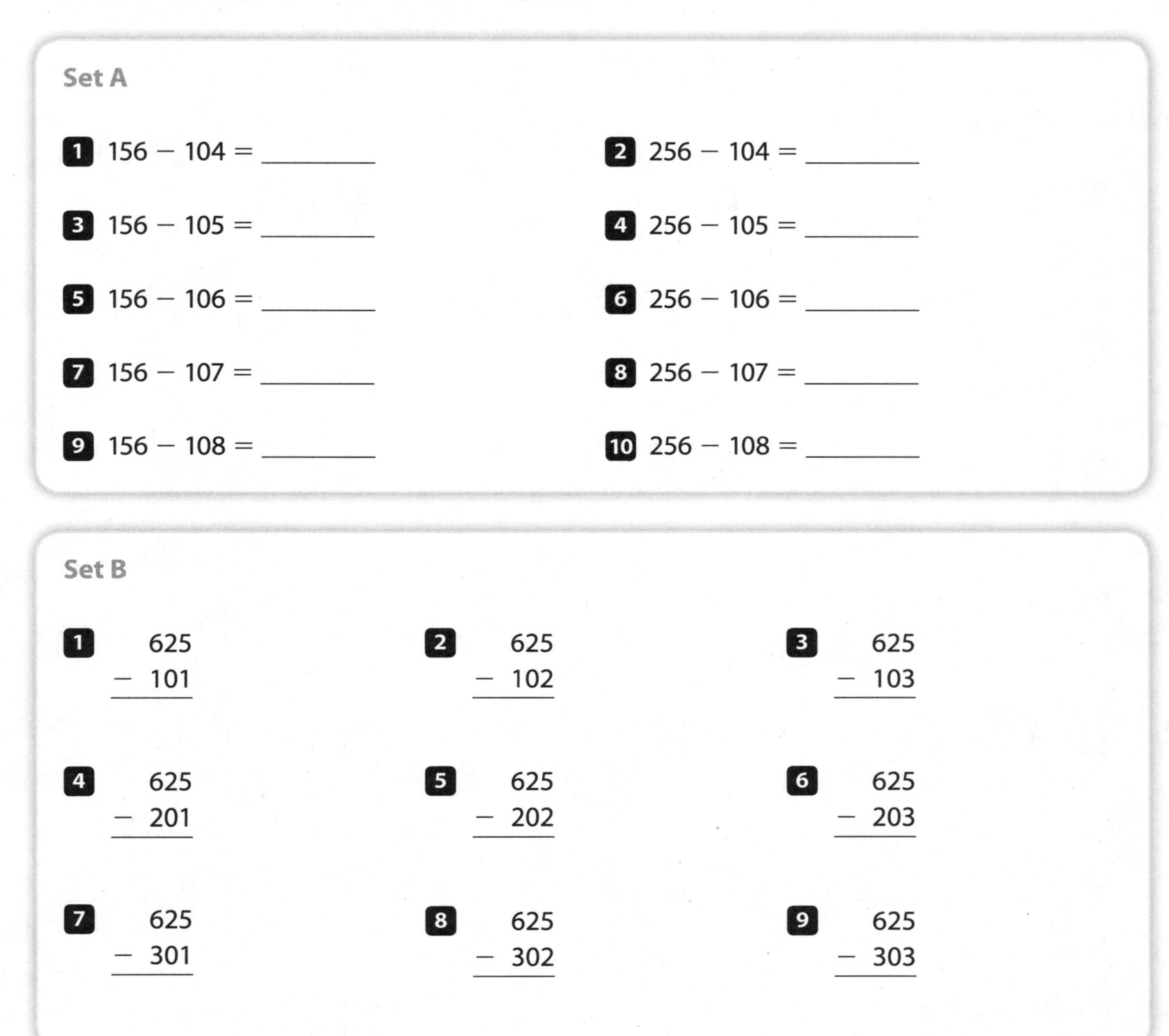

Set A

1. $156 - 104 =$ ________
2. $256 - 104 =$ ________
3. $156 - 105 =$ ________
4. $256 - 105 =$ ________
5. $156 - 106 =$ ________
6. $256 - 106 =$ ________
7. $156 - 107 =$ ________
8. $256 - 107 =$ ________
9. $156 - 108 =$ ________
10. $256 - 108 =$ ________

Set B

1. $625 - 101$
2. $625 - 102$
3. $625 - 103$
4. $625 - 201$
5. $625 - 202$
6. $625 - 203$
7. $625 - 301$
8. $625 - 302$
9. $625 - 303$

Describe a pattern you see in one of the sets of problems above.

____

____

____

Fraction Addition—Skills Practice

Name: ____________________

Add fractions.

Form A

1. $\frac{1}{4} + \frac{1}{4} =$ ______
2. $\frac{1}{6} + \frac{1}{6} =$ ______
3. $\frac{1}{3} + \frac{2}{3} =$ ______
4. $\frac{1}{10} + \frac{2}{10} =$ ______
5. $\frac{1}{5} + \frac{3}{5} =$ ______
6. $\frac{5}{8} + \frac{2}{8} =$ ______
7. $\frac{3}{12} + \frac{5}{12} =$ ______
8. $\frac{5}{100} + \frac{5}{100} =$ ______
9. $\frac{6}{10} + \frac{3}{10} =$ ______
10. $\frac{4}{3} + \frac{1}{3} =$ ______
11. $\frac{4}{8} + \frac{5}{8} =$ ______
12. $\frac{1}{2} + \frac{1}{2} =$ ______
13. $\frac{2}{6} + \frac{5}{6} =$ ______
14. $\frac{3}{12} + \frac{7}{12} =$ ______
15. $\frac{80}{100} + \frac{8}{100} =$ ______
16. $\frac{1}{4} + \frac{4}{4} =$ ______
17. $\frac{3}{4} + \frac{5}{4} =$ ______
18. $\frac{2}{8} + \frac{3}{8} =$ ______
19. $\frac{8}{5} + \frac{2}{5} =$ ______
20. $\frac{8}{10} + \frac{3}{10} =$ ______
21. $\frac{1}{3} + \frac{2}{3} + \frac{1}{3} =$ ______
22. $\frac{4}{5} + \frac{2}{5} + \frac{3}{5} =$ ______
23. $\frac{2}{6} + \frac{1}{6} + \frac{2}{6} =$ ______
24. $\frac{5}{8} + \frac{2}{8} + \frac{1}{8} =$ ______
25. $\frac{2}{10} + \frac{1}{10} + \frac{5}{10} =$ ______
26. $\frac{1}{2} + \frac{1}{2} + \frac{1}{2} =$ ______
27. $\frac{7}{12} + \frac{1}{12} + \frac{3}{12} =$ ______

Fraction Addition—Skills Practice

Name: ______________________

Add fractions.

Form B

1. $\frac{1}{3} + \frac{1}{3} =$ ______
2. $\frac{1}{5} + \frac{2}{5} =$ ______
3. $\frac{1}{2} + \frac{1}{2} =$ ______
4. $\frac{3}{10} + \frac{2}{10} =$ ______
5. $\frac{2}{12} + \frac{5}{12} =$ ______
6. $\frac{2}{4} + \frac{1}{4} =$ ______
7. $\frac{3}{6} + \frac{2}{6} =$ ______
8. $\frac{2}{100} + \frac{8}{100} =$ ______
9. $\frac{60}{100} + \frac{30}{100} =$ ______
10. $\frac{9}{10} + \frac{3}{10} =$ ______
11. $\frac{3}{5} + \frac{4}{5} =$ ______
12. $\frac{5}{2} + \frac{1}{2} =$ ______
13. $\frac{3}{8} + \frac{2}{8} =$ ______
14. $\frac{4}{3} + \frac{1}{3} =$ ______
15. $\frac{30}{100} + \frac{300}{100} =$ ______
16. $\frac{4}{12} + \frac{5}{12} =$ ______
17. $\frac{7}{10} + \frac{2}{10} =$ ______
18. $\frac{2}{5} + \frac{3}{5} =$ ______
19. $\frac{3}{2} + \frac{4}{2} =$ ______
20. $\frac{5}{4} + \frac{2}{4} =$ ______
21. $\frac{3}{10} + \frac{5}{10} + \frac{1}{10} =$ ______
22. $\frac{1}{4} + \frac{2}{4} + \frac{3}{4} =$ ______
23. $\frac{2}{8} + \frac{1}{8} + \frac{4}{8} =$ ______
24. $\frac{2}{12} + \frac{3}{12} + \frac{5}{12} =$ ______
25. $\frac{1}{2} + \frac{1}{2} + \frac{1}{2} =$ ______
26. $\frac{9}{10} + \frac{3}{10} + \frac{1}{10} =$ ______
27. $\frac{4}{5} + \frac{3}{5} + \frac{2}{5} =$ ______

Fraction Addition—Skills Practice

Name: ______________

Add mixed numbers.

Form A

1. $2\frac{1}{3} + \frac{1}{3} =$ ________
2. $2\frac{1}{5} + 1\frac{3}{5} =$ ________
3. $1\frac{1}{2} + 1\frac{1}{2} =$ ________
4. $2\frac{5}{12} + 3\frac{1}{12} =$ ________
5. $3\frac{2}{4} + 2\frac{1}{4} =$ ________
6. $\frac{5}{6} + 4\frac{1}{6} =$ ________
7. $3\frac{20}{100} + 4\frac{5}{100} =$ ________
8. $9\frac{2}{10} + 3\frac{7}{10} =$ ________
9. $2\frac{3}{5} + 4\frac{1}{5} =$ ________
10. $10\frac{3}{8} + 2\frac{3}{8} =$ ________
11. $9\frac{1}{3} + \frac{2}{3} =$ ________
12. $7\frac{10}{100} + \frac{7}{100} =$ ________
13. $5\frac{4}{10} + 1\frac{6}{10} =$ ________
14. $4\frac{2}{5} + 5\frac{4}{5} =$ ________
15. $3\frac{1}{2} + 4\frac{1}{2} =$ ________
16. $3\frac{5}{10} + 5\frac{1}{10} =$ ________
17. $6\frac{3}{4} + 4\frac{2}{4} =$ ________
18. $6\frac{2}{8} + 2\frac{5}{8} =$ ________
19. $\frac{8}{12} + 2\frac{7}{12} =$ ________
20. $3\frac{2}{10} + 4\frac{1}{10} =$ ________
21. $10\frac{1}{5} + 8\frac{3}{5} =$ ________
22. $5\frac{3}{4} + 2\frac{3}{4} =$ ________
23. $7\frac{90}{100} + 7\frac{10}{100} =$ ________
24. $6\frac{2}{3} + 4\frac{2}{3} =$ ________

Fraction Addition—Skills Practice

Name: ___________

Add mixed numbers. **Form B**

1. $2\frac{1}{4} + 3\frac{1}{4} =$ ______

2. $3\frac{4}{6} + 4\frac{1}{6} =$ ______

3. $2\frac{1}{3} + 6\frac{2}{3} =$ ______

4. $1\frac{4}{5} + 2\frac{3}{5} =$ ______

5. $5\frac{3}{8} + 7\frac{2}{8} =$ ______

6. $2\frac{3}{12} + 3\frac{9}{12} =$ ______

7. $6\frac{9}{10} + 3\frac{2}{10} =$ ______

8. $4\frac{2}{3} + 1\frac{2}{3} =$ ______

9. $4\frac{3}{8} + 5\frac{4}{8} =$ ______

10. $2\frac{5}{6} + 8\frac{4}{6} =$ ______

11. $1\frac{3}{12} + 6\frac{5}{12} =$ ______

12. $15\frac{80}{100} + 4\frac{20}{100} =$ ______

13. $5\frac{3}{4} + 6\frac{2}{4} =$ ______

14. $3\frac{1}{8} + 7\frac{4}{8} =$ ______

15. $8\frac{1}{5} + 7\frac{2}{5} =$ ______

16. $3\frac{2}{3} + 3\frac{2}{3} =$ ______

17. $3\frac{4}{5} + 5\frac{2}{5} =$ ______

18. $2\frac{5}{6} + 9\frac{3}{6} =$ ______

19. $7\frac{8}{10} + 5\frac{9}{10} =$ ______

20. $20\frac{1}{2} + 10\frac{1}{2} =$ ______

21. $7\frac{3}{12} + 2\frac{11}{12} =$ ______

22. $3\frac{7}{8} + 4\frac{5}{8} =$ ______

23. $\frac{32}{100} + 3\frac{55}{100} =$ ______

24. $3\frac{5}{6} + 8\frac{3}{6} =$ ______

Fraction Addition— Repeated Reasoning

Name: ____________________

Find patterns in adding fractions.

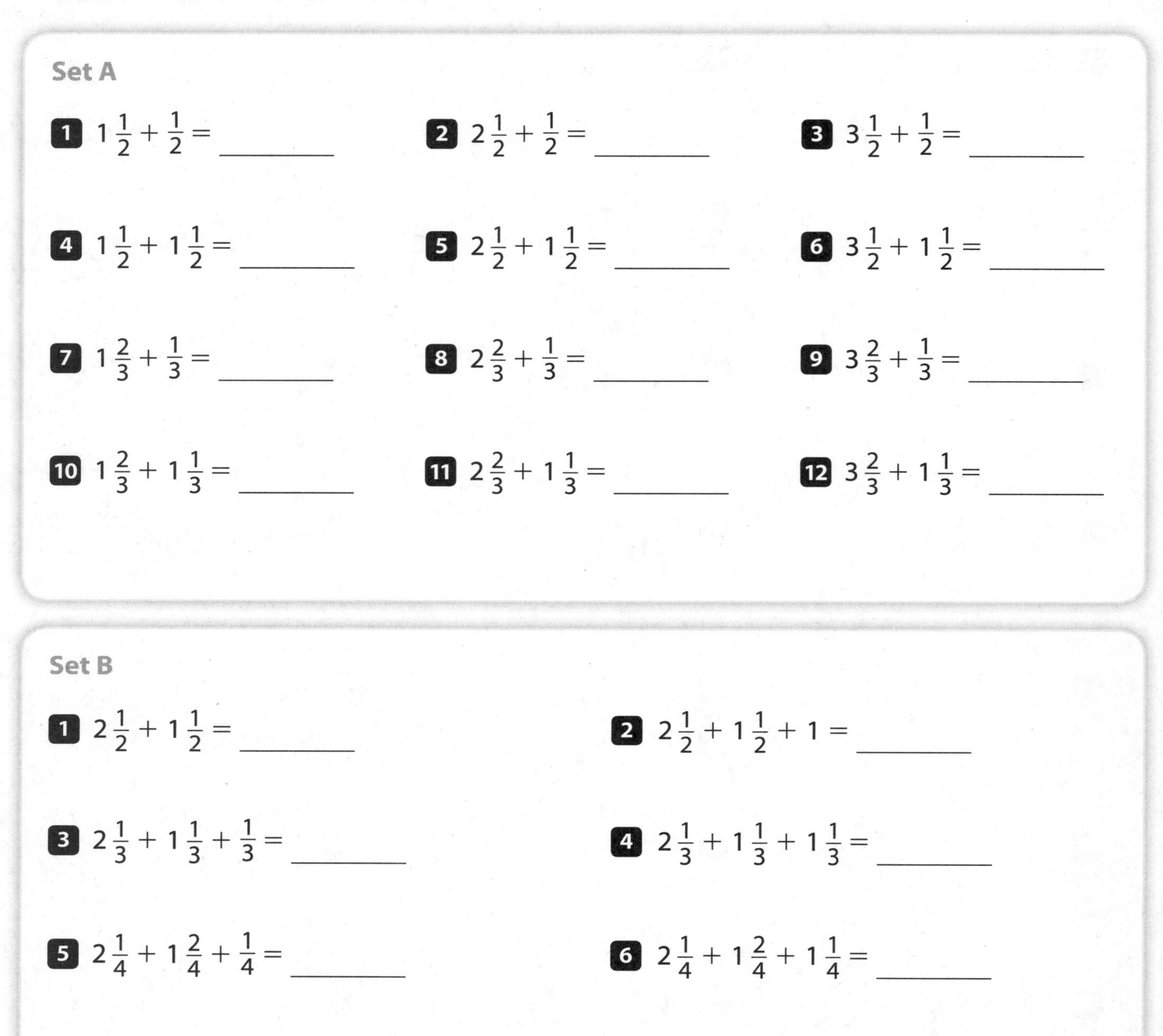

Set A

1. $1\frac{1}{2} + \frac{1}{2} =$ ________
2. $2\frac{1}{2} + \frac{1}{2} =$ ________
3. $3\frac{1}{2} + \frac{1}{2} =$ ________
4. $1\frac{1}{2} + 1\frac{1}{2} =$ ________
5. $2\frac{1}{2} + 1\frac{1}{2} =$ ________
6. $3\frac{1}{2} + 1\frac{1}{2} =$ ________
7. $1\frac{2}{3} + \frac{1}{3} =$ ________
8. $2\frac{2}{3} + \frac{1}{3} =$ ________
9. $3\frac{2}{3} + \frac{1}{3} =$ ________
10. $1\frac{2}{3} + 1\frac{1}{3} =$ ________
11. $2\frac{2}{3} + 1\frac{1}{3} =$ ________
12. $3\frac{2}{3} + 1\frac{1}{3} =$ ________

Set B

1. $2\frac{1}{2} + 1\frac{1}{2} =$ ________
2. $2\frac{1}{2} + 1\frac{1}{2} + 1 =$ ________
3. $2\frac{1}{3} + 1\frac{1}{3} + \frac{1}{3} =$ ________
4. $2\frac{1}{3} + 1\frac{1}{3} + 1\frac{1}{3} =$ ________
5. $2\frac{1}{4} + 1\frac{2}{4} + \frac{1}{4} =$ ________
6. $2\frac{1}{4} + 1\frac{2}{4} + 1\frac{1}{4} =$ ________

Describe a pattern you see in one of the sets of problems above.

____

____

____

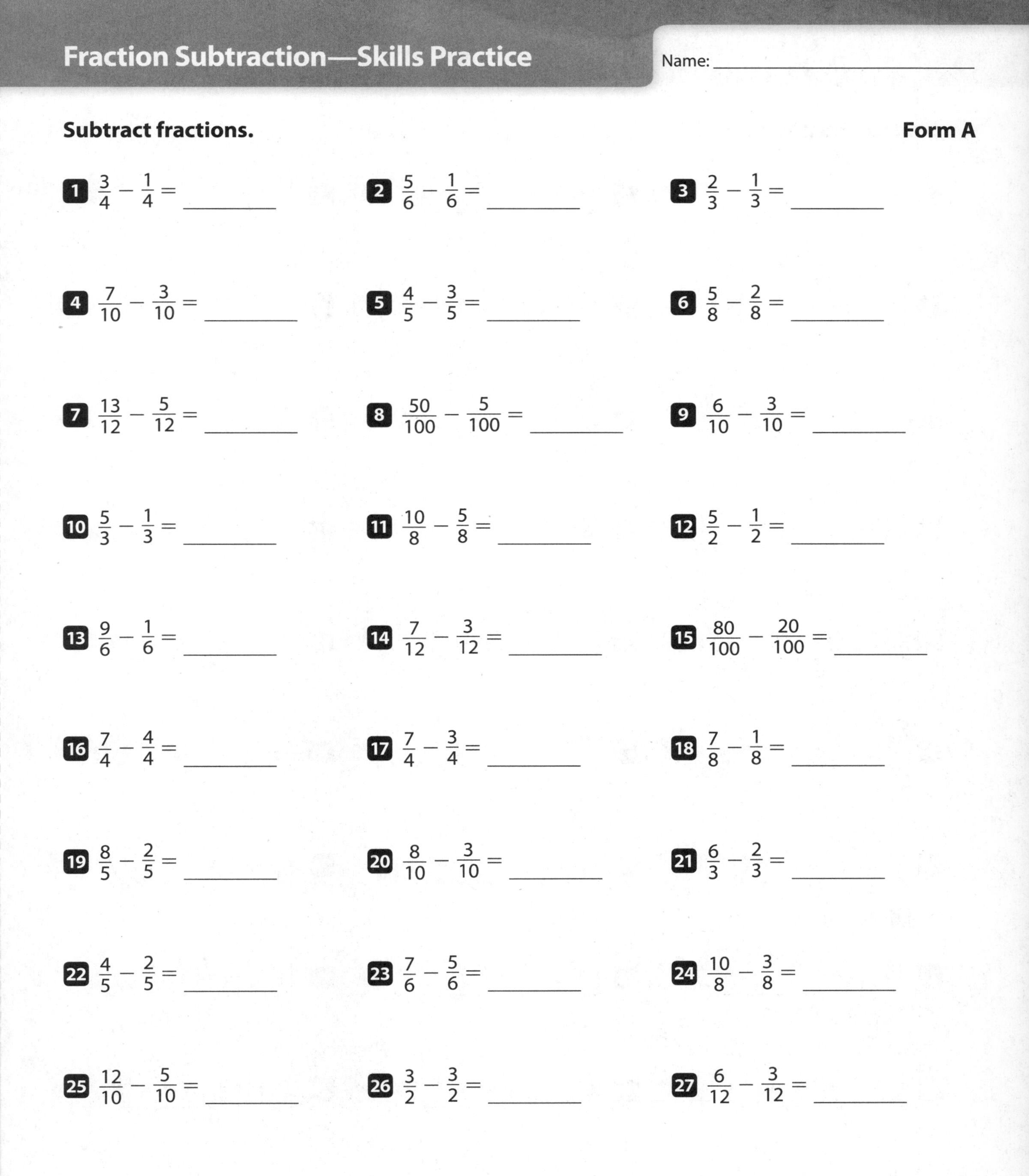

Fraction Subtraction—Skills Practice

Name: ______________________

Subtract fractions. **Form A**

1. $\frac{3}{4} - \frac{1}{4} =$ ________
2. $\frac{5}{6} - \frac{1}{6} =$ ________
3. $\frac{2}{3} - \frac{1}{3} =$ ________
4. $\frac{7}{10} - \frac{3}{10} =$ ________
5. $\frac{4}{5} - \frac{3}{5} =$ ________
6. $\frac{5}{8} - \frac{2}{8} =$ ________
7. $\frac{13}{12} - \frac{5}{12} =$ ________
8. $\frac{50}{100} - \frac{5}{100} =$ ________
9. $\frac{6}{10} - \frac{3}{10} =$ ________
10. $\frac{5}{3} - \frac{1}{3} =$ ________
11. $\frac{10}{8} - \frac{5}{8} =$ ________
12. $\frac{5}{2} - \frac{1}{2} =$ ________
13. $\frac{9}{6} - \frac{1}{6} =$ ________
14. $\frac{7}{12} - \frac{3}{12} =$ ________
15. $\frac{80}{100} - \frac{20}{100} =$ ________
16. $\frac{7}{4} - \frac{4}{4} =$ ________
17. $\frac{7}{4} - \frac{3}{4} =$ ________
18. $\frac{7}{8} - \frac{1}{8} =$ ________
19. $\frac{8}{5} - \frac{2}{5} =$ ________
20. $\frac{8}{10} - \frac{3}{10} =$ ________
21. $\frac{6}{3} - \frac{2}{3} =$ ________
22. $\frac{4}{5} - \frac{2}{5} =$ ________
23. $\frac{7}{6} - \frac{5}{6} =$ ________
24. $\frac{10}{8} - \frac{3}{8} =$ ________
25. $\frac{12}{10} - \frac{5}{10} =$ ________
26. $\frac{3}{2} - \frac{3}{2} =$ ________
27. $\frac{6}{12} - \frac{3}{12} =$ ________

Fraction Subtraction—Skills Practice

Name: ____________________

Subtract fractions. **Form B**

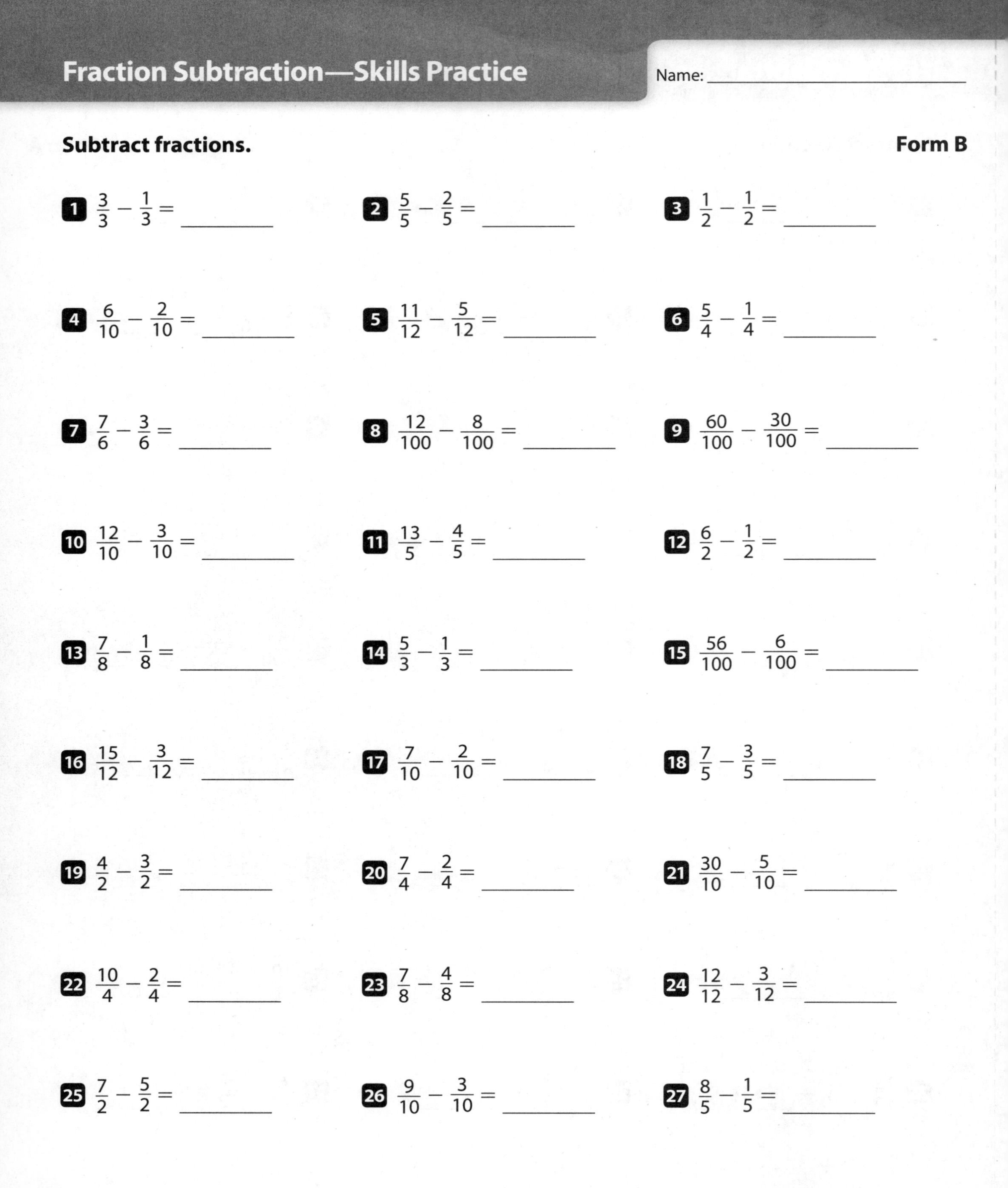

1. $\frac{3}{3} - \frac{1}{3} =$ ________
2. $\frac{5}{5} - \frac{2}{5} =$ ________
3. $\frac{1}{2} - \frac{1}{2} =$ ________
4. $\frac{6}{10} - \frac{2}{10} =$ ________
5. $\frac{11}{12} - \frac{5}{12} =$ ________
6. $\frac{5}{4} - \frac{1}{4} =$ ________
7. $\frac{7}{6} - \frac{3}{6} =$ ________
8. $\frac{12}{100} - \frac{8}{100} =$ ________
9. $\frac{60}{100} - \frac{30}{100} =$ ________
10. $\frac{12}{10} - \frac{3}{10} =$ ________
11. $\frac{13}{5} - \frac{4}{5} =$ ________
12. $\frac{6}{2} - \frac{1}{2} =$ ________
13. $\frac{7}{8} - \frac{1}{8} =$ ________
14. $\frac{5}{3} - \frac{1}{3} =$ ________
15. $\frac{56}{100} - \frac{6}{100} =$ ________
16. $\frac{15}{12} - \frac{3}{12} =$ ________
17. $\frac{7}{10} - \frac{2}{10} =$ ________
18. $\frac{7}{5} - \frac{3}{5} =$ ________
19. $\frac{4}{2} - \frac{3}{2} =$ ________
20. $\frac{7}{4} - \frac{2}{4} =$ ________
21. $\frac{30}{10} - \frac{5}{10} =$ ________
22. $\frac{10}{4} - \frac{2}{4} =$ ________
23. $\frac{7}{8} - \frac{4}{8} =$ ________
24. $\frac{12}{12} - \frac{3}{12} =$ ________
25. $\frac{7}{2} - \frac{5}{2} =$ ________
26. $\frac{9}{10} - \frac{3}{10} =$ ________
27. $\frac{8}{5} - \frac{1}{5} =$ ________

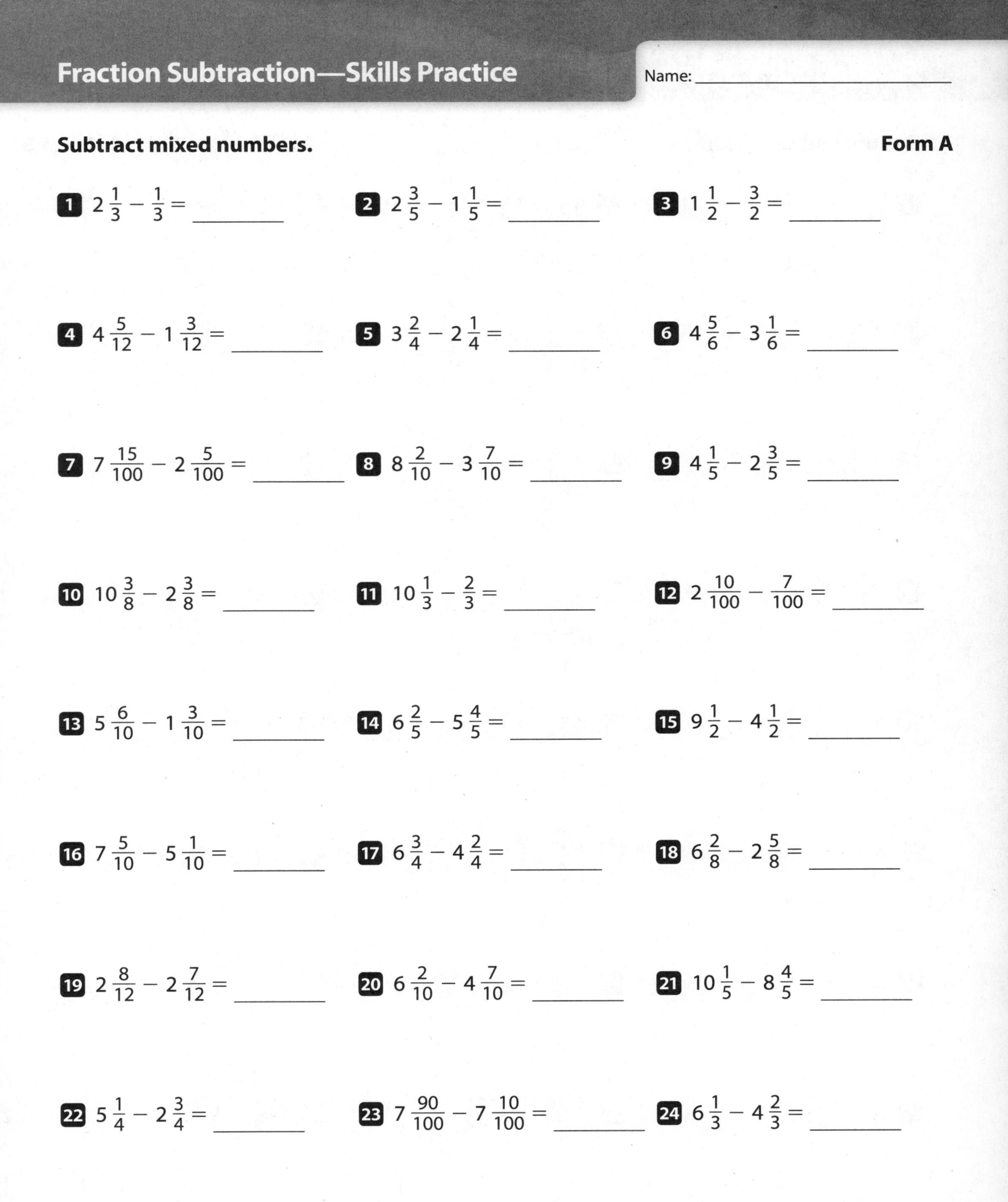

Fraction Subtraction—Skills Practice

Name: ____________________

Subtract mixed numbers. **Form A**

1. $2\frac{1}{3} - \frac{1}{3} =$ ________
2. $2\frac{3}{5} - 1\frac{1}{5} =$ ________
3. $1\frac{1}{2} - \frac{3}{2} =$ ________
4. $4\frac{5}{12} - 1\frac{3}{12} =$ ________
5. $3\frac{2}{4} - 2\frac{1}{4} =$ ________
6. $4\frac{5}{6} - 3\frac{1}{6} =$ ________
7. $7\frac{15}{100} - 2\frac{5}{100} =$ ________
8. $8\frac{2}{10} - 3\frac{7}{10} =$ ________
9. $4\frac{1}{5} - 2\frac{3}{5} =$ ________
10. $10\frac{3}{8} - 2\frac{3}{8} =$ ________
11. $10\frac{1}{3} - \frac{2}{3} =$ ________
12. $2\frac{10}{100} - \frac{7}{100} =$ ________
13. $5\frac{6}{10} - 1\frac{3}{10} =$ ________
14. $6\frac{2}{5} - 5\frac{4}{5} =$ ________
15. $9\frac{1}{2} - 4\frac{1}{2} =$ ________
16. $7\frac{5}{10} - 5\frac{1}{10} =$ ________
17. $6\frac{3}{4} - 4\frac{2}{4} =$ ________
18. $6\frac{2}{8} - 2\frac{5}{8} =$ ________
19. $2\frac{8}{12} - 2\frac{7}{12} =$ ________
20. $6\frac{2}{10} - 4\frac{7}{10} =$ ________
21. $10\frac{1}{5} - 8\frac{4}{5} =$ ________
22. $5\frac{1}{4} - 2\frac{3}{4} =$ ________
23. $7\frac{90}{100} - 7\frac{10}{100} =$ ________
24. $6\frac{1}{3} - 4\frac{2}{3} =$ ________

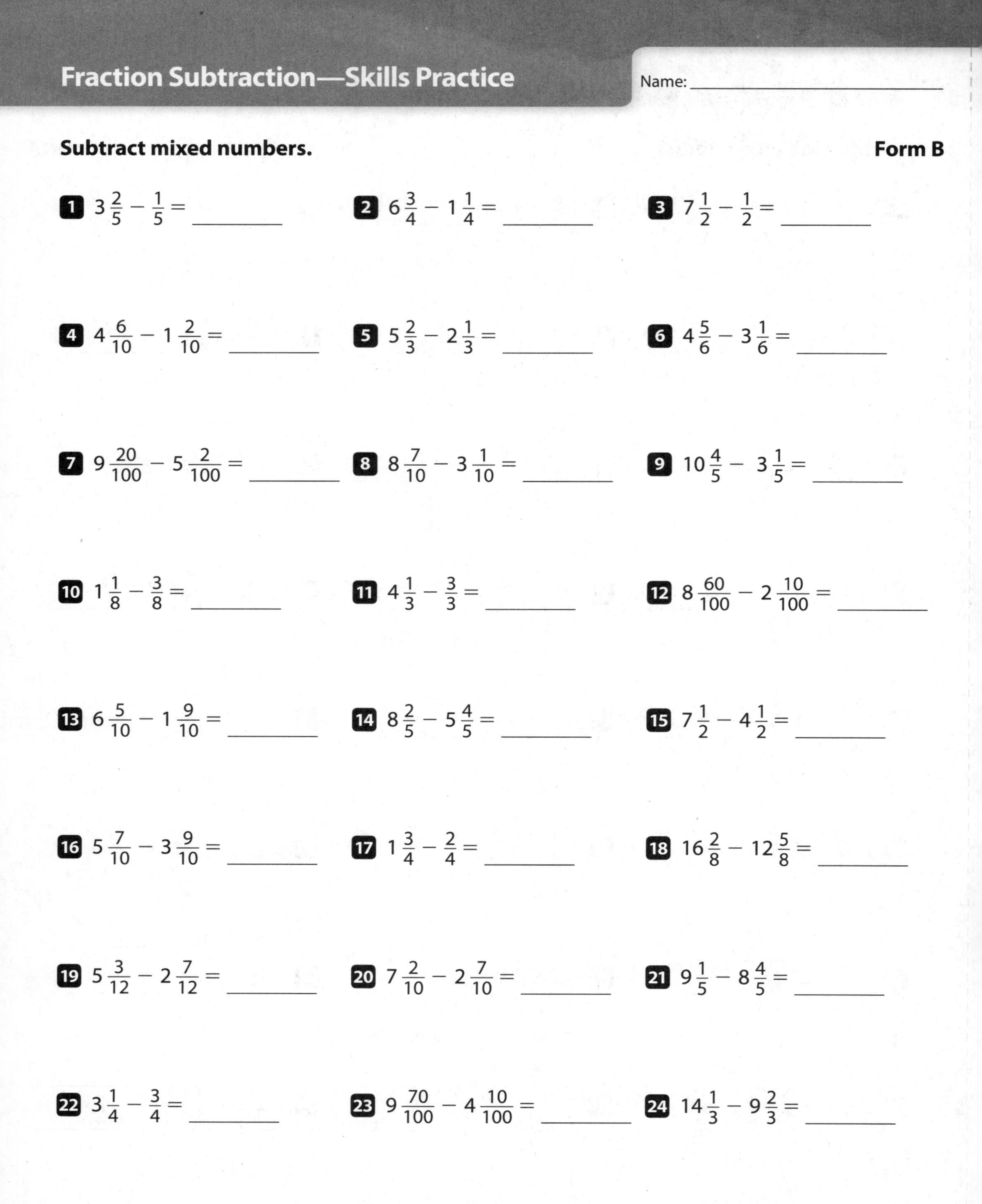

Fraction Subtraction—Skills Practice

Name: ______________

Subtract mixed numbers.

Form B

1. $3\frac{2}{5} - \frac{1}{5} =$ ________
2. $6\frac{3}{4} - 1\frac{1}{4} =$ ________
3. $7\frac{1}{2} - \frac{1}{2} =$ ________
4. $4\frac{6}{10} - 1\frac{2}{10} =$ ________
5. $5\frac{2}{3} - 2\frac{1}{3} =$ ________
6. $4\frac{5}{6} - 3\frac{1}{6} =$ ________
7. $9\frac{20}{100} - 5\frac{2}{100} =$ ________
8. $8\frac{7}{10} - 3\frac{1}{10} =$ ________
9. $10\frac{4}{5} - 3\frac{1}{5} =$ ________
10. $1\frac{1}{8} - \frac{3}{8} =$ ________
11. $4\frac{1}{3} - \frac{3}{3} =$ ________
12. $8\frac{60}{100} - 2\frac{10}{100} =$ ________
13. $6\frac{5}{10} - 1\frac{9}{10} =$ ________
14. $8\frac{2}{5} - 5\frac{4}{5} =$ ________
15. $7\frac{1}{2} - 4\frac{1}{2} =$ ________
16. $5\frac{7}{10} - 3\frac{9}{10} =$ ________
17. $1\frac{3}{4} - \frac{2}{4} =$ ________
18. $16\frac{2}{8} - 12\frac{5}{8} =$ ________
19. $5\frac{3}{12} - 2\frac{7}{12} =$ ________
20. $7\frac{2}{10} - 2\frac{7}{10} =$ ________
21. $9\frac{1}{5} - 8\frac{4}{5} =$ ________
22. $3\frac{1}{4} - \frac{3}{4} =$ ________
23. $9\frac{70}{100} - 4\frac{10}{100} =$ ________
24. $14\frac{1}{3} - 9\frac{2}{3} =$ ________

Fraction Subtraction—Repeated Reasoning

Name: ____________________

Find patterns in subtracting fractions.

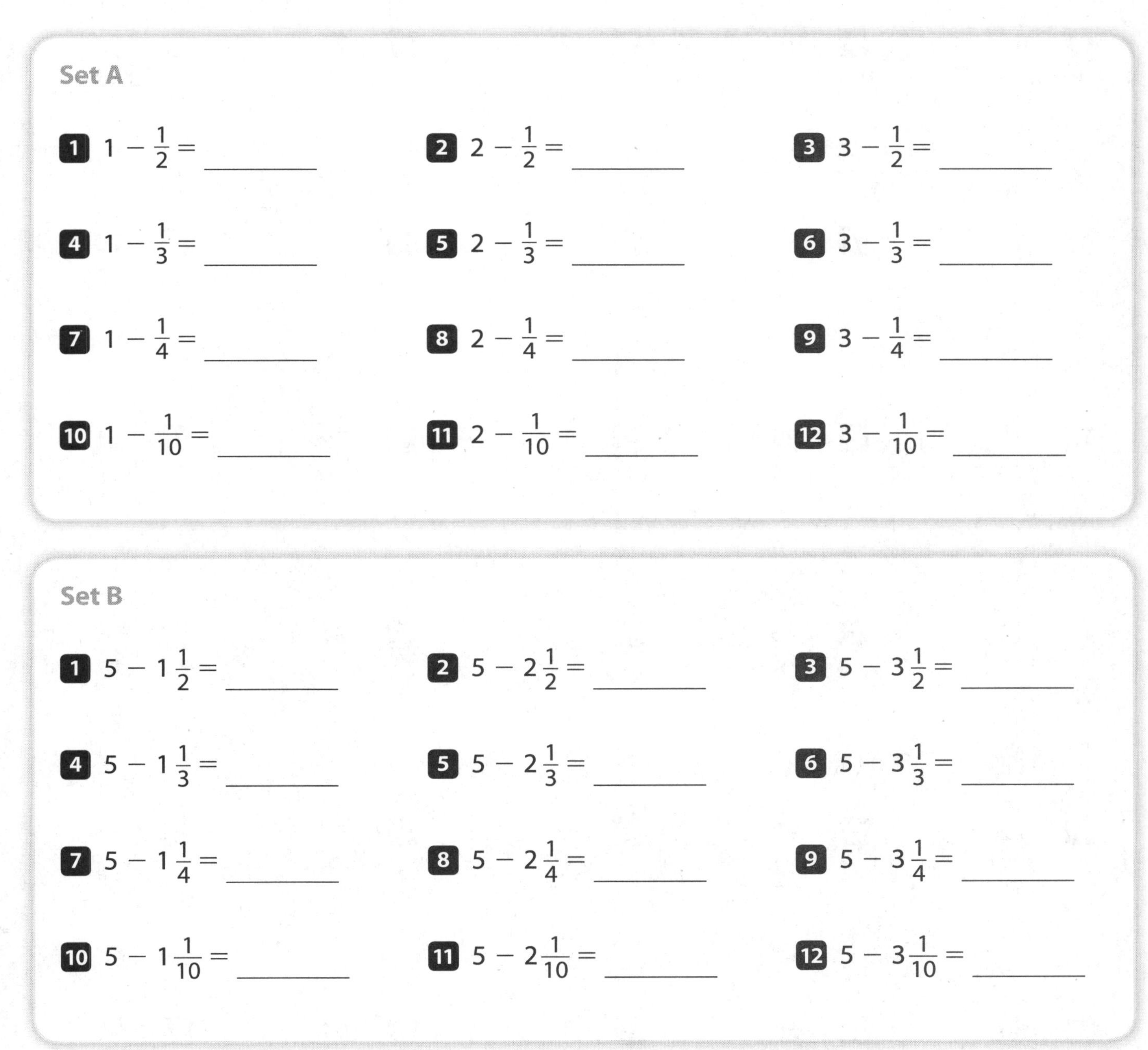

Set A

1. $1 - \frac{1}{2} =$ ________
2. $2 - \frac{1}{2} =$ ________
3. $3 - \frac{1}{2} =$ ________
4. $1 - \frac{1}{3} =$ ________
5. $2 - \frac{1}{3} =$ ________
6. $3 - \frac{1}{3} =$ ________
7. $1 - \frac{1}{4} =$ ________
8. $2 - \frac{1}{4} =$ ________
9. $3 - \frac{1}{4} =$ ________
10. $1 - \frac{1}{10} =$ ________
11. $2 - \frac{1}{10} =$ ________
12. $3 - \frac{1}{10} =$ ________

Set B

1. $5 - 1\frac{1}{2} =$ ________
2. $5 - 2\frac{1}{2} =$ ________
3. $5 - 3\frac{1}{2} =$ ________
4. $5 - 1\frac{1}{3} =$ ________
5. $5 - 2\frac{1}{3} =$ ________
6. $5 - 3\frac{1}{3} =$ ________
7. $5 - 1\frac{1}{4} =$ ________
8. $5 - 2\frac{1}{4} =$ ________
9. $5 - 3\frac{1}{4} =$ ________
10. $5 - 1\frac{1}{10} =$ ________
11. $5 - 2\frac{1}{10} =$ ________
12. $5 - 3\frac{1}{10} =$ ________

Describe a pattern you see in one of the sets of problems above.

____

____

____

Multi-Digit Multiplication—Skills Practice

Name: ______________________________

Multiply a 2-digit number by a 1-digit number.

Form A

1 12×2	**2** 10×3	**3** 21×4	**4** 23×1	**5** 33×2
6 11×8	**7** 35×4	**8** 46×5	**9** 51×3	**10** 70×5
11 10×9	**12** 88×4	**13** 78×5	**14** 29×6	**15** 61×6
16 12×7	**17** 26×8	**18** 58×9	**19** 81×7	**20** 75×3
21 72×3	**22** 92×3	**23** 49×7	**24** 31×6	**25** 56×4
26 34×6	**27** 58×5	**28** 37×7	**29** 64×8	**30** 98×9

Multi-Digit Multiplication—Skills Practice

Name: ______________________

Multiply a 2-digit number by a 1-digit number. **Form B**

1 21×2

2 10×6

3 41×3

4 32×1

5 22×4

6 11×7

7 54×9

8 64×5

9 55×8

10 75×5

11 12×9

12 84×8

13 57×4

14 96×7

15 41×6

16 82×7

17 26×5

18 92×6

19 81×3

20 35×7

21 62×8

22 43×8

23 98×2

24 36×9

25 28×4

26 53×4

27 38×5

28 24×7

29 48×3

30 99×9

Multi-Digit Multiplication—Skills Practice

Name: ______________________

Multiply 2-digit numbers. **Form A**

1 21×35	**2** 18×16	**3** 24×12	**4** 32×15	**5** 12×37
6 11×77	**7** 54×92	**8** 64×35	**9** 75×28	**10** 43×15
11 42×96	**12** 40×88	**13** 57×64	**14** 96×70	**15** 61×54
16 82×27	**17** 26×45	**18** 82×34	**19** 63×36	**20** 35×27
21 20×16	**22** 41×30	**23** 98×20	**24** 36×79	**25** 28×49

Multi-Digit Multiplication

Name: ____________________

Multiply 2-digit numbers.

Form B

1 12×53	**2** 86×11	**3** 55×43	**4** 23×15	**5** 12×83
6 11×66	**7** 94×25	**8** 46×53	**9** 37×62	**10** 78×18
11 24×96	**12** 14×85	**13** 74×36	**14** 97×40	**15** 41×56
16 92×57	**17** 63×45	**18** 52×27	**19** 84×29	**20** 99×34
21 50×26	**22** 74×30	**23** 89×40	**24** 36×29	**25** 98×90

Multi-Digit Multiplication—Skills Practice

Name: ______________________

Multiply a 3-digit number by a 1-digit number. **Form A**

1. $\begin{array}{r} 513 \\ \times \quad 2 \\ \hline \end{array}$

2. $\begin{array}{r} 120 \\ \times \quad 3 \\ \hline \end{array}$

3. $\begin{array}{r} 612 \\ \times \quad 4 \\ \hline \end{array}$

4. $\begin{array}{r} 711 \\ \times \quad 5 \\ \hline \end{array}$

5. $\begin{array}{r} 460 \\ \times \quad 3 \\ \hline \end{array}$

6. $\begin{array}{r} 325 \\ \times \quad 7 \\ \hline \end{array}$

7. $\begin{array}{r} 940 \\ \times \quad 5 \\ \hline \end{array}$

8. $\begin{array}{r} 518 \\ \times \quad 3 \\ \hline \end{array}$

9. $\begin{array}{r} 105 \\ \times \quad 9 \\ \hline \end{array}$

10. $\begin{array}{r} 862 \\ \times \quad 4 \\ \hline \end{array}$

11. $\begin{array}{r} 728 \\ \times \quad 5 \\ \hline \end{array}$

12. $\begin{array}{r} 429 \\ \times \quad 6 \\ \hline \end{array}$

13. $\begin{array}{r} 123 \\ \times \quad 7 \\ \hline \end{array}$

14. $\begin{array}{r} 256 \\ \times \quad 8 \\ \hline \end{array}$

15. $\begin{array}{r} 908 \\ \times \quad 9 \\ \hline \end{array}$

16. $\begin{array}{r} 381 \\ \times \quad 2 \\ \hline \end{array}$

17. $\begin{array}{r} 712 \\ \times \quad 3 \\ \hline \end{array}$

18. $\begin{array}{r} 923 \\ \times \quad 3 \\ \hline \end{array}$

19. $\begin{array}{r} 752 \\ \times \quad 7 \\ \hline \end{array}$

20. $\begin{array}{r} 310 \\ \times \quad 6 \\ \hline \end{array}$

21. $\begin{array}{r} 304 \\ \times \quad 6 \\ \hline \end{array}$

22. $\begin{array}{r} 502 \\ \times \quad 5 \\ \hline \end{array}$

23. $\begin{array}{r} 837 \\ \times \quad 6 \\ \hline \end{array}$

24. $\begin{array}{r} 604 \\ \times \quad 8 \\ \hline \end{array}$

Multi-Digit Multiplication—Skills Practice

Name: ______________________

Multiply a 3-digit number by a 1-digit number.

Form B

1. 100×7
2. 421×3
3. 324×1
4. 202×4
5. 504×9
6. 614×5
7. 945×8
8. 157×5
9. 624×8
10. 457×3
11. 967×4
12. 804×6
13. 250×4
14. 512×9
15. 381×5
16. 336×7
17. 843×2
18. 938×6
19. 362×9
20. 278×4
21. 308×5
22. 724×7
23. 548×3
24. 909×9

Multi-Digit Multiplication—Skills Practice

Name: ____________________

Multiply a 4-digit number by a 1-digit number.

Form A

1 5,213 × 2	**2** 6,120 × 4	**3** 5,332 × 3	**4** 5,201 × 4
5 4,360 × 5	**6** 7,025 × 3	**7** 1,945 × 6	**8** 3,518 × 7
9 2,075 × 9	**10** 4,208 × 6	**11** 7,528 × 2	**12** 5,299 × 3
13 1,234 × 7	**14** 2,048 × 5	**15** 9,088 × 3	**16** 8,301 × 8
17 7,302 × 4	**18** 9,423 × 2	**19** 7,526 × 4	**20** 4,610 × 6
21 3,604 × 8	**22** 5,902 × 9	**23** 8,637 × 6	**24** 6,804 × 5

Multi-Digit Multiplication—Skills Practice

Name: ______________________

Multiply a 4-digit number by a 1-digit number. **Form B**

1. $4{,}130 \times 2$
2. $5{,}212 \times 4$
3. $3{,}023 \times 3$
4. $1{,}200 \times 4$
5. $5{,}170 \times 5$
6. $6{,}047 \times 8$
7. $2{,}593 \times 6$
8. $8{,}350 \times 7$
9. $3{,}084 \times 9$
10. $2{,}708 \times 6$
11. $8{,}925 \times 2$
12. $7{,}599 \times 3$
13. $9{,}423 \times 4$
14. $2{,}048 \times 5$
15. $4{,}625 \times 7$
16. $5{,}304 \times 8$
17. $2{,}730 \times 3$
18. $9{,}067 \times 2$
19. $7{,}199 \times 4$
20. $5{,}402 \times 7$
21. $6{,}521 \times 8$
22. $3{,}207 \times 9$
23. $8{,}022 \times 6$
24. $4{,}635 \times 5$

Multi-Digit Multiplication— Repeated Reasoning

Name: ______________________

Find place value patterns.

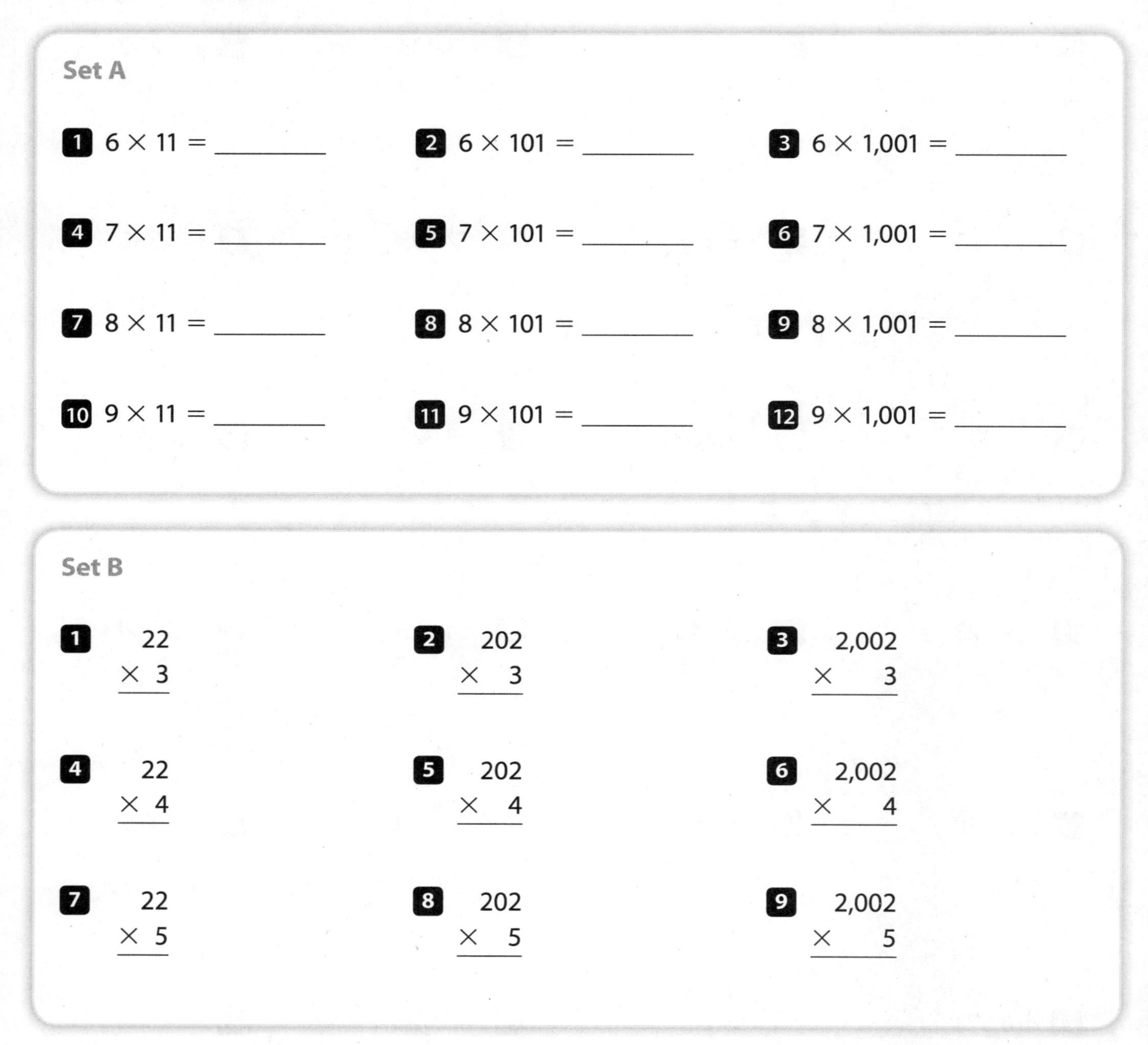

Set A

1. $6 \times 11 =$ ______
2. $6 \times 101 =$ ______
3. $6 \times 1{,}001 =$ ______
4. $7 \times 11 =$ ______
5. $7 \times 101 =$ ______
6. $7 \times 1{,}001 =$ ______
7. $8 \times 11 =$ ______
8. $8 \times 101 =$ ______
9. $8 \times 1{,}001 =$ ______
10. $9 \times 11 =$ ______
11. $9 \times 101 =$ ______
12. $9 \times 1{,}001 =$ ______

Set B

1. 22×3
2. 202×3
3. $2{,}002 \times 3$
4. 22×4
5. 202×4
6. $2{,}002 \times 4$
7. 22×5
8. 202×5
9. $2{,}002 \times 5$

Describe a pattern you see in one of the sets of problems above.

____

____

____

Multi-Digit Multiplication—Repeated Reasoning

Name: ______________________

Find patterns multiplying by 98 and 99.

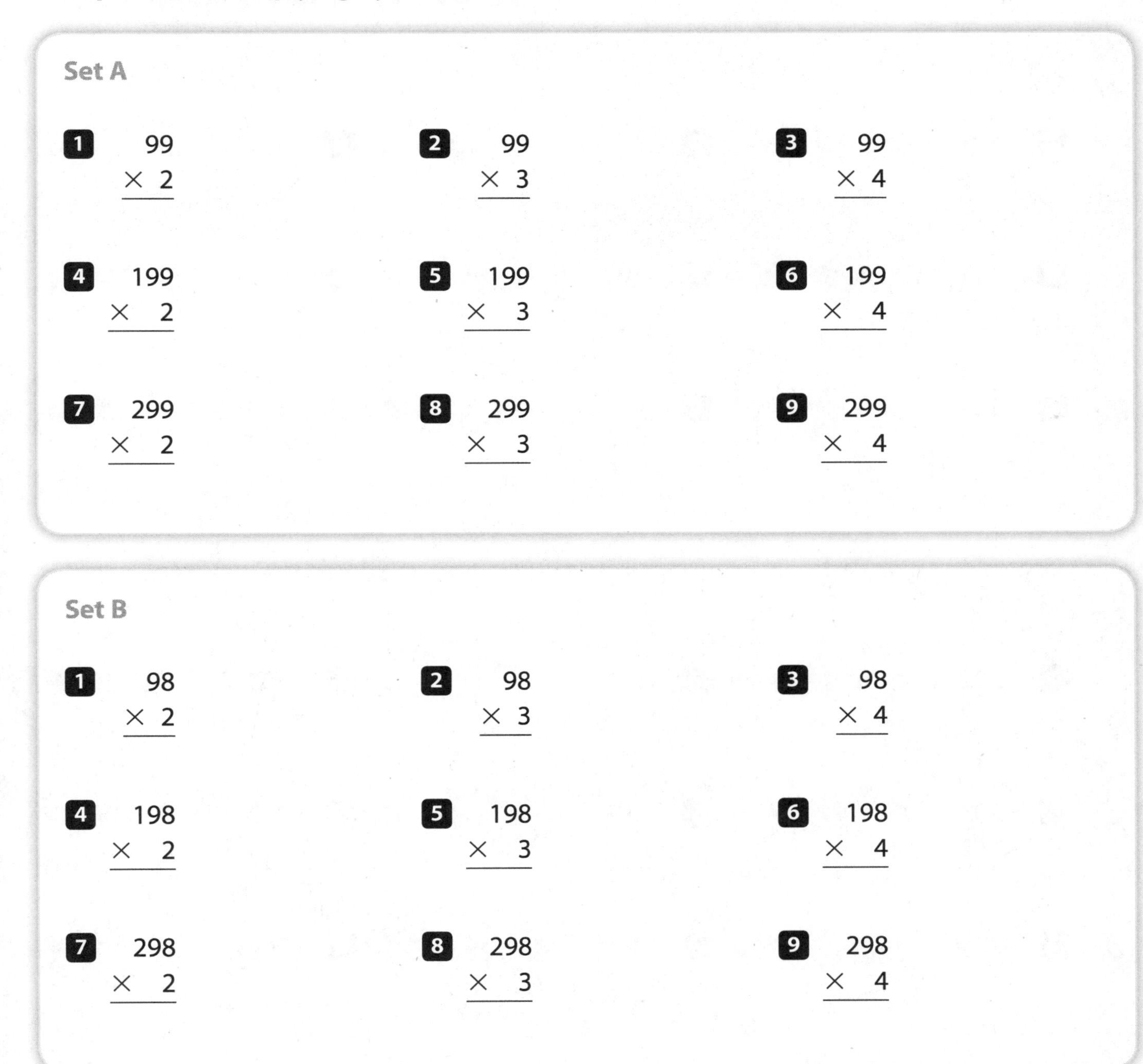

Describe a pattern you see in one of the sets of problems above.

____

____

____

Multi-Digit Multiplication—Repeated Reasoning

Name: ____________________

Find patterns multiplying by near-hundreds.

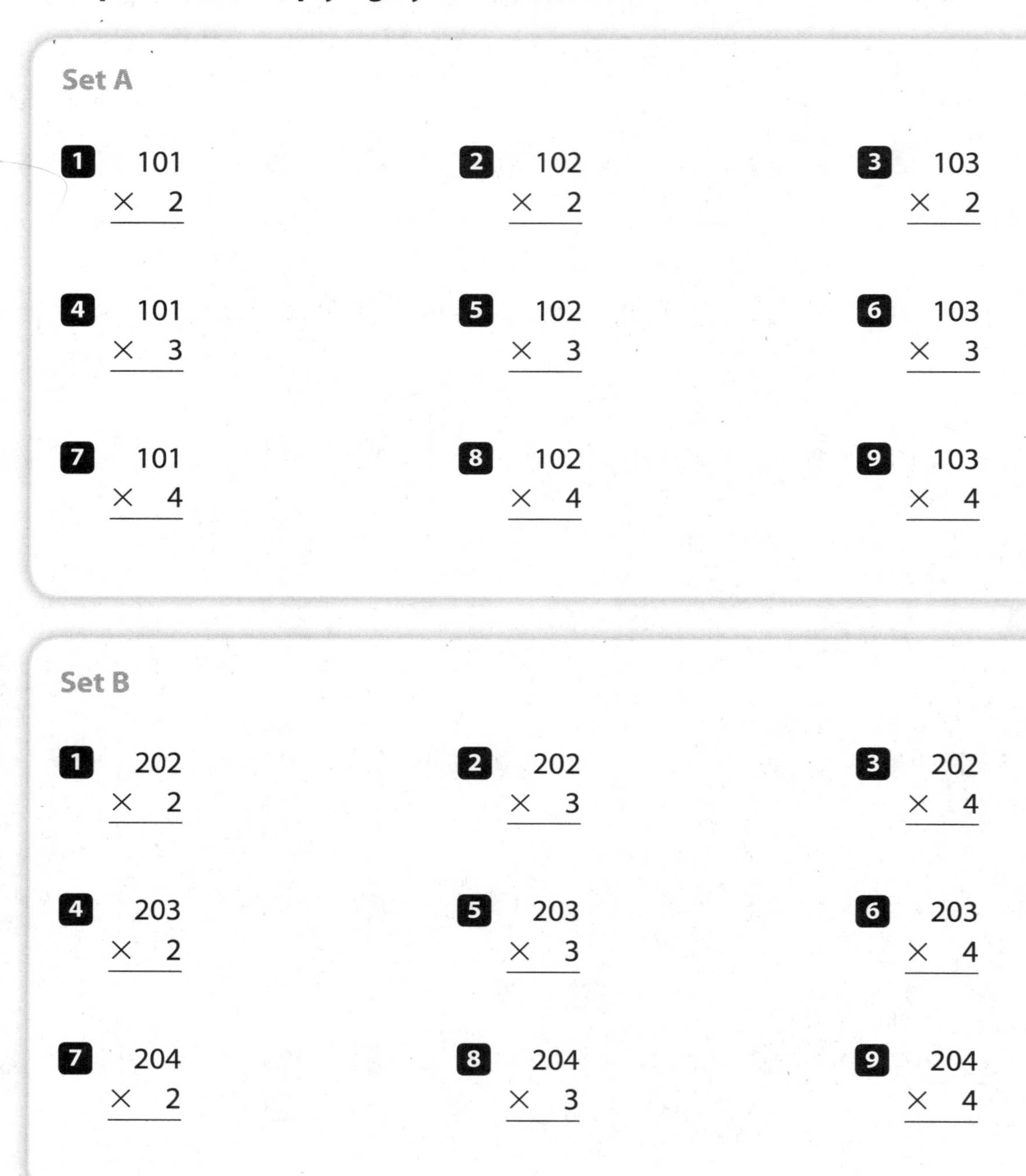

Set A

1. 101×2
2. 102×2
3. 103×2
4. 101×3
5. 102×3
6. 103×3
7. 101×4
8. 102×4
9. 103×4

Set B

1. 202×2
2. 202×3
3. 202×4
4. 203×2
5. 203×3
6. 203×4
7. 204×2
8. 204×3
9. 204×4

Describe a pattern you see in one of the sets of problems above.

____

____

____

Multi-Digit Division—Skills Practice

Name: ______________________

Divide 2-digit dividends.

Form A

1 $3\overline{)81}$	**2** $4\overline{)52}$	**3** $5\overline{)90}$	**4** $2\overline{)78}$
5 $6\overline{)85}$	**6** $9\overline{)63}$	**7** $3\overline{)92}$	**8** $7\overline{)81}$
9 $2\overline{)73}$	**10** $5\overline{)70}$	**11** $8\overline{)99}$	**12** $4\overline{)95}$
13 $9\overline{)98}$	**14** $3\overline{)99}$	**15** $6\overline{)38}$	**16** $5\overline{)95}$
17 $7\overline{)87}$	**18** $8\overline{)62}$	**19** $4\overline{)82}$	**20** $2\overline{)87}$

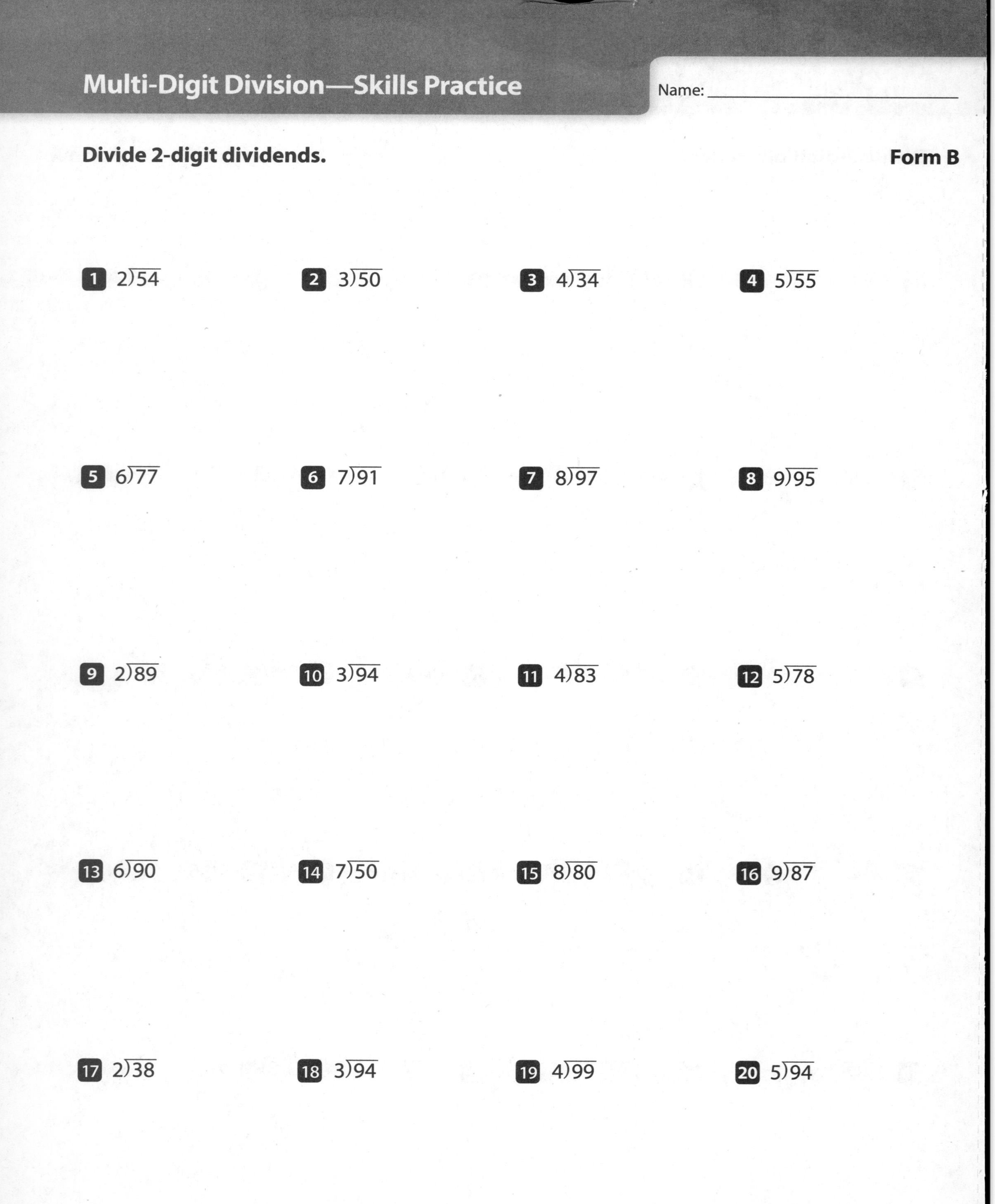

Multi-Digit Division—Skills Practice

Name: ____________________

Divide 2-digit dividends.

Form B

1 $2\overline{)54}$	**2** $3\overline{)50}$	**3** $4\overline{)34}$	**4** $5\overline{)55}$
5 $6\overline{)77}$	**6** $7\overline{)91}$	**7** $8\overline{)97}$	**8** $9\overline{)95}$
9 $2\overline{)89}$	**10** $3\overline{)94}$	**11** $4\overline{)83}$	**12** $5\overline{)78}$
13 $6\overline{)90}$	**14** $7\overline{)50}$	**15** $8\overline{)80}$	**16** $9\overline{)87}$
17 $2\overline{)38}$	**18** $3\overline{)94}$	**19** $4\overline{)99}$	**20** $5\overline{)94}$

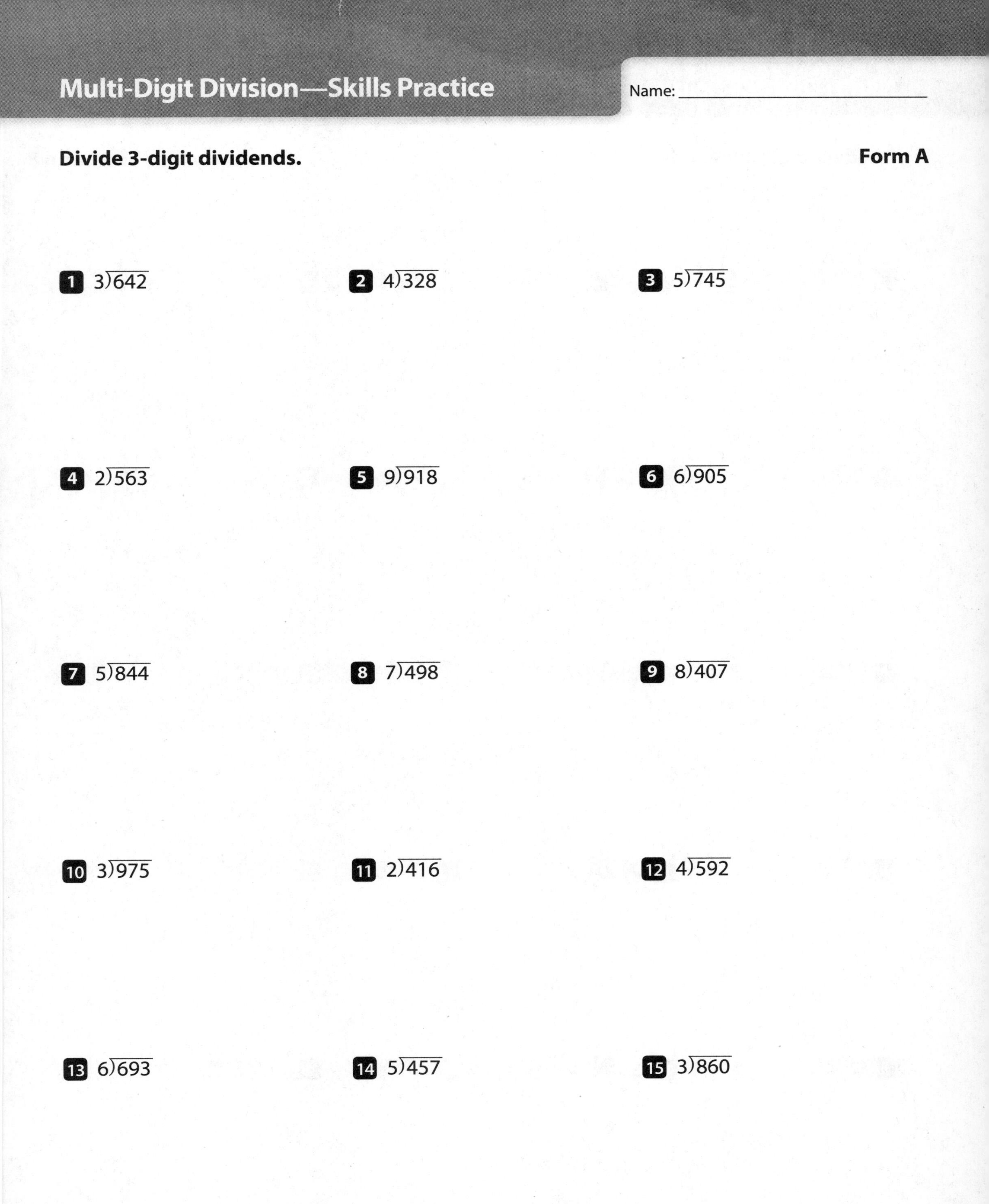

Multi-Digit Division—Skills Practice

Name: ______________________________

Divide 3-digit dividends.

Form A

1 $3\overline{)642}$

2 $4\overline{)328}$

3 $5\overline{)745}$

4 $2\overline{)563}$

5 $9\overline{)918}$

6 $6\overline{)905}$

7 $5\overline{)844}$

8 $7\overline{)498}$

9 $8\overline{)407}$

10 $3\overline{)975}$

11 $2\overline{)416}$

12 $4\overline{)592}$

13 $6\overline{)693}$

14 $5\overline{)457}$

15 $3\overline{)860}$

Multi-Digit Division—Skills Practice

Name: ______________________

Divide 3-digit dividends.

Form B

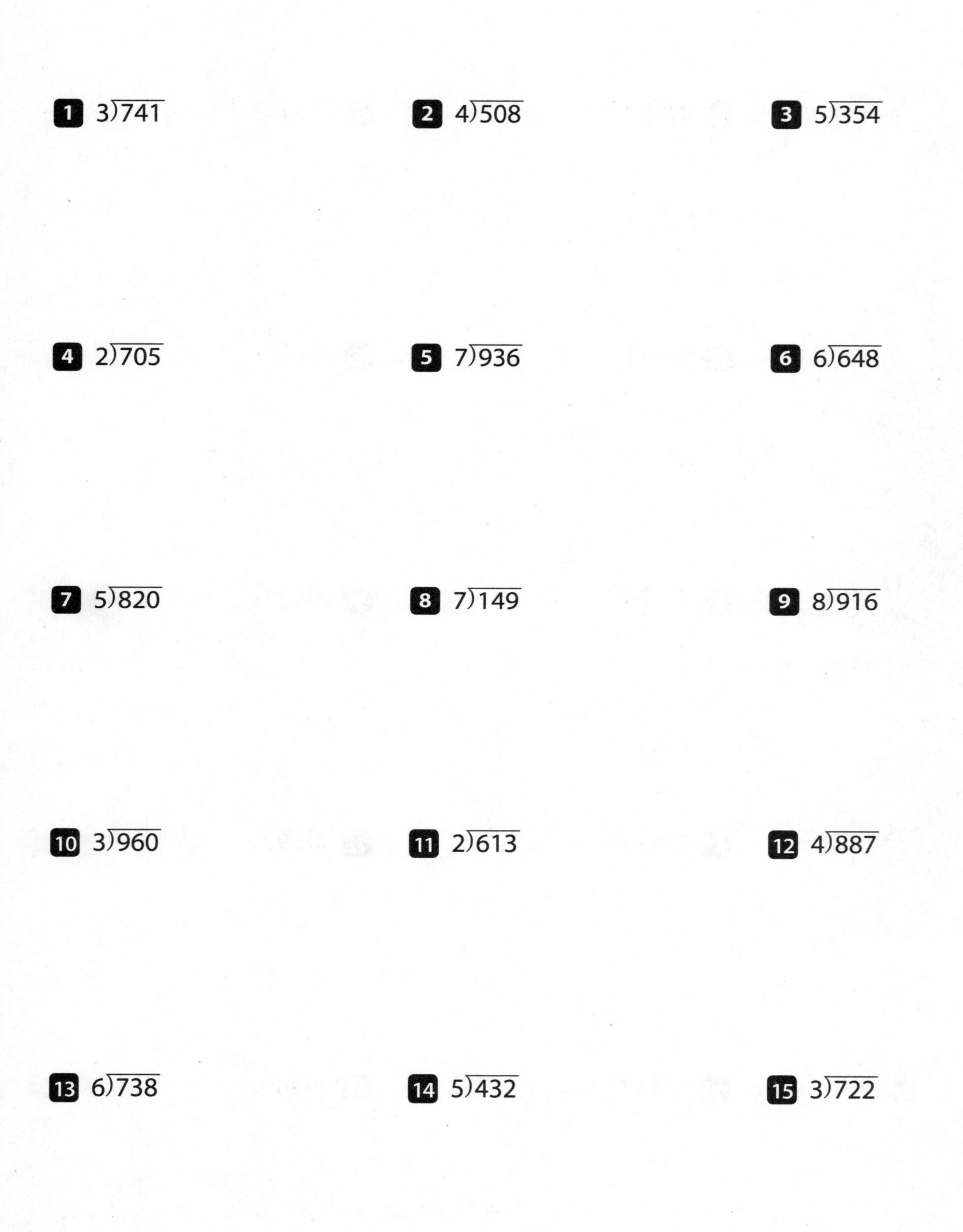

1 $3\overline{)741}$

2 $4\overline{)508}$

3 $5\overline{)354}$

4 $2\overline{)705}$

5 $7\overline{)936}$

6 $6\overline{)648}$

7 $5\overline{)820}$

8 $7\overline{)149}$

9 $8\overline{)916}$

10 $3\overline{)960}$

11 $2\overline{)613}$

12 $4\overline{)887}$

13 $6\overline{)738}$

14 $5\overline{)432}$

15 $3\overline{)722}$

Multi-Digit Division—Skills Practice

Name: ____________________

Divide 4-digit dividends. **Form A**

1. $3\overline{)6,933}$
2. $4\overline{)1,304}$
3. $5\overline{)1,234}$
4. $2\overline{)7,350}$
5. $7\overline{)1,589}$
6. $6\overline{)1,574}$
7. $5\overline{)2,648}$
8. $3\overline{)2,845}$
9. $8\overline{)6,014}$
10. $3\overline{)8,574}$
11. $2\overline{)5,318}$
12. $4\overline{)2,583}$
13. $6\overline{)3,754}$
14. $5\overline{)7,138}$
15. $3\overline{)5,002}$

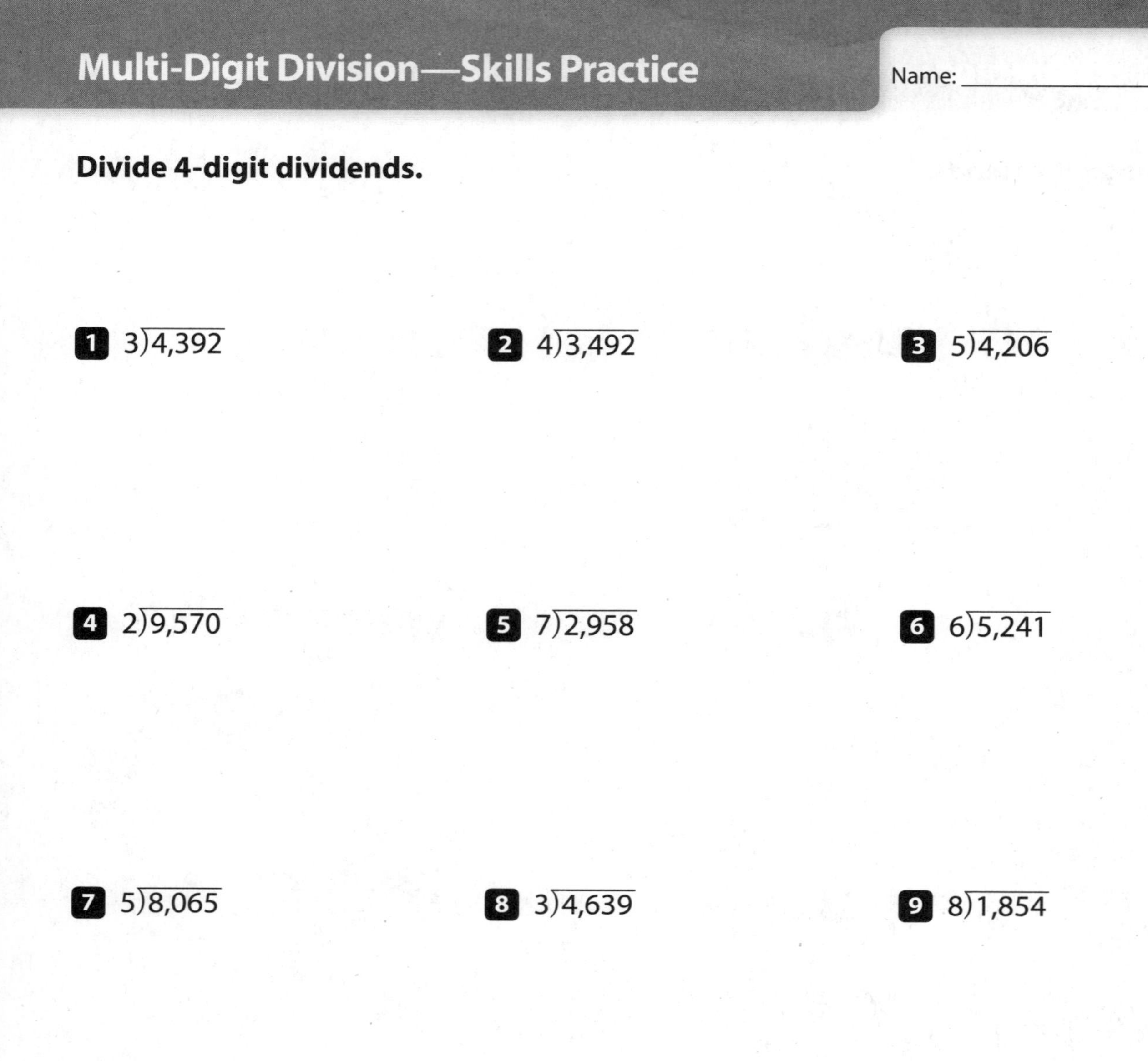

Multi-Digit Division—Skills Practice

Name: ______________________

Divide 4-digit dividends.

Form B

1. $3\overline{)4,392}$
2. $4\overline{)3,492}$
3. $5\overline{)4,206}$
4. $2\overline{)9,570}$
5. $7\overline{)2,958}$
6. $6\overline{)5,241}$
7. $5\overline{)8,065}$
8. $3\overline{)4,639}$
9. $8\overline{)1,854}$
10. $3\overline{)5,740}$
11. $2\overline{)7,356}$
12. $4\overline{)3,820}$
13. $6\overline{)4,523}$
14. $5\overline{)6,148}$
15. $3\overline{)2,005}$

Multi-Digit Division—Repeated Reasoning

Name: ______________________

Find patterns in quotients.

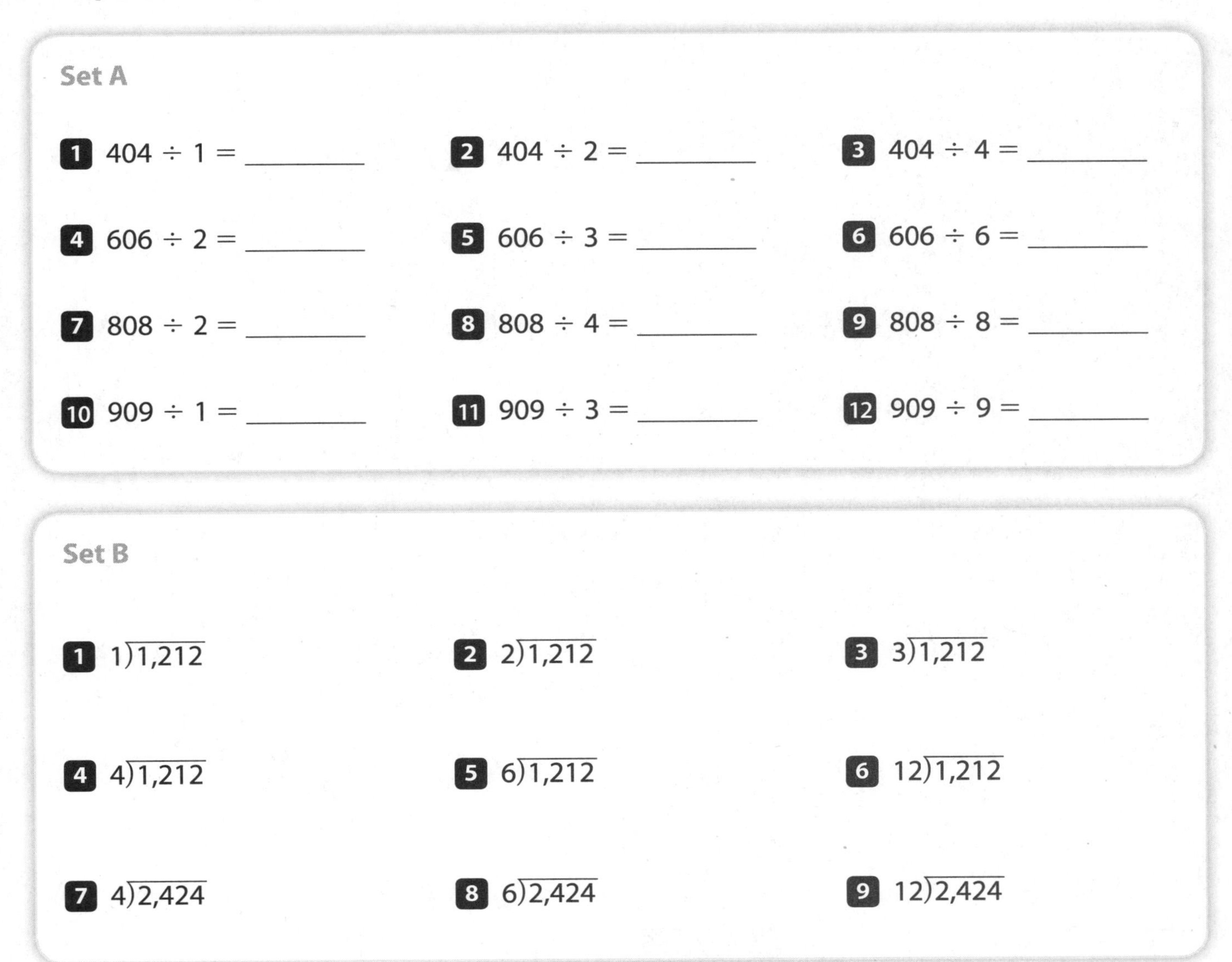

Set A

1. 404 ÷ 1 = ________
2. 404 ÷ 2 = ________
3. 404 ÷ 4 = ________
4. 606 ÷ 2 = ________
5. 606 ÷ 3 = ________
6. 606 ÷ 6 = ________
7. 808 ÷ 2 = ________
8. 808 ÷ 4 = ________
9. 808 ÷ 8 = ________
10. 909 ÷ 1 = ________
11. 909 ÷ 3 = ________
12. 909 ÷ 9 = ________

Set B

1. $1\overline{)1,212}$
2. $2\overline{)1,212}$
3. $3\overline{)1,212}$
4. $4\overline{)1,212}$
5. $6\overline{)1,212}$
6. $12\overline{)1,212}$
7. $4\overline{)2,424}$
8. $6\overline{)2,424}$
9. $12\overline{)2,424}$

Describe a pattern you see in one of the sets of problems above.

____

____

____

$6 \div 2 = 30$

$42 \div 6 = 70$

$27 \div 9 = 3$

2700 | 90

00 | 30